All About Full Production

Other Books by Christoph Roser

"Faster, Better, Cheaper" in the History of Manufacturing: From the Stone Age to Lean Manufacturing and Beyond, 439 pages, Productivity Press, 2016. ISBN 978-1-49875-630-3.

Fertigungstechnik für Führungskräfte. 2. überarbeitete und erweiterte Auflage, 293 pages, AllAboutLean Publishing, 2019. ISBN 978-3-96382-004-5 (Manufacturing fundamentals textbook for my lectures, in German)

Collected Blog Posts of AllAboutLean.com 2013, 112 pages, AllAboutLean Publishing, 2020. ISBN 978-3-96382-007-6.

Collected Blog Posts of AllAboutLean.com 2014, 332 pages, AllAboutLean Publishing, 2020. ISBN 978-3-96382-010-6.

Collected Blog Posts of AllAboutLean.com 2015, 413 pages, AllAboutLean Publishing, 2020. ISBN 978-3-96382-013-7.

Collected Blog Posts of AllAboutLean.com 2016, 352 pages, AllAboutLean Publishing, 2020. ISBN 978-3-96382-016-8.

Collected Blog Posts of AllAboutLean.com 2017, 371 pages, AllAboutLean Publishing, 2020. ISBN 978-3-96382-019-9.

Collected Blog Posts of AllAboutLean.com 2018, 384 pages, AllAboutLean Publishing, 2020. ISBN 978-3-96382-022-9.

Collected Blog Posts of AllAboutLean.com 2019, 339 pages, AllAboutLean Publishing, 2020. ISBN 978-3-96382-025-0.

Collected Blog Posts of AllAboutLean.com 2020, 356 pages, AllAboutLean Publishing, 2021. ISBN 978-3-96382-030-4.

All About **Pull Production**

Designing, Implementing, and Maintaining Kanban, CONWIP, and other Pull Systems in Lean Production

With a Foreword by John Shook

Christoph Roser

AllAboutLean.com Publishing
Offenbach, Deutschland
2021

AllAboutLean.com Publishing, Christoph Roser, Hafeninsel 14, 63067 Offenbach, Deutschland, printed by Amazon Media EU S. à r. l., 5 Rue Plaetis, L-2338, Luxembourg

ISBN of the different versions

- 978-3-96382-028-1 Paperback
- 978-3-96382-029-8 E-Book

Bibliographic information published by the Deutsche Nationalbibliothek. The Deutsche Nationalbibliothek lists this publication in the Deutsche Nationalbibliografie. Detailed bibliographic data are available on the internet at http://dnb.dnb.de.

Version 1.00 03.04.2021 1st Edition

A Blind Date on Valentine's Day in the Haymarket.

Legal Disclaimer

This book was prepared with great care and a lot of effort. I believe the content is correct and the recommendations are sensible. As in any work, there may be errors and mistakes, albeit I hope there are only a few of them. Because of the wide variety of different production systems or even other non-production systems, I had to make generalizations and assumptions. These may not apply to all possible systems. I provide this book and its contents on an "as- is" basis and make no representations or warranties of any kind regarding this book or its contents. I assume no responsibility for errors, inaccuracies, omissions, or any other inconsistencies. Hence, I hereby **disclaim any liability** to any party for any loss, damage, or disruption caused by errors or omissions, whether such errors or omissions result from negligence, accident, or any other cause. Please don't sue me.

Table of Contents

Praise for All About Pull Production

In this book you will find many techniques and tools that will help you reconfigure your supply chain operations. But more importantly, by exploring numerous approaches and methods, this book will challenge you to rethink your strategy, to reconsider what your supply system needs to accomplish and why. This book provides you the means to create supply systems for the rapidly evolving complexities of the twenty-first century, anywhere, in any industry.

John Shook
Chairman, Lean Global Network

Prof. Roser is the go-to source for anything about lean. With this comprehensive book on pull production he has written an authoritative work. Highly recommended for anyone interested in getting to the heart of Toyota's pull principle.

Dr. Torbjørn Netland
Professor of Production and Operations Management, ETH Zürich

This book explains pull production very well and in an excellent style. The book definitely demystifies pull. Without doubt, the book will be the go-to guide for both beginners and experienced practitioners.

Cheong Tsang
Bosch Plant Manager (Retired)

Prof. Dr. Roser is an irreplaceable professional in teaching and studying production management systems. He has both brilliant academic talent as a researcher and rich technical skills as a practitioner and a consultant. He has long experience and much knowledge in both Europe and Japan. Readers will definitely obtain a lot of valuable insights and new ideas from his book on pull production.

Dr. Masaru Nakano
Professor, Keio University; Former Toyota Manager

This is by far the best in-depth exploration of pull. It is amazingly comprehensive, including warnings, common errors, and applicability of various pull systems. I am sure that it will become THE standard reference book on pull systems.

Dr. John Bicheno
Emeritus Professor of Lean Enterprise, University of Buckingham

According to the lean principle "Flow where you can, pull where you can't", Christoph Roser presents production control methods based on the pull principle in a comprehensive and practice-oriented way. This book is worth reading for everyone dealing with mura (i.e. variability in value streams), and is my recommendation for students and industry practitioners alike.

Dr.-Ing. Jochen Deuse
Professor, Head of Institute of Production Systems, TU Dortmund University; Director Centre for Advanced Manufacturing, University of Technology Sydney

The book provides well structured, in-depth insights in the application of pull systems, from Kanban to less-known but powerful alternatives. The book is a valuable source for students and practitioners in industry, from lean experts to production managers.

Dr.-Ing. Ralph Richter
Former Head of the Bosch Production System and Plant Manager at Bosch

With this deeply researched and considered book, Prof. Roser goes beyond the simple explanations of pull to reveal pull production in its compelling simplicity. The results provide a convincing case and trusty guide.

Peter Willats
Professor, University of Buckingham, Co-Founder, Kaizen Institute of Europe

This book is so comprehensive in its scope, anyone considering a pull system should read it to make sure they have made the correct choice. So many are only aware of the kanban system and consider it the default. This book offers options for them to consider in light of their needs.

Mark Warren
Manufacturing Engineer and Production Historian

What you have put together in this book is amazing—this may become your magnum opus in due course! It's going to be a great reference resource for practitioners and academics.

Dr. Rajan Suri
Emeritus Professor of Industrial Engineering, University of Wisconsin-Madison, Inventor of POLCA

This book is excellent material for understanding and using pull production. It is very informative and written in a very polite and pleasant personal style with good reflections and clarifications.

Dr. Björn Johansson
Professor of Sustainable Production, Chalmers University of Technology, Sweden

Foreword by John Shook, Chairman, Lean Global Network

Christopher Roser has written a timely and important book. Global supply chains in every industry are broken. That fact is not new, though conditions as I write this in 2021 are even more dire than usual. What is new is not that they are broken, but the fact that now everyone *knows* they are broken. Also not new is the fact that the method that could dramatically improve the situation is getting blamed for the failure: the pull system devised by Toyota more than half a century ago, known as Just-In-Time.

PULL?

What is a pull system? I will not try to summarize here what author Roser spends an entire book explaining in detail – be prepared, you will need to exert some energy to do justice to the various methods detailed in this book! Here, I will merely offer a few words of context.

The definitive academic definition of pull has been offered by Wally Hopp and Mark Spearman, who claim in their influential 2004 paper[1] that the defining characteristic of a pull system is the presence of inventory control limits: "A pull production system is one that explicitly limits the amount of work in process that can be in the system".

Much harm has been done by this simple and incorrect definition. As it was developed through real-world practice at Toyota at a time when it had no access to automotive suppliers and therefore *needed* to innovate, "pull" begins from a totally different starting point. Inventory was in fact not even the main problem they were trying to solve (nor is it today). The critical supply chain (or, as lean thinkers prefer to call it, a value stream) problem to solve is for each point in the chain to know at any given moment exactly what to make and what to move. This does indeed entail the problem of inventory and inventory leads to many other associated problems (including carrying costs, among others). For this reason, pundits, academicians and even practitioners tend to focus on the piles of stuff we

---

1   Wallace J. Hopp and Mark L. Spearman, *To Pull or Not to Pull: What Is the Question?*, Manufacturing & Service Operations Management 6, no. 2 April 1, 2004: 133–48.

call inventory without looking further to understand the deeper causes. The piles are there. They continue to grow. They block our view.

A pull system approaches the problem of supply chain design from a very different perspective. How can we organize all the work, all the material, and all of the *time* entailed in a long supply chain so that it operates as effectively and efficiently as possible? How can we have each step producing precisely what the next step needs when it needs it, in the amount needed? Is a top-down planning process the best way, informing each step in a large supply system what to make and when? Such an approach might work, if everything went according to said plan. But, alas, in the real world, that is rarely the case. Things go wrong. Machines stop running. Trucks break down. Humans make mistakes. And, anyway, in today's world, customers make last-minute decisions. People change their minds. So, how can we organize all this complexity when the beginning of the supply chain is half a world and half a year away from the customer?

These are the problems that pull systems tackle from an unconventional set of assumptions. Minimum inventory is desirable, to be sure, but setting inventory limits is by no means the defining characteristic. The amount of inventory needed is the result of actions taken and decisions geared to address other problems – how to ensure that what is needed is where it is needed when it is needed.

Toyota discovered early on that the auto industry presented a multitude of deeply complex problems beyond the obvious ones of designing, building, and marketing the product. There are employees to hire and train, parts and materials to source, products to sell and service, regulatory concerns to contend with. And there is the thorny problem of managing the thousands of parts and materials that go into a car. As straightforward as it may sound, this can be as difficult as transforming those materials into the product.

Toyota auto company founder Kiichiro Toyoda came up with the concept – and even the curious name – of "Just In Time" in the 1930s on a reconnaissance mission to the UK. He missed a train connection, providing him a lesson he would never forget in the value of promptness and inspiring the insight that one should never fail to arrive where one needs to be *just in time*. As his company was figuring out how to actually build the automobiles that he designed, the factory was facing the problem of constantly running out of parts and materials. As a startup, the fledgling company didn't have the capital to purchase large stockpiles. The answer was to bring in parts and materials daily, just in time, to be fabricated or assembled.

A decade later, Kiichiro's machine shop manager Taiichi Ohno began experimenting with simple pull systems on the plant floor. He found that workers at downstream processes were frequently out of the materials they needed to do their work, while upstream processes were busy producing the wrong thing. He decided to reverse the direction of the flow of information that instructed each operation what to produce and move. (As Roser will explain, Ohno was not the first to tackle this problem via "pull", but he was the first to come up with a systematic way to make pull work sustainably.)

In the end, two simple rules prevailed: 1) never make or move too much or 2) too little.

Simple indeed. But to actualize these simple rules in the real world requires turning things upside down: pull, don't push. Start by connecting individual processes. Make production flow wherever possible. Wherever it isn't possible to flow from value creating step to value creating step, connect disparate processes through some sort of mechanism (such as Kanban) to enable downstream processes to pull from upstream processes what they need when they need it. Simple! And brilliant!

But simple doesn't mean easy and brilliant doesn't necessarily mean intuitive.

My first exposure to Toyota's pull system was in the first half of 1984 on the stamping shop floor of Toyota's Takaoka Assembly Plant. Toyota was preparing for the beginning of operations at NUMMI (New United Motor Manufacturing Inc.), the company's joint venture with General Motors in Fremont, California. My aha moment – "Oh, *that's* what JIT means!" – came after, not during, my plant training, which was when I was supposed to learn all about TPS.

Though I was still new to the process, I was already in the position of explaining TPS to visitors, mostly from General Motors. While I had learned enough to be able to walk through a basic explanation of Kanban and "pull vs push", I didn't really get it. Then one day, as I was being backed into a corner to explain, really, what pull was and why it was so important, I became frustrated with one particular production manager from GM as he was frustrated with me.

A practical mid-level manager with decades of experience, he pressured me: "I don't get it. So what? I hear what you're saying but I don't see the big deal. Why should I care about 'pull instead of push'? I don't see the advantage". I was as frustrated as he, annoyed that he couldn't understand the same explanations that had seemed to suffice for others. Our frustrations rose as we egged each other on. I recall my face reddening as I realized that I couldn't explain it well because I myself didn't *really* know what the big deal was. I understood the rudiments in terms of the actions on the plant floor. And I understood to some extent the big-picture argument for what pull was and how it was unconventional, in abstract terms. But I didn't know how to connect the dots and hadn't fully grasped what was so revolutionary about JIT and pull.

I think my frustration – first toward my guest and then gradually but steadily toward myself – was the spark that led to insight and my aha moment. I was suddenly, finally, struck by the power of all these quick cycle replenishment loops that were repeating seemingly endlessly throughout the entire supply chain. The small loop of material and information flow that we were observing was fractal. What we were witnessing at the end of a big press line as stamped steel was taken away every few minutes to a store located just a short walk away, which was then connected in a similar way to the process that followed (the body welding shop), was taking place all up and down the supply chain. The next day, we visited some outside suppliers connected with the assembly plant by Kanban: they were cycling between the two factories as frequently as eight times per day. It is a *system* with feedback loops, self-correcting and, indeed, revolutionary.

Within a few months, NUMMI was up and running and the world outside Toyota was getting its first close look at a successful pull system in operation. Still, what observers can see on the surface – such as low inventory – is only the result. The work behind the scenes to execute a system that looks so simple is in fact *deceptively simple*. Toyota had established an entire department to innovate every aspect of the design and operation of its supply system. To this day, it is the rare company (especially outside the auto industry) that is willing to invest in *developing the organizational capability* required to successfully transform to a pull system. (Toyota views conversion from push to pull as a defining characteristic of the higher-level functioning of its system of Just In Time – which is in turn a major component of its Toyota Production System – but pull is just one piece of JIT, along with the concepts and practices of Takt Time and creating continuous flow.)

MISUNDERSTANDINGS, FALLACIES, CONFUSION AND DAMAGE DONE

It is unfortunate indeed that the most viable way forward to fix what ails supply chains is frequently blamed for their failure. Academicians (such as those referenced above) do not have a monopoly on spreading misunderstandings about supply chain dynamics. Periodically, even the most highly esteemed journals publish articles blaming the supply crisis on Just in Time or lean manufacturing. Shortages of goods following 9/11, during the great recession of 2008-09, or during the Covid-19 pandemic invariably lead to nonsense such as this headline article in the Wall Street Journal in late 2020:

> *Why Are There Still Not Enough Paper Towels? Blame lean manufacturing. A decades long effort to eke out more profit by keeping inventory low left many manufacturers unprepared when Covid-19 struck. And production is unlikely to ramp up significantly any time soon.*[2]

Now in early 2021 the latest global supply chain crisis – progressing to items perhaps more challenging than toilet paper – entails semiconductors and geopolitics. Policies that led to three decades of chasing lowest piece prices in China are being reversed. The pendulum swings again. Through it all, there is a better way.

A WAY FORWARD

Enter Christoph Roser's timely expose *All About Pull*. This book makes no pretense at being a sound bite for casual readers of 1500 word simplifications on social media. The content in these pages will require you, dear reader, to do some work.

Christoph Roser has spent decades studying multiple dimensions of lean thinking and practice. As a researcher at the Toyota Central Research and

---

[2] Sharon Terlep and Annie Gasparro, *Why Are There Still Not Enough Paper Towels?*, *Wall Street Journal*, August 21, 2020, sec. US, https://www.wsj.com/articles/why-arent-there-enough-paper-towels-11598020793.

Development Laboratories in Nagoya, Japan, he had direct access to knowledge of practices along with the inquiry process which is essential to that organization's mission. From there, he continued his learning through his work with McKinsey & Company and various divisions of the Bosch group of enterprises. Roser's inquiry continues through his research and teaching as a professor of production management at the University of Applied Sciences in Karlsruhe, Germany. In addition to this book, there are many opportunities to profit from Roser's expertise through more than 50 academic journal articles, hundreds of postings on this blog All About Lean, and his book *Faster, Better, Cheaper in the History of Manufacturing*.

Within these pages, you will find many techniques and tools that will help you reconfigure your supply chain operations. But more importantly, by exploring numerous approaches and methods, author Roser will challenge you to rethink your strategy, to reconsider what your supply system needs to accomplish and why. How can you get each item to be in the right place at the right time? How can the thousands of people and processes of an extended value stream do the right work at the right time? Supply system designers have no end of problems to solve and approaches to tackle them. The shift to pull is a technical challenge but it also requires a fundamental shift in the mindsets of not only supply chain professionals but also of chief executives. This book provides you the means to create supply systems for the rapidly evolving complexities of the 21st Century, anywhere, in any industry.

John Shook
Chairman, Lean Global Network
Ann Arbor Michigan USA

Acknowledgements

It is completed! This is my first book focusing solely on lean manufacturing. Almost three years of writing and editing, creating images, designing the cover, and many other tasks to present you this work that you have in front of you. This does not even count the almost a decade of blog-post writing that also contributed to this book, although all blog posts have been significantly reworked and modified. I sincerely hope that it will help you in your work.

I could not have written this book without the help of others. I would especially like to thank all the reviewers that gave input and made this book better. These are, in alphabetical order, Michel Baudin, John Bicheno, Karl Ludwig Blocher, Jochen Deuse, Björn Johansson, David Lenze, Masaru Nakano, Torbjørn Netland, Ralph Richter, John Shook, Ambika Sriramakrishna, Rajan Suri, Matthias Thürer, Cheong Tsang, Mark Warren, and Peter Willats.

Special thanks also to John Shook for writing the foreword in addition to giving me feedback on the manuscript.

I would also like to thank my proofreader and copyeditor, Christy Distler. Since English spelling and grammar are not my strong suit, she surely had her work cut out for her. Many thanks also to Iryna Makarevych for her help with the cover design and the interior layout.

Most of the images are my own. However, occasionally I use images by others. Some of these were public domain or under a Creative Commons license, others I purchased the rights for. Many thanks to the creators of these artworks. As I am a great fan and supporter of the Creative Commons license, I would like to thank especially those that provided their images free of charge or under a Creative Commons license. A detailed list of the images of other authors is at the end of this book in the image credits.

edition, and not to future updated editions, although they may have similar conditions.

On a side note, if you are wondering about the ball bearings on the cover... I thought quite a bit on how the cover should look. First, I had a kanban diagram, but it just looked ugly. But a ball bearing is a nice illustration for pull or kanban. The balls go round and round in a loop, just like kanban in a pull system. Three ball bearings represent a series of kanban loops. Hence, I believe these three ball bearings are a nice illustration of pull systems.

Above all, I sincerely hope that this book, *All About Pull Production*, will help you improve your system performance and increase the competitiveness and profitability of your company!

Chapter 1
Introduction

Pull is an excellent tool to establish flow and limit your inventory. With very few exceptions, all production systems would benefit from pull. Pull is a cornerstone of lean production.

This book on pull production is **written for the practitioner**. Focus is on **actual use of pull systems in real-world applications**. However, before we start with the actual details on pull systems, here is some advice on whom this book is for, and when you should use pull. I will also give you some guidance on reading this book, and a bit on the history of pull systems.

In this book, I go into detail on the **selection, calculation, implementation, and maintenance of the various pull systems**. The book is based on my experience in implementing and using pull on actual shop floors. It also includes academic research to explain the theories behind it. Again, the primary aim of this book is to help the practitioner on the shop floor.

1.1 Whom This Book Is For

This book is a practical guide for anyone looking to implement pull systems. It does not try to explain all of lean manufacturing, but has a **rigorous focus on pull**. I find it difficult to fit all of lean production into a single book. After all, it was difficult enough to fit *All About Pull Production* into a single book!

This book focuses heavily on practical application. It values functionality over theory, albeit I point out the underlying relations. It is not a high-level philosophical discussion of lean, but a book to help you roll up your sleeves and get the job done. It is **written for the practitioner**, especially in **small and medium enterprises** that may not have a lean back office for support. If you are in charge of a (or part of a) small- or medium-sized company and want to implement pull, then this book is for you. It can also be used in **larger corporations**. However, it also serves as a useful **reference for students and researchers of lean manufacturing**.

It serves as a guide for anyone connected to manufacturing. It can help **people in charge of manufacturing** and other systems, from the supervisor to middle management, to the COO and CEO. It is also relevant for **people supporting manufacturing** or other systems. This could include people responsible for designing, maintaining, and planning such systems, including operators in maintenance, production planning, line layout, and line design, industrial engineering, and others. More broadly it can help with **any kind of processing system that could use pull, including healthcare, services, administration, military, government, banking**, and many more.

Since people in industry are under constant time pressure, I structured this book to support **selective reading**. While I would love for you to read this book cover to cover, I completely understand if **you just need a solution for your problem… fast!** Hence, I tried to point out which type of pull system is useful for you, and structured the book to allow skipping to the most interesting parts. For the same reason, I have a list of variables close to the equations that use them, even if I have explained the variables before. A complete list of variables can be found in the appendix. The table of contents has quite a few levels more than what may be esthetically pleasing, but this also helps you to quickly find what you need. **Text in bold highlights key points**, helping you to scan the pages for the parts relevant to you.

This book should ideally be read before you implement pull in your system. However, it can also help you if you already have an existing pull system and want to improve or maintain it. Overall, the goal of this book is to help you to **go out and organize your industry!**

1.2 When Do You Need Pull?

Pull production is part of the lean manufacturing *kaizen* improvement process. **Lean should always start with a problem**, and from there work toward the solution. Deciding top down that you need pull and then looking for a problem to match is the wrong direction. **If the only tool you have is a hammer, everything will look like a nail.**

Hence, the first step is to figure out **what problems you want to solve**. Usually, the answer is that there are only three problems: cost, quality, and delivery time. However, these are all the problems a production system can normally have (assuming operators' safety is ensured and that the law is not looking for you). Try to narrow down which of these problems, and where, is most relevant to you.

Pull can help you with **improving lead times** and therefore **improving delivery times**. Pull is a common solution that helps you to stabilize and control your material flow. This reduces lead times and improves delivery performance.

Pull can also help to **reduce cost**. However, there are many ways to reduce cost. This includes design changes, process optimization, and waste reduction. Pull is a possible answer, but not the only one and not necessarily the best, if cost is your biggest problem. However, pull can **reduce inventory**, which will have a lot of benefits, including cost reduction.

Implementing pull is also a way to **build lean capability for you and your operators**. It also helps **to establish trust in lean**. By establishing a pull system, the operators become familiar with the underlying principles of lean. This can help with a cultural shift toward continuous improvement and lean. If capability building and trust building is your goal, establish a pull system where the chances of success are high. Tackling the trickiest production system first with a workforce unfamiliar with pull can lead to failure and hence mistrust.

But again, **start with the problem, and then work your way forward from there**.

1.3 How to Read This Book

Pull is one of the key concepts of lean manufacturing. While it did not originate with Toyota, the Toyota Production System made pull in general and kanban in particular famous. It helped Toyota to grow and become the largest carmaker in the world. This book is targeted primarily at production; however, pull can also be used in many other areas, like service, healthcare, call centers, retail, logistics, administration, development, construction, and others.

However, the concept of pull is often misunderstood. It is often defined as the direction of the information flow, when in reality it is all about **limiting the inventory combined with a system to replenish this inventory**. Whenever a part leaves the system, a replacement is produced or shipped. Whenever a job is completed, the next job is released for production. Hence pull will prevent overloading the system. You will find more on this in Chapter 2.

This book can be read cover to cover, but it also allows selective reading. The best-known variant of pull production is kanban, but there are many more. If you make custom products or products in small quantities, you should also read CONWIP (constant work in process), but you may skip CONWIP if you only have make-to-stock production. If you have only flow production, you may not be interested in POLCA (paired-cell overlapping loops of cards with authorization). The aim is to give you practical advice beyond pure theory to help you decide which pull system is right for you, and how to set it up and maintain it. Chapter 3 compares the different approaches to pull production. This guides you in selecting the pull system best suited to your situation. Which one should you use for your situation? Which ones can be combined with others? As shown in Figure 1, Chapter 3 helps you to decide which pull system is most relevant to you.

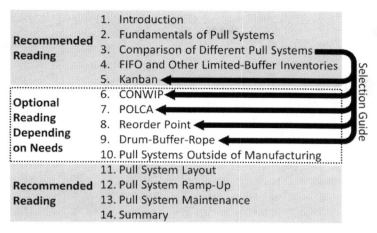

Figure 1: Overview of the chapters of this book (Image Roser)

Chapter 4 goes into the details of FIFO and its variants. Chapter 5 presents the important kanban system. Chapter 2 to Chapter 5 should be read regardless of your selected pull system, as they include many basics that will be helpful for other approaches. However, Chapter 6 to Chapter 10 can be read selectively based on your interests. Chapter 6 presents the CONWIP system for make-to-order. Chapter 7 introduces POLCA for job shops. Chapter 8 describes reorder points, which are well suited for purchasing. Chapter 9 outlines the drum-buffer-rope system popular with fans of the Theory of Constraints.

Chapter 10 goes into pull systems outside of traditional manufacturing and logistics. This includes healthcare, project management, development, administration, and construction. This chapter is not intended to be an in-depth coverage of these topics, but to give you inspiration about adaptations of pull outside of manufacturing.

Chapter 11 goes into more details on the layout of the pull system and helps you to decide where to make your pull loops. Chapter 12 describes how to ramp up a pull production, and Chapter 13 how to maintain it. Chapter 11 to Chapter 13 are again suggested reading for everybody, as they contain information relevant to any pull system.

Throughout this book I have hundreds of illustrations. Many of them are loosely based on value stream mapping. If you are unfamiliar with basic value stream maps, you will find a brief explanation in the appendix. The appendix also contains a list of variables, the theoretical COBACABANA pull method, and some recommended reading.

1.4 A Brief History of Pull Production

The concept of pull production is most commonly associated with kanban invented by Toyota. However, the idea itself precedes Toyota. One of the earliest instances of pull I know of were retail supermarkets. Before supermarkets, typical grocery stores had an attendant behind the counter. This person picked the goods you wanted from the shelf, calculated the prices, and then completed the transaction, handing you the goods in exchange for money. An example of a typical grocery store from around 1900 is shown in Figure 2.

Figure 2: A traditional grocery store around 1900, with attendants behind the counter (Image unknown author in public domain)

The Piggly Wiggly supermarket chain radically changed this concept in 1916 with their store in Memphis, Tennessee, USA. The customer walked in the store, picked up whatever they wanted, and then went to the checkout to pay. This was the first modern supermarket, a system you are surely familiar with. All items are labeled with prices. You have a basket, or a shopping cart, and your only human interaction is when you pay at the checkout. This was a radical change for its time, with large savings in labor cost far exceeding the losses due to theft. Nowadays it is the norm in most retail stores. One of the first Piggly Wiggly supermarkets from 1918 is shown in Figure 3.

Figure 3: The first Piggly Wiggly supermarket in Memphis, Tennessee, opened 1916. Photo from 1918. (Image Clarence Saunders in public domain)

The interesting part related to pull production, however, was behind the scenes. Piggly Wiggly had a system with a target stock level, and each day they simply reordered whatever they sold. Since they ordered only enough to refill the inventory to the target level, this, in effect, was a **reorder system**, and hence a pull system.

The idea of a supermarket also helped Toyota to develop kanban. The person responsible for the development of kanban at Toyota was Taiichi Ohno. At the beginning, Toyota was a spinning and weaving company. Their chief competitor, Nichibo (also known as Dai Nippon Spinning), outperformed Toyoda[3] both in quality and in cost. Ohno and his team studied Nichibo. Among other things, they learned that Nichibo had much less inventory and produced material in smaller batches.

Ohno, like many other Japanese at that time, were also very interested in the much more advanced technologies and methods of the United States. Back then, there were no retail supermarkets in Japan. However, Ohno had

---

[3]   The family name is Toyoda with a "D". The car company eventually changed its name to Toyota with a "T" for easier international pronunciation and to have a lucky number of strokes in the Japanese writing, トヨタ. Hence, nowadays some companies in the group are called Toyoda (e.g., Toyoda Gosei), and others Toyota (e.g., Toyota Motor).

heard about these in high school, when a classmate made a presentation about his visit to the USA. This included pictures of modern supermarkets.[4] He took inspiration (and the name *supermarket* for the managed inventory) from America for his production system at Toyota. The first implementation of these supermarkets at Toyota was by Taiichi Ohno in 1948.[5]

Continuously improving on these processes, the workers wrote small sheets of paper from 1953 onward to inform the production which parts to replenish. Soon, these scribbled notes turned into organized and color-coded cards. Taiichi Ohno visited the United States himself in 1956 and saw his first retail supermarket there. At this time, most material flow in his workshop was already controlled by pull, using these cards, although they were not yet known as **kanban**.[6]

Figure 4: Traditional engraved wooden kanban signboard over the entrance to a modern fashion store in Ginza, Tokyo, Japan (Image Roser)

---

[4] Masaaki Sato, *The Toyota Leaders: An Executive Guide* New York: Vertical, 2008, ISBN 1-934287-23-7.

[5] Christoph Roser, *"Faster, Better, Cheaper" in the History of Manufacturing: From the Stone Age to Lean Manufacturing and Beyond*, 1st ed. Productivity Press, 2016, ISBN 978-1-4987-5630-3.

[6] Please note that Ohno was not the only one experimenting with such pull systems. For example, in 1954 Lockheed also used similar systems in their production of jet aircraft.

Not until 1964 were those cards named kanban. In Japanese, *kanban* is written 看板. While commonly translated as "card", the original meaning is "signboard, billboard, or doorplate". Kanban is the proper name for the sign over a shop. An example of a traditional kanban over a modern store is shown in Figure 4.

In traditional Japan, this **kanban represents the reputation and honor of the store**. Maybe you have seen a kitschy martial arts movie, where the bad guy goes to another training hall (dojo), defeats the master, and then steals or destroys the sign (kanban) of the dojo. This destruction of the kanban is an additional act of humiliation for the defeated dojo master, as it also "destroys his honor".

It is said that when Taiichi Ohno named the cards for his production system, he named them *kanban* to emphasize the importance of this information for the proper functioning of the production system. The kanban is the honor of the factory, and you must not lose it! This kanban system as part of the Toyota Production System helped Toyota to become very successful. Toyota is still considered financially the most successful large car company, and it is the role model for lean manufacturing.

The Western world eventually noticed the different performance of car makers during the 1973 oil crisis, although lean itself only became popular around 1990. When the members of the Organization of Arab Petroleum Exporting Countries proclaimed an oil embargo, the world quickly ran short on fuel. Car sales fell. Gas stations ran out of gas, as shown in Figure 5.

Figure 5: "No gas" sign at a gas station during the 1973 oil crisis (Image David Falconer in public domain)

Especially American car makers with gas-guzzling vehicles had problems. They soon were overwhelmed by their unsold stock of cars. Toyota, on the other hand, could ramp down production reasonably well. After the crisis, carmakers had the opposite problem of ramping up production again. With the help of their pull production system, Toyota also managed much better.

A report by MIT and the subsequent book, *The Machine that changed the World*, summarized these achievements.[7] This publication put the Toyota Production System and hence pull production on the agenda of Western manufacturing. They found many facts embarrassing to the Western world. American carmakers needed twice as much labor time to make a car. German carmakers needed as many employees at the end of the line to fix problems as they needed to make a car to begin with. In pretty much all aspects, Toyota fared much better. This started the rest of the world's interest in the Toyota Production System, later renamed **lean production**. In the Western world, kanban is sometimes even used as a synonym for pull, as it is the best-known pull system.

However, there are more pull systems, as we will see later in this book. While their history is not as extensive, I would also like to briefly mention where they originated. Chronologically closest to kanban is **drum-buffer-rope**. This approach was coined by Eliyahu Goldratt as part of his "Theory of Constraints" (TOC) philosophy starting with the book *The Goal* in 1984.[8] The term *drum-buffer-rope*, however, got its name only later in his book *The Race*.[9]

Goldratt took inspiration for this from many other ideas, usually without giving credit. There are many similar but less famous methods by others that precede *The Goal*, as for example "Systems Dynamics" developed by Jay Forrester in the 1950s; "Critical Path Method" by Morgan R. Walker in the 1950s; "Program Evaluation and Review Technique" (PERT) by the US Navy in 1957; and Wolfgang Mewes' "Bottleneck-focused Strategy" in 1963.

---

[7] James P. Womack, *The Machine That Changed the World: Based on the Massachusetts Institute of Technology 5-Million-Dollar 5-Year Study on the Future of the Automobile* New York: Rawson Associates, 1990, ISBN 0-89256-350-8.

[8] Eliyahu M. Goldratt and Jeff Cox, *The Goal: A Process of Ongoing Improvement*, 2nd revised ed. North River Press, 1992, ISBN 0-88427-178-1.

[9] Eliyahu M. Goldratt and Robert E. Fox, *The Race* Croton-on-Hudson, New York, USA: North River Press Inc., 1986, ISBN 978-0-88427-062-1.

Many other respected scientists claim that Goldratt's methods often lack mathematic rigor and are inferior to other methods.[10, 11]

Goldratt promoted his methods heavily, just when "lean" was gaining ground in the West. Some rejected the "Japanese lean" and preferred the "Western" Goldratt simply because the Japanese were, in their mind, still the enemy defeated in World War II with two nuclear bombs. Goldratt gained popularity, and even though he died in 2011, his methods still have a strong following.

Another pull system called **CONWIP** (constant work in process) was coined in an often-cited paper by Hopp and Spearman in 1990.[12] It is used for make-to-order production. It is also very similar to kanban and easy to use. This is especially noteworthy as, unlike drum-buffer-rope, there was not any major commercial promotion for CONWIP. However, it is usually not known under the name CONWIP, and often is not even properly named at all. The most common usage is as a make-to-order production line, where the limited number of slots on the line represents the target limit on inventory. The method is important, but lacks a well-recognized name. Within this book I will use the name CONWIP to explain the details behind this approach. However, please don't get hung up on the name, as the approach itself is quite useful.

The lesser-known **POLCA** pull system is a method developed by Rajan Suri in the 1990s. His first book, *Quick Response Manufacturing: A Companywide Approach to Reducing Lead Times*, was published in 1998.[13] POLCA has a

[10] Dan Trietsch, *Why a Critical Path by Any Other Name Would Smell Less Sweet? Towards a Holistic Approach to PERT/CPM*, Project Management Journal 36 2005: 27–36.

[11] Dan Trietsch, *From Management by Constraints (MBC) to Management by Criticalities (MBC II)*, Human Systems Management 24 January 1, 2005: 105–15.

[12] Mark L. Spearman, David L. Woodruff, and Wallace J. Hopp, *CONWIP: A Pull Alternative to Kanban*, International Journal of Production Research 28, no. 5 May 1, 1990: 879–94.

[13] Rajan Suri, *Quick Response Manufacturing: A Companywide Approach to Reducing Lead Times* Portland, Oregon, USA: Taylor & Francis Inc, 1998, ISBN 978-1-56327-201-1.

small but dedicated group of followers. If you want to explore POLCA, a later book by Suri, *The Practitioner's Guide to POLCA,* is more helpful.[14]

---

[14] Rajan Suri, *The Practitioner's Guide to POLCA: The Production Control System for High-Mix, Low-Volume and Custom Products* Productivity Press, 2018, ISBN 978-1-138-21064-6.

Chapter 2
Fundamentals of Pull Systems

Pull in its essence is a structured way to manage your material flow. **You have an inventory limit. Whenever an item or job leaves the system, the system automatically takes actions either to replace this item (if it is make-to-stock) or to start the next job (if it is make-to-order).** Hence, this limit on the inventory controls the start of production of additional parts or jobs and prevents the overloading of the system as well as accidental underutilization of the system. However, there are many misconceptions on what "pull" actually is, especially contrasted with its opposite, "push".

2.1 Misconceptions on Push Versus Pull

One of the key features in lean production is to **use pull rather than push**. While pretty much everyone knows (at least in theory) how to implement pull using kanban, the underlying fundamental differences are fuzzier. But what exactly is the difference between push and pull? Also, what makes pull systems so superior to push systems?

It turns out that most definitions are going in the wrong direction, or are at least somewhat confusing. Even the names *push* and *pull* are not well suited to describe the concept, although these terms are even used at Toyota. Neither are common illustrations, similar to the one shown in Figure 6.

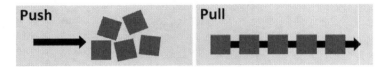

Figure 6: Inaccurate illustration for push and pull. Similar illustrations are often used to visualize push and pull. Unfortunately, the illustration and even the names push *and* pull *are very misleading. (Image Roser)*

Let me start with a selection of different definitions of push and pull that are commonly used. While these are not actual quotes, similar descriptions can be found all over the internet and in other sources.

2.1.1 Misconception 1: Make-to-Stock and Make-to-Order

Push is make-to-stock, not based on actual demand. Pull is make-to-order, based on actual demand.

Often, push and pull are (incorrectly) explained through "make-to-stock" and "make-to-order", similar to the fictitious quote above and visualized in Figure 7. Supposedly, a push production creates products without having a specific customer request (make-to-stock). A pull production supposedly produces only if there is a request for a product by the end customer (make-to-order).

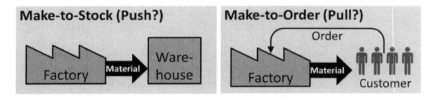

Figure 7: Incorrect concept of push being make-to-stock and pull being make-to-order (Image Roser)

That is a very flawed view of the difference between push and pull. Even Toyota produces some of their cars make-to-stock without a specific customer order. They build up stock of popular models for walk-in customers. Hence, it is perfectly possible to manage a make-to-stock system using pull production. Kanban is a perfect example of a make-to-stock production system.

Furthermore, using this definition, pull production would be centuries old, since make-to-order is an ancient concept. Every cobbler before the Industrial Revolution made shoes only if a customer requested them. However, these cobblers were anything but lean, and were usually surrounded by piles of material.

Finally, if you get an order from a subsequent warehouse for a make-to-stock item, it is both make-to-stock and an order, as shown in Figure 8. Is this approach pull or push?

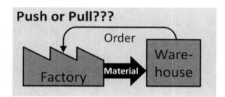

Figure 8: If push would be make-to-stock and pull would be make-to-order, what would an order from the warehouse be? (Image Roser)

Sometimes it is attempted to correct the above definition by stating that the *order* in *make-to-order* does not have to be an end customer, but could be a stage in between. However, even for make-to-stock, somebody somewhere has to give the order to produce. Here, this *somebody* would be the customer, and any make-to-stock would be identical to make-to-order.

2.1.2 Misconception 2: Market Forecast Versus Actual Demand

Push is planned based on a market forecast. Pull is planned based on actual customer demand.

This (also incorrect!) definition uses slightly different words but is otherwise similar to the make-to-stock and make-to-order definitions above. No factory produces anything unless they expect to sell the item to a customer eventually. This example is visualized in Figure 9 and Figure 10.

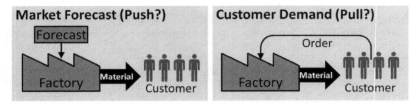

Figure 9: Incorrect model for push and pull based on a forecast (Image Roser)

Any forecast is influenced by current customer orders. The forecast just tries to predict future customer orders. Pretty much all make-to-stock production is based on a forecast, hoping the customer will show up and eventually buy the goods.

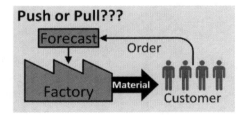

Figure 10: At the end, some signal must come from the customer. (Image Roser)

2.1.3 Misconception 3: Direction of Information Flow

The difference between push and pull is the direction of the information flow. Push has a central logistic plan, and the information flows in the same direction as the material. Pull has an information flow opposite of the material flow.

Often, the fundamental difference between push and pull is seen as the difference between having a central logistic plan versus information directly from the customers. This is illustrated in Figure 11. If there is a central logistic plan, it is supposedly push. If the orders come directly from the customer, it is supposedly pull.

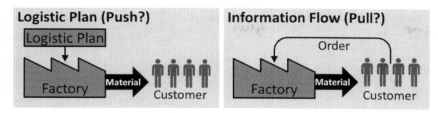

Figure 11: Misleading model for push and pull based on the direction of information flow (Image Roser)

This explanation is also often used at Toyota, and as such is not wrong. However, I believe this definition describes pull only on a very high level, and can easily be misunderstood.

We have again the same problems as before. The logistic plan is not created out of thin air, but based on the expected demands of the customer, as shown in Figure 12.

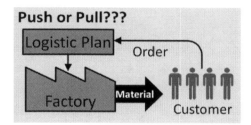

Figure 12: If the customer input goes into the production plan, would it be push or pull? (Image Roser)

2.1.4 Misconception 4: ERP and Kanban

ERP is push, kanban is pull.

A well-implemented kanban system (i.e., not just a plant where every paper is miraculously called *kanban*) is indeed a pull system. However, it is not the only way to create a pull system. You could also use CONWIP, POLCA, reorder points, or other methods.

Also, while a functioning kanban system is a pull system, it does not have to be based on paper kanbans. A kanban system can also be digital using an ERP[15] system, in which case the logistic plan would create its orders based on kanbans. Hence, you would have a pull system with a central logistic plan. Therefore, this definition of push and pull does not work either, as it is entirely feasible to implement pull using ERP.

2.2 Pull Is an Inventory Limit That Is Replenished!

All the definitions above do not capture the true essence of a pull system. The confusion probably stems from the rather unfortunate names *push* and *pull*, which are misleading. Regrettably, that is what it is called. Regarding the true difference between push and pull, Hopp and Spearman are probably closer to the truth. They require an explicit **limit on inventory**, which for me makes half of a pull system.

> *A pull production system is one that explicitly limits the amount of work in process that can be in the system. [...] a push production system is one that has no explicit limit on the amount of work in process that can be in the system.*[16]

However, they overlooked the **signal when an item leaves the system**. This signal **must start a replenishment of make-to-stock items or release the next job for make-to-order items**. Therefore, my definition of push and pull is as follows. This is also illustrated in Figure 13.

- A pull system must have an explicit target limit on your inventory or workload!
- A pull system must **release a signal when an item or batch of items leaves the system**. For batches of material, the signal can be with either the first or the last item in a batch.
- This **signal must start replenishment** for make-to-stock items **or release the next job** for make-to-order items. The replenishment or

---

15 ERP stands for Enterprise Resource Planning, and is a software system for managing your company. The largest ERP systems vendors are SAP and Oracle.

16 Wallace J. Hopp and Mark L. Spearman, *To Pull or Not to Pull: What Is the Question?*, *Manufacturing & Service Operations Management* 6, no. 2 April 1, 2004: 133–48.

---

release must be the same quantity or the same workload as the items that left the system.

- A system missing any of these three requirements above is a push system.

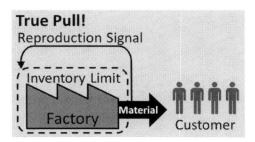

Figure 13: Pull systems are systems with a fixed target limit on the inventory and a signal to replenish. (Image Roser)

Whenever an item leaves the system and the inventory falls below the target, actions have to be taken to increase the inventory to the target again. This usually means producing or purchasing. It has nothing to do with physical pulling or pushing of material or information.

A true pull system produces only if the inventory limit has not yet been reached. It must stop if the limit on the inventory has been reached. Production can only start again if another completed part leaves the system.

Even with push, any shop floor eventually has an upper limit. Yet, this is not determined rationally, but coincidentally by the available space. If all available space is crammed full with inventory, at one point the production will stop. However, this limit is not well defined as it depends on the creativity of the logistics people to find more spaces to put items. Additionally, any space may be taken up by any type of part. A part that may need the space more urgently may be out of luck just because another less important part was put there already.

For example, a kanban system has a limit on the inventory for every part type. You cannot have more material than what is allowed by your number of kanbans. This limit is explicitly defined by the number of kanbans. When an item leaves the system, the kanban is the signal to replenish this item.

Similarly, for CONWIP systems, a job in the backlog of open orders is only started if there is a free CONWIP card available. While an order is not rejected in a CONWIP system, it still has to wait until a slot in the form of a free CONWIP card becomes available.

Overall, many sources or practitioners define push and pull misleadingly or incorrectly. This is probably because the names *push* and *pull* are actually quite misrepresentative. This confusion is unfortunate, since pull is one of the key elements of a successful manufacturing system. The major difference is the inventory limit coupled with automatic replenishment. **A pull system has an explicit limit on the inventory.** This limit is for each part individually if make-to-stock and for all jobs combined if make-to-order. A part leaving the system gives a **signal that starts a process to reach the inventory limit again**, either through replenishment or through the release of the next job. If you have such a clearly defined inventory limit with a signal to replenish, you have a pull system and hence have access to all the benefits of a lean pull production. **If there is no clearly defined limit on inventory, or no signal to replenish, you have a push system**.

2.3 Alternatives to an Inventory Limit

Key to any pull system is the limit of the inventory. The system automatically aims to always reach this inventory limit. If an item leaves the system, another item is released for production in the system. This inventory limit is often defined as a **number of products** for any product type for make-to-stock production.

However, there are also alternatives on how to define this inventory limit. Limiting the number of products is common for make-to-stock pull production of individual parts. However, if you have a make-to-order system, you may limit the **number of jobs** or the **number of orders** in your system.

To increase the precision of the inventory limit for jobs of different sizes, it is also possible to limit not the number of jobs or parts, but the **workload** of these jobs or parts. This is often called **workload control**. Rather than limiting the system to a number of parts, the system is limited to a number of machining or process hours.

A new job is only started if the new job does not push the workload over the target limit. This approach is the default for drum-buffer-rope, but it can also be adapted to any of the other pull systems presented in this book.

Measuring the workload instead of the quantity gives a more leveled pull system, especially for jobs with varying workload.

It is not that the workload is an approximation for the quantity. Instead, the quantity is an approximation for the workload. What we truly want to limit in our pull system is the workload. For make-to-order, this is more precise than a limit on the number of jobs.

A simple limit on the number of jobs makes no difference between small and quick jobs versus large and cumbersome jobs. However, estimating and tracking the workload requires significantly more effort compared to just counting the number of jobs. For most cases, simply limiting the quantity is fine, and the more cumbersome limit on the total workload is usually not necessary.

In process industry, however, the production may not always be measured in pieces. Sometimes it is measured in a continuous quantity like liters, kilograms, cubic meters, etc. Here, you can limit the **continuous quantity** to establish pull.

This works also for a truly continuous process where there is an uninterrupted stream of your product. An example would be the water treatment plant, where tap water is produced in a continuous process. Your target limit on your continuous quantity would be your storage capacity (water tower, cistern, etc.). Your plant produces water until the tanks are full, and then stops. If the level in your tanks drop, you start producing again.

Contrarily, if your process industry works in batches (one vat of beer, one barrel of whiskey, etc.), then a batch may be an adequate substitute for a continuous quantity that can be measured simply by counting. Here a "normal" pull system that simply counts the units will suffice.

You will also find other workload measures outside of the conventional productive industry. You may have a target limit on the number of **calls** in a call center, or the number of **customers** for your shop. You may limit the number of **patients** in your hospital (for optional treatment only, please!), or separately for individual departments like radiology, therapy, laboratory, etc. You can limit the number of **documents in progress** for your accounting service.

In software development or technical design, the target limit is often on the number of **projects** that are worked on simultaneously. This limit can also be applied not only to the entire department but also to individual programmers or designers. There can also be individual target limits for different stages along the value chain, like "write bids", "analyze", "develop", or "testing".

The possibilities here are as endless as the economy, and many different limits are imaginable. **Create a target limit in units that approximate your workload. Include a process to track the limit and release more work into the system if the workload falls below the limit.** Do this with a system that is also easy to understand and measure, and you will have a pull system.

2.4 Why Pull Is So Superior

Pull systems helped Toyota and many other companies to become successful. It is widely regarded as superior to push. But why does this limit on inventory make so much difference? Why do pull systems vastly outperform push production systems? Pull production has several beneficial effects. The most important one is the limit on the inventory. Pull helps you to keep your inventory level at a sweet spot for your manufacturing system. There are even more positive effects of pull on the stability of your production system. But first let's look deeper at inventory.

2.4.1 Effect of Inventory on Performance

The optimal state of many performance indicators is often either the maximum (e.g., productivity, delivery speed) or the minimum (e.g., defects, cost). Inventory, however, is different. Too much can be as bad as too little. Find a sweet spot with just the right amount of inventory. You also have to stay close to this spot for a continuously good performance.

A study found that between 1986 and 2000, the average inventory of US manufacturing firms decreased from 96 days to 81 days.[17] Pretty much all the reduction was in the work-in-process inventory, and not in the finished-goods inventory. This study also found that companies with comparatively high inventory had the worst stock performance. Companies with the smallest inventories performed much better. Surprisingly, companies with slightly less than average inventory levels performed best. This shows that cutting inventory too much or too fast may bring little benefit, but not reducing the inventory is even worse.

Other reports show that the trend of reducing inventory continues.[18] Toyota is among the leanest companies I know. They have only two hours' worth of inventory in their inbound warehouses, and not much more within the factory itself. Good Western companies have two days' worth of inbound inventory. However, an average company often has over two weeks or more of inventory in the inbound warehouse alone.

Inventory is one of the seven types of waste (*muda* in Japanese) in lean production. Having too much inventory has many negative side effects and induces hidden and not-so-hidden costs. Besides the obvious **tied-up capital**, there is **storage, handling, taxes, insurance, administration, obsolescence**, and **theft**, to name only the most significant effects.

On top of that, and probably as detrimental as all the previous negative effects, **a large inventory makes your system sluggish**. If the customer demand stays constant and you increase your inventory, all parts have to wait longer until they reach the customer. Hence, new products or new orders will take longer to reach the market. Yet especially in today's fast-paced business, companies can ill afford to delay production because they have to produce and/or sell off the old ones first. Similar applies to a change in the product or the fixing of a newly discovered systematic defect. The higher the inventory, the more troublesome it is to fix it all.

---

[17] Hong Chen, Murray Z. Frank, and Owen Q. Wu, *What Actually Happened to the Inventories of American Companies Between 1981 and 2000?*, Management Science, July 1, 2005.

[18] The Economist, *Supple Supplies - Businesses Are Proving Quite Resilient to the Pandemic | Briefing, The Economist*, May 16, 2020, https://www.economist.com/briefing/2020/05/16/businesses-are-proving-quite-resilient-to-the-pandemic.

Overall, both the expenses and the delays will cost you anywhere between 30% and 65% of the value of the goods per year.[19] Hence, having an average inventory of one million euro will cost you between one-third and one-half of that sum per year. I am not sure if all companies have understood this expense associated with inventory yet.

But do not reduce too much either. Many companies are reducing their inventory, even if all too often the reason is simply that Toyota does it. However, simply reducing the inventory brings up another problem.

In any production system, there are fluctuations. Different products are produced. Parts may arrive early or late. Processes will take longer than expected or will be faster. Operators may be available or not. In essence, material does not flow at an even speed, but often moves in waves, sometimes faster and sometimes slower.

This is especially true if you do not look at the total inventory, but at each individual part number. Your individual part types inventory will fluctuate much more proportionally than your total inventory across all part types. Your material flow on a part number basis is much more uneven. The effect is similar with other disturbances. In general, the smaller your produced quantity of a product, the more it fluctuates.

Reducing fluctuations is a major part of lean manufacturing. In particular, leveling aims to reduce fluctuations originating from the production program. However, there are more possible methods, like reducing part variants, line balancing, preventive maintenance, and many more.

Even with your best effort, you cannot eliminate all fluctuations. A second option is to decouple these fluctuations. For this, **inventory** is your friend. Depending on the pull loop, this can include raw materials, work in process (WIP), and finished goods. Inventory can be used for decoupling. The buffer inventory going up and down like waves decouples the fluctuations. This allows the machines and operators to work at a constant speed. Hence, you can provide the customer with material despite a fluctuating demand. However, if you cut your inventory, your ability to decouple these

---

[19] Helen Richardson, *Control Your Costs–Then Cut Them, Transportation & Distribution* 36, no. 12 December 1995: 94.

fluctuations decreases. These unchecked fluctuations will cause more problems for you.

Besides inventory, there are two more ways you can decouple fluctuations. After inventory, the second option is **capacity** adjustments. You ramp up your capacity when needed and reduce it when not. However, this is often not feasible on short notice in most modern production systems.

If you cannot use inventory or capacity to decouple these fluctuations, by default the third option will apply: **time**! Your manufacturing system will have plenty of waiting times. Operators, machines, and customers will all be waiting for material. The more you cut inventory below the sweet spot, the lower your utilization and delivery performance will be. Altogether, your cost will go up since you have a lot of processes that you do not use because of the lack of material. At the same time, you will have unhappy customers waiting for products—if they have not yet switched to the competition already.

If you reduce your inventory too much, your efficiency goes down and your cost goes up. This can soon be more expensive than the buffer inventory in the first place. To add insult to injury, your inventory won't really go down that much either. If the system lacks the internal capacity because of lack of material but you still order parts like you have full capacity, you will end up with piles of material anyway. Except that it is mostly the wrong kind. If you need 100 parts to make a product, you will have 99 on hand, but one is missing because of fluctuations that are not decoupled. Hence, the other 99 parts are lying around and cannot be used.

Overall, **too little inventory can be as bad as or even worse than too much inventory.** Somewhere in between there is a sweet spot where your total cost is minimal. Your system works more efficiently if there is not too much but also not too little inventory. Finding this exact spot is difficult, and it is pretty much impossible to calculate with any practical accuracy. Luckily, this spot is usually a wider valley. Therefore, having a small bit more or less inventory does not have such a drastic impact. Also, please remember that such a sweet spot is not static. It can change by itself, or—much better—you can improve your system to move the sweet spot to an even sweeter spot.

While most companies understand that lean production involves a reduction of inventory, they often miss the point that the system has to be improved too. Wannabe-lean companies that simply reduce inventory even past the sweet spot have too little inventory. This decreases performance.

They should actually increase inventory. Also, do not forget that it is possible to change these underlying relations by improving (or worsening) the system itself. But overall, having the right level of inventory is important for the success of the company. **Pull helps you to stay at or near a good level of inventory.** Pull helps you to avoid a lot of cost and delays that happen if you have too much or too little inventory.

2.4.2 It Reduces and Stabilizes Lead Time

Pull controls and manages the inventory. The production lead time is heavily influenced by the inventory. The relation between inventory, lead time, and throughput is described in Little's law, which I will show you in Chapter 5.4.1.3.

Pull helps you to both reduce the inventory and to keep it stable. This will reduce not only the overall lead time but also the fluctuations thereof. Especially this reduction in fluctuations makes it much easier to plan your system. Just in Time (JIT) is pretty much impossible to do without a good pull system.

Please note that while pull production limits the inventory to a target limit, inventories still can fluctuate below this limit. For example, with kanban systems, theoretically, all the kanbans could sit in the supermarket with their associated material. We would have our maximum inventory in the supermarket. However, it is also possible that all kanbans are waiting for production and our inventory would be zero. The reality is usually something in between. However, these fluctuations will probably be smaller than in a push system. One major factor here is that the signal for replenishment is happening almost automatically, whereas in a push system it may be delayed until a human notices the issue and starts production.

But keep in mind that pull does not prevent an empty inventory if major problems stop you from replenishing your goods for longer durations than the pull system was set up to handle. If your suppliers fail you, you will eventually run out of goods, no matter what type of pull or push system you are using. The same applies if the demand exceeds your capacity. No pull (or push) system can help you with that.

2.4.3 It Does It (Almost) Automatically

Having a pull system in place is like having an automatic system that keeps your inventory near the sweet spot below a certain target limit. This applies no matter if you implement pull using kanban (for make-to-stock), CONWIP (for make-to-order), or any other pull system or combination thereof. If the system is working, it needs only a little maintenance to check for lost cards or to update the number of cards occasionally.

2.4.4 It Is Suited for Almost Any Production System

Pull systems are suitable for almost any production system, no matter if you are mass producing a few part types (often called high-volume-low-mix) or customizing every individual product (often called low-volume-high-mix). It works with flow shops and job shops, and even with project shops like construction sites (limit the number of construction sites to your capacity). It works for big and small parts. Pull can be implemented for discrete parts (things you can count like screws or cars), for continuous production (chemicals, oils, gases), and even digital calculation and information processing. Pull can be used in administrative processes, services, product design, and even in hospitals (although you have to get the prioritization process right for the last one!).

2.4.5 It Is Robust!

There are different ways to control your production system. You could plan using available capacity and required deadlines, which would be the conventional push approach. Unfortunately, both capacity and deadlines are usually rather volatile and can change quickly. Hence, planning ahead is difficult, and frequent changes to the production plan are needed to match changing situations. Overall, it is very tricky to plan reliably using conventional push production.

With pull production, however, you merely plan the limit on inventory, and establish a system for automatic replenishment or release of the next jobs if the inventory falls below the limit. Especially for releasing jobs in make-to-order production, pull usually includes a prioritization on which job to produce next. There is no need to plan the capacity in detail, or the deadlines, as long as your system has enough capacity and material. **Pull**

eliminates a big part of your planning effort, and hence also a lot of possibilities for mistakes.

Additionally, the system is very robust against the limit on inventory. It doesn't matter if your limit is a bit too high or a bit too low, your system is probably still going to work fine, even if you haven't hit the perfect inventory levels. Minor changes in the inventory limit do not lead to larger changes in the performance. Pull production is overall very robust and insensitive to fluctuations in the system.

Hence, overall pull systems are so great because they have a cap on inventory and can—if set up correctly—keep the inventory close to the sweet spot between too much and too little inventory. Pull systems can do this regardless of whether they are set up using kanban, CONWIP, or any other method for inventory caps. They can be used with almost any production system. Hence, if you can change your system from a push system to a pull system, do it! It will help you to get your industry organized.

2.5 What Helps You With Pull?

Pull is a very useful tool for manufacturing and other types of processes. However, the advantages can be enhanced (or watered down) by other factors. Pull benefits from many other tools in the lean toolbox, as well as the underlying lean philosophy. Most of these tools help to reduce the inventory limit (or workload limit), allowing you to produce even more efficiently.

Here I will show what can help with pull. For some of these criteria below, a poor performance could require improving the criteria first before implementing new pull systems. Others are beneficial to pull, but not strictly required. It goes without saying that if your biggest issue is the safety of your operators, then this should be your top priority before anything else.

2.5.1 Process Stability

An important basis for any pull system is a reasonably stable production or logistic system. The processes in the system should run stable, without significant downtimes or other delays. Stability is beneficial, but it is not a binary on/off situation. You can also implement pull if your system is less stable, but you would need a larger inventory limit to cover eventualities. The more stable the system runs, the lower your inventory limit can be.

If your process stability is very far off the mark, invest time and effort to improve stability before you start to implement pull systems. Large instabilities would require very large target inventories to buffer them, leading to a lot of other problems. Hence, having an at least somewhat stable process is often seen as a prerequisite for good pull production. Instabilities lead to either large inventories or stock-outs despite pull production due to insufficient buffer inventories.

2.5.2 Material Availability

This stability also extends to the material availability. Pull systems assume that the necessary materials from the preceding processes are available. For the pull system to work, this should (mostly) be the case. Granted, even the best plants will have a lack of raw materials eventually. Yet, this requires extra work to handle the problem and might also cause delays downstream. The higher your material availability, the more stable your production system can run, which allows you to lower your inventory. **If your material availability is very far off the mark, invest time and effort to improve material availability before you start to implement pull systems.**

2.5.3 Quality

While the vision is zero defects, few plants can achieve this. For a pull system to run well, you would need reasonable product (or service) quality. The higher your quality, the less effort is needed to fix quality issues, and the more stable your production system can run. **If your quality performance is very far off the mark, invest time and effort into improving quality before you start to implement pull systems.**

2.5.4 Flow

Flow is an important but also very general concept in lean. It is more of a philosophy that your material should move along the value stream instead of idling and waiting. In reality, some waiting times are hard to avoid, but improving flow is beneficial not only for pull but for the entire system. Simultaneously, a good pull system also helps to improve flow. This is easiest in a **flow shop**, and it is always recommended to change from a job shop to a flow shop if you can.

Often, the term **one-piece flow** is used, although with different definitions. One-piece flow is a part that moves downstream right after completion at a process. It is not collected in a batch before the entire batch is moved. Some definitions also require that there be no inventory buffers between processes, but this is often highly impractical in reality. Sometimes it is also defined as lot size one, but this is a different aspect. For me, one-piece flow also works with larger lot sizes, as long as the parts don't have to wait for the entire lot before moving forward.

Regardless of how you define flow, it helps with pull if your material is actually flowing and not idling in warehouses. However, even the best companies have material in a warehouse, and some idling of material is unavoidable. A lack of process stability, material availability, and quality may take priority over implementing a new pull system. However, it is rare for a lack of flow to prevent the implementation of a pull system. Nevertheless, **better flow is beneficial for a pull system.**

2.5.5 Small Lot Sizes

Similar to flow, small lot sizes are not strictly necessary for pull systems, but can help to improve the performance of pull systems. As we will see later during the calculation of the inventory limit, the lot size has a large impact on the inventory limit. Smaller lot sizes will allow smaller target inventories. **True north is a lot size of one**, although this may be hard to achieve if you have larger changeover times. Reducing changeover times will allow you smaller lot sizes. I have even seen lot size one for automated aluminum casting at Denso, which was quite impressive.[20]

---

[20] Christoph Roser, *Toyota's and Denso's Relentless Quest for Lot Size One*, in *Collected Blog Posts of AllAboutLean.Com 2016*, Collected Blog Posts of AllAboutLean.Com 4 Offenbach, Germany: AllAboutLean Publishing, 2020, 250–55, ISBN 978-3-96382-016-8.

2.5.6 Leveling

Another factor to improve your pull system is leveling. There are different methods of leveling. You can **level by volume** and **level by variety**. Please stay away from things like a two-week pattern, often called EPEI (Every Part Every Interval) leveling. Those are very difficult to maintain. The chaos resulting from changes to these long-term patterns neutralizes the benefit of leveling in the first place, and you are worse off than before.[21]

Mixing up your daily production plan into a pattern with small lot sizes is possible for most production systems.[22] You can also try to **level your capacity**, producing similar quantities every day.[23] As with lot sizes and flow, leveling is not necessarily a prerequisite for pull, although pull and your entire organization will benefit from it.

2.6 When NOT to Pull

Pull systems overall are very robust and stable and well suited for pretty much any production system. In fact, pull can also be used outside normal industry (e.g., in healthcare, military, call centers, and other service industries, banking, or data processing). Pull is highly advisable for almost any production system. However, there are a few — very few — exceptions.

---

[21] Christoph Roser, *Theory of Every Part Every Interval (EPEI) Leveling & Heijunka*, in *Collected Blog Posts of AllAboutLean.Com 2014*, Collected Blog Posts of AllAboutLean.Com 2 Offenbach, Germany: AllAboutLean Publishing, 2020, 287–92, ISBN 978-3-96382-010-6.

[22] Christoph Roser, *Introduction to One-Piece Flow Leveling – Part 1 Theory*, in *Collected Blog Posts of AllAboutLean.Com 2015*, Collected Blog Posts of AllAboutLean.Com 3 Offenbach, Germany: AllAboutLean Publishing, 2020, 1–5, ISBN 978-3-96382-013-7.

[23] Christoph Roser, *An Introduction to Capacity Leveling*, in *Collected Blog Posts of AllAboutLean.Com 2014*, Collected Blog Posts of AllAboutLean.Com 2 Offenbach, Germany: AllAboutLean Publishing, 2020, 281–86, ISBN 978-3-96382-010-6.

2.6.1 Lack of Control of Arriving Parts or Jobs

Pull has one requirement for it to work: **You need to control the number of new parts or tasks arriving.** This is usually the case in manufacturing. Parts arrive only when you explicitly order or produce them. Without a purchase or production order, you will not get any parts. Thus, you can limit the maximum inventory simply by not ordering or producing more when you reach that limit. A counterexample would be a repair store or a key-copying location. A typical store usually has no influence on when a customer shows up. They usually choose not to limit the number of customers in the store to prevent bad reviews. Instead, if multiple customers arrive, the customer has to wait. If very few customers arrive, the staff has to wait. There is usually no defined limit on the upper number of customers, although at one point the location is simply so crowded that no one can enter anymore.

However, it is also often possible to limit the number of customers. Restaurants are usually limited by the number of seats. During the 2020 coronavirus crisis, many stores were ordered to limit the number of shoppers. It is quite possible to create such an upper limit. Furthermore, it is also possible to decouple the uncontrollable arrival, and have pull systems supplying the fluctuating demand. For example, a restaurant kitchen can use pull for ordering raw materials and cooking, even though the queue of customers goes around the block.

2.6.2 Difficult or Expensive to Turn Off Process

Another case against pull is if **it is very expensive or impossible to turn off the process**. Even if the customer purchases less, you may have to produce and build up inventory to avoid the even larger expense of shutting down your process. This may happen in blast furnaces for steel smelting. Conventional wisdom is to turn on the furnace and then run it for twenty years without break until the inner lining is getting too thin and needs to be replaced. Stopping and restarting this process is very expensive, and companies try to avoid this. Another example may be oil platforms, where the major cost is setting up the platform and drilling a hole.

Once the platform is running, it often makes economic sense to keep operating even if the demand and the oil price go down. For example, extraction oil from oil sands may require heating the ground to liquefy tar.

Turning off the heat not only would require a lot of energy to reheat it, but may also permanently damage the output of the well.

Finally, some plastic processing may prefer to keep the process running rather than turning it off and having the plastic solidify in the machine, requiring expensive clean-ups. A buffer after such an expensive process decouples the material flow. This avoids pushing material into the rest of the value stream. A downstream pull system is quite possible even with a push material source, as long as it is decoupled by a buffer. Note, however, that this buffer can become very large.

2.6.3 Very Long Replenishment Time

Pull may also be difficult **if you have very long replenishment times**, especially **if the shelf life of your product is significantly shorter than your replenishment time**. For example, take a strawberry farmer. The farmer has to decide a year ahead which crops and how many to plant. Once the strawberries are ready for harvesting, the farmer has to sell them at whatever the market prices are. There are few options to store strawberries for extended periods.

Even more extreme would be a forest owner producing lumber. Depending on the type of lumber, it can take decades for the product to be ready for harvesting. In such situations, it is very difficult to create a pull system, albeit the quantity is usually constrained by the available farmland. However, here, too, large inventories can decouple this tree farm from the downstream lumberyards. These allow pull to be used downstream of the decoupling buffers.

2.6.4 Very Short Shelf Life

Related to the long replenishment time, there may also be instances where push may be better than pull if the product has a **very short shelf life**. Larger inventory limits may lead to inventory expiring in your warehouse. If other measures you could take do not rectify this, then you may use push instead of pull. However, you should first try other approaches to reduce inventory or extend the shelf life. See Chapter 5.7.5 for more details on the other options.

2.6.5 High Level of Control and Superior Knowledge

Finally, push may be better than pull if **you have a very high level of control of your system and an excellent knowledge of upcoming fluctuations** (i.e., you can use push if you are close to all knowing and all seeing in your production system). Even then, pull would still work. It is imaginable to have a push-type system that outperforms a pull system, but only if you have such an excellent understanding of your system. A pull system reacts immediately whenever a part is consumed or completed. A push system controlled by humans, computer logic, or artificial intelligence would have to outperform pull systems. For the same inventory, this should give better availability, better utilization, or better lead time, or a combination thereof. Alternatively, you should get a lower inventory for the same availability, utilization, or lead time.

Hence, if the knowledge of the human, computer logic, or artificial intelligence on the future fluctuations and disruptions is exceptional, they may manage a push production system better than pull production. Yet, I believe such companies are as rare as unicorns. While you can sometimes meet managers that believe they or their organization is all knowing (usually in the higher ranks far removed from the shop floor), it is rarely true.

2.6.6 Invalid Reasons for Push

Some sources mention **using push if the demand is exceedingly high**, although I would advise against this. For example, during the 2020 coronavirus pandemic, masks were in demand much higher than supply could provide. The idea of using push is to produce whatever you can and not worry about target inventories.

However, every demand peak will end, either because demand goes down or because, as in 2020, supply goes up. At this point, your push system will overflow and your inventory will spiral out of control. Judge if pushing is worth the risk of having excess inventory when the demand and supply normalizes. I would still recommend using pull and adjust the inventory limits rather than throw it all out for an uncontrolled push system.

Similarly, you could **use pull if supply is exceedingly low**, albeit I would advise against it for similar reasons. Using again the 2020 pandemic as an example, customers ordered many more masks than they needed, hoping that at least some of them would be delivered. You would order twice your needs, hoping to get at least half of what you actually need. This game may or may not bring a benefit to your company, but if everybody does it, all will be worse off. And again, you risk having way too much inventory arrive once the supply normalizes. This negative effect on the supply chain is known as the bullwhip effect. Use it at your own risk.

Other than that, I am always hard pressed to find good examples where pull is not superior to push. In literature, you can find many scientific articles claiming that push is better in some cases, but if you dig deeper, you find that they just did not understand what pull actually is. Pull is almost always much better at handling uncertainty and faster at maintaining your inventory buffer.

In reality, pull production takes care of all the regular everyday production. If you know your upcoming fluctuations, it may be better to adjust the pull system. Fluctuations could be seasonal demand changes, or your ship with goods just sunk, or all your products failed the safety test and need to be remade, or there is a craze for your products just because Beyoncé said she loves them, or your products sit like lead on the shelves just because Beyoncé said she hates them, or... or... or... I am sure you are familiar with many such examples in your industry.

2.7 What Problems Does Pull NOT Help With?

Pull is a great tool to improve your material flow. However, it is not a catch-all universal solution for all of your problems. Here are a few examples where pull will not help you, although it won't make it worse either.

2.7.1 Lack of Capacity

I am sometimes asked if pull can help with a lack of production capacity. No, **pull does not help if you have not enough production capacity**. It can help with producing the right stuff, but if your production system is simply too small, pull will not help. If your process can make 100 parts per day but you need 200 per day, pull will not fix this. You would need other tools to find and improve the bottleneck.[24, 25, 26]

This being said, there may be some side benefits of pull that impact capacity. Pull helps your system to run smoothly and reduces chaos. Less chaos often means that the system can focus more on production, and you have less waiting times for materials or searching for jobs. Hence, pull can have a beneficial impact on your production system capacity, but pull should not be your primary focus if you have capacity problems.

2.7.2 Quality Problems

Similarly, **pull does not help with quality problems**. Pull is a better way to tell your system *what* to produce and *when*, but it does not tell your system *how* to produce it. Hence, the quality is usually not affected by a pull system. But again, there may be spin-off effects. Having less chaos thanks to a pull system may reduce errors and mistakes, hence pull could improve the quality. Smaller lots in pull systems also allow you to find quality problems earlier. Nevertheless, if your biggest problem is quality, then pull should not be the focus of your improvement efforts.

2.7.3 Breakdowns and Lack of Material

Pull also does not help you with unstable processes and logistics. **Pull does not help if your processes misbehave or break frequently. Pull does not help if your supplier fails you**. Frequent downtimes and lack of materials will cause confusion regardless of whether it is a push or pull system. Lack

---

[24] Christoph Roser, *Mathematically Accurate Bottleneck Detection 1 – The Average Active Period Method*, in *Collected Blog Posts of AllAboutLean.Com 2014*, Collected Blog Posts of AllAboutLean.Com 2 Offenbach, Germany: AllAboutLean Publishing, 2020, 133–36, ISBN 978-3-96382-010-6.

[25] Christoph Roser, *The Bottleneck Walk – Practical Bottleneck Detection Part 1*, in *Collected Blog Posts of AllAboutLean.Com 2014*, Collected Blog Posts of AllAboutLean.Com 2 Offenbach, Germany: AllAboutLean Publishing, 2020, 1, ISBN 978-3-96382-010-6.

[26] Christoph Roser, *Bottleneck Management Part 1 – Introduction and Utilization*, in *Collected Blog Posts of AllAboutLean.Com 2014*, Collected Blog Posts of AllAboutLean.Com 2 Offenbach, Germany: AllAboutLean Publishing, 2020, 246–51, ISBN 978-3-96382-010-6.

of materials also throws a production system into chaos. In such cases, your improvement focus should be on creating a stable system. Can you reduce the frequency and/or duration of breakdowns, using for example total preventive maintenance or other tools? Can you arrange for a more stable material supply? Again, since pull helps to reduce chaos, there may be some side benefits from pull in such cases. For example, the causes of disruptions may be understood earlier because of pull. But again, if your biggest problem is an unstable production or logistic system, wait with pull and reduce your instabilities first.

Chapter 3
Comparison of Different Pull Systems

There are many ways to create a pull production system. All of them have in common that they limit the material to an upper maximum limit within their segment of the value stream. This is combined with a system to replenish if material leaves the system. They control the material flow for a segment of your value stream. This segment is usually between an inventory at the end, and another inventory or a production process somewhere upstream. For kanban this would be called the kanban loop, similarly for CONWIP this is the CONWIP loop. An example of a kanban loop is shown in Figure 14.

The most famous pull system is kanban, but even there you have different options. However, there are even more pull systems, like CONWIP, drum-buffer-rope, POLCA, or even simple reorder point systems.

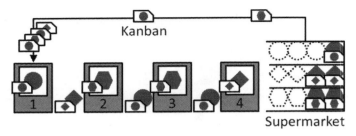

Figure 14: Example of a typical kanban loop across four processes. The material with kanbans flows from left to right to the supermarket. After taking a part out of the supermarket, the kanbans flow back to the beginning of the loop. (Image Roser)

3.1 Criteria for Pull System Selection

Depending on your system, different pull methods may be suitable for implementation. Let me show you the relevant factors before helping you to decide which pull system is best for you.

3.1.1 Make-to-Stock Versus Make-to-Order

There are different criteria that you have to look at when selecting the flavor of your pull system. The most important criteria is if your process precedes the customer order, or if the customer order precedes the process. **Was the item produced, transported, or purchased before the customer order, or after the customer order?**

If the goods are produced before a specific customer order and where the products usually wait in inventory for a customer order, it is called **make-to-stock** (MTS). If the goods are produced only after a specific customer order, it is called **make-to-order** (MTO).

Similar systems exist for logistics. It is often called **purchase-to-stock** (PTS) or **purchase-to-order** (PTO). However, for pull systems it is irrelevant if you pay for the goods or not, so it would be more accurate to call these **ship-to-stock** (STS) or **ship-to-order** (STO). Ship-to-stock may also benefit from a pull system. However, ship-to-order is usually not managed by pull; you just purchase or ship whatever you need. Only if irregular large ship-to-order processes risk overwhelming the supplier should you consider limiting your shipping quantity through a pull system. But even then, this is uncommon.

Development is usually based on a custom order or a new product, and you do not develop the same product twice, hence development would always be **development-to-order**. Subsequently we will call these concepts make-to-stock and make-to-order for simplicity's sake, although they also apply to purchasing, development, and others.

In industry, the distinction between **high-volume-low-mix** and **low-volume-high-mix** is sometimes used. It differentiates if you make a lot of identical parts, or if your parts are usually different. This is related, but not the key decision parameter for pull systems. For pull, the key question is still if you aim to always have a product in inventory (make-to-stock), or if you produce only if there is an order and the customer has to wait (make-to-order).

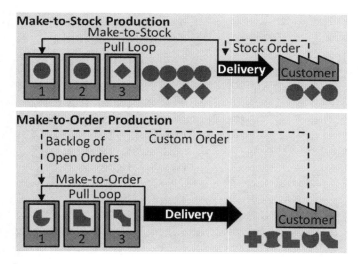

Figure 15: Visualization of a make-to-stock and a make-to-order production system. Notice the difference in the end of the pull loops and the entry of the orders. (Image Roser)

Usually, high-volume-low-mix is well suited for make-to-stock, and low-volume-high-mix is well suited for make-to-order. However, there may be cases where you decide to still make a high-volume product on order or a low-volume product to stock. Hence, **make-to-order and make-to-stock is the key factor for selecting a pull system**, as shown in Figure 15. This is probably the most fundamental factor for selecting your pull system, as make-to-stock and make-to-order have two fundamentally different goals.

With make-to-stock, the goal is to always have parts available, while requiring as little inventory as possible. You typically produce large quantities of identical products (high-volume-low-mix). The customer order starts a delivery of the item in stock, followed by the replenishment of an identical item. The item was produced in advance, and the customer (ideally) does not have to wait.

With make-to-order, production starts only after a customer order. You usually have a backlog of open orders waiting to enter the pull system. This backlog may also be sequenced according to its priority. Furthermore, a completed part is usually delivered right away after production, and you have little or no finished-goods inventory. Hence, **with make-to-stock, the goal is to minimize the time between receiving the order and delivering the product, while keeping the system utilization reasonably high.** You typically produce many different products in small quantities or even completely unique items (low-volume-high-mix). Only after a customer order does production start. The customer always has to wait for delivery after making an order.

As for keeping the make-to-order utilization reasonably high, please note that this means neither a utilization of 100%, nor all processes having a high utilization. Especially for imbalanced systems, as commonly found in job shops, many processes will be idle frequently because they are not needed as much as other processes. Artificially increasing the utilization of such infrequently needed processes will increase the lead time and create havoc with your production system.

One important effect of this factor on your pull system is the level of detail needed for controlling your pull system. **For make-to-order production, it suffices to have only a generic inventory limit across all of your parts within your pull loop.** Different parts all contribute to the same inventory limit. **For make-to-stock production, however, you have to set a limit separately for every single part type** that is in your pull loop.

Unfortunately, you do not always have a system that is purely make-to-stock or purely make-to-order. Most of you will have systems that are a mix of both. You may hold your high-runner completed goods in inventory just in case a customer orders one item (make-to-stock). Your more exotic and less frequently ordered items, however, are produced only if there is a specific customer requesting this item (make-to-order). Both may be produced in the same manufacturing system. In this case, you would need a pull system capable of handling both situations. **This mix of make-to-order and make-to-stock is usually a combination of two different pull systems**, often kanban and CONWIP, as shown in Figure 16. Such combinations of pull systems are absolutely feasible and can handle a mix of make-to-order and make-to-stock production.

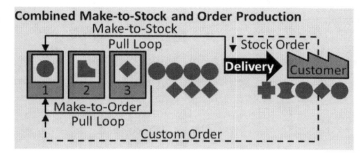

Figure 16: Visualization of a mixed make-to-stock and a make-to-order production system, where two different pull systems are used to control one production (Image Roser)

You may also produce custom make-to-order end products that you assemble based on standard parts that you produce or order in larger quantities and hold in inventory (make-to-stock). In this case, the last part or parts of your value stream may be make-to-order or a mixed system, while upstream systems can be make-to-stock. This is shown in Figure 17. Here it may be advisable to create different pull loops for different segments of the value stream, where the downstream loops are make-to-order and the upstream ones are make-to-stock. See Chapter 11 for more details on where to make pull loops.

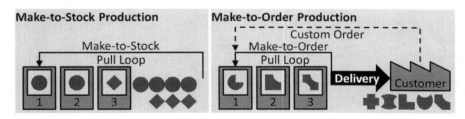

Figure 17: Make-to-stock loop feeding into a make-to-order production (Image Roser)

3.1.2 Production/Development Versus Purchasing

A second important distinction is the **capacity limitation**. Are you producing or developing, or are you purchasing items from an external supplier? This is based on the capacity limit of your system. **Can you get all the items you want at once (purchasing), or do you have to do it one at a time (development or production)? Do you have to worry about the production sequence of your items, or is it no problem to just get them all at the same time?** In practicality, this is often the difference if you produce or develop items yourself or if you order them from suppliers.

Production systems usually produce one item after another. Hence the sequence of your orders is relevant. Your production system has a limited capacity, which could be measured in parts per day. If you want to produce too much at the same time, your production system gets clogged up. Some products may be completed early, others may take longer.

However, if you order different goods from different suppliers, you need not think about the sequence of your order. You don't think if you should order parts A from supplier X first and then parts B from supplier Y. You just order them all at the same time. Even if you order multiple parts from the same supplier, you rarely worry about the sequence of the order. Instead, you let the supplier figure it out.

In reality, of course, purchasing items also has a capacity limit. If you order too much at the same time from a smaller supplier, their system may clog up, and your deliveries will be late. Hence, different from make-to-order and make-to-stock, this distinction also has a gray zone in between.

3.1.3 Flow Shop Versus Job Shop

Another less important factor relevant only to production but not to purchasing is if you have a job shop or a flow shop. Examples are shown in Figure 18.

Flow shops are much easier to handle. If you can turn your system into a flow shop, it will almost always be beneficial for your system. You only need to control the first process; the others are usually controlled automatically through a FIFO (First-In-First-Out).

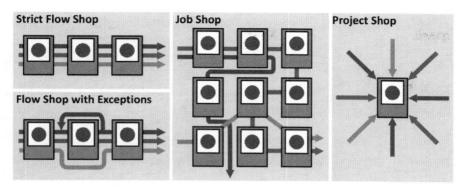

Figure 18: Illustration of a normal flow shop, a flow shop with some exceptions, a job shop, and a project shop. The different arrows represent different material flows. (Image Roser)

If, however, you have a job shop, you need to manage not only what to produce with your system, but have to manage every process in the job shop. POLCA specializes in job shops, but requires more effort because job shops in general require more effort. Another method, COBACABANA, also specializes in job shops, but there is no actual real-world implementation yet. Hence, you can find COBACABANA in the appendix.

For mixed systems that have some elements of a flow shop and some elements of a job shop, you may choose which concept fits your system better. Have you arranged your processes in a sequence that fits most products? Then it is probably closer to a flow shop. Were you unable to find a sequence since so many different products have different sequences? Then it is probably closer to a job shop.

3.1.4 High Demand Versus Low Demand

Another smaller factor relevant only for make-to-stock or ship-to-stock is the demand of a particular item. Do you sell large quantities or only a few items? This is also a relative factor. Judging if an item is high demand or low demand is relative to your system. This may also be very different depending on the product type. In particular, it may influence kanban systems to decide what variant of kanban you should use.

3.1.5 Small and Cheap Versus Expensive or Large

Finally, a consideration for make-to-stock systems is also the cost and effort of having the item in inventory. Most times, this is based mostly on the value and the size of the item. **If the item is expensive, you probably don't want to tie up too much capital in excess inventory. If the item is large, you probably don't want to use up too much storage space.** In both cases you may invest additional effort to reduce the quantity and hence reduce the tied-up capital or required storage space. For example, if you make cars, you don't want to put too many expensive and bulky engine drive trains on stock.

If the items are neither large nor expensive, you probably don't worry too much about your inventory as long as you have enough. In this case, having a bit more material than needed is usually nothing to worry about. Hence, here you may choose a method that may not have the smallest possible inventory limit, but is easier on the management of the pull system. Let's take again the example of building cars. You probably care little if you have 500 sheet metal screws for 1 cent each in inventory (in sum $5) or 5000 screws (in sum $50), as long as you have enough and it does not take up your valuable time for managing the inventory.

3.1.6 Discrete Versus Continuous Quantities

Many production systems measure the inventory limit in pieces or jobs. In this case, a kanban or CONWIP card simply represents a certain number of pieces or jobs. Other production systems, however, produce continuous quantities like liters or cubic meters. Even then, depending on the system, a card can represent a fixed quantity of products or workload. This is often a packaging size of the final product or a batch size during production.

However, there are production systems that produce in **truly continuous quantities**, like a water treatment plant, where the quantity is measured for example using a liquid height marker. In this case, all card-based systems are hard to use. Instead of cards, you would have to adapt to track the quantity in production and always replenish to the inventory limit. Most systems can be adapted for this, but the reorder point is by its nature well suited to this type of system.

3.2 Which Pull System Is Right for You?

In an academic publication, normally all the options are explained first and at the end they are compared. While I would of course love it if you read this book cover to cover, I assume you are a professional under time pressure and are just looking for a solution. Hence, I don't want you to read fifty pages on kanban only to find out that kanban won't work for you since you produce make-to-order. Therefore, I give you guidance on which pull system to use first, even if I have not yet explained the details of these pull systems.

3.2.1 Suitability of Pull Systems

Let me first give you an (admittedly very subjective) evaluation of the different pull systems I will present later in this book, and how well they fare with different requirements. In Figure 19, I summarize which type of pull system is compatible with make-to-stock, make-to-order, ship-to-stock, ship-to-order, and flow shops or job shops, as well as truly continuous processing of bulk materials.

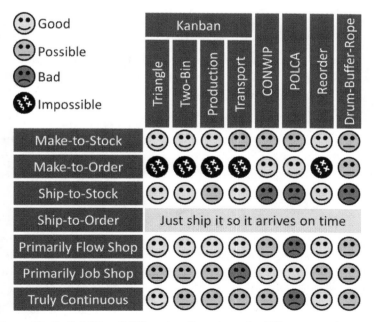

*Figure 19: Suitability of different pull systems for different requirements
(Image Roser)*

Please note that any kanban system and reorder systems are fundamentally incompatible with make-to-order. Also note that if you are shipping items based on a customer order, you do not really need a pull system; you merely need to ship the items so they arrive on time.

3.2.2 Pull System Selection Decision Tree

To help you in your decision of which pull system to use, I have created decision trees shown in Figure 20 and Figure 21. Please be aware that these recommendations include a lot of assumptions and generalizations. Yet overall, these recommended systems are all feasible options. Because of the length of these options, I have split them into a decision tree for production or development in Figure 20 and a decision tree for purchasing in Figure 21.

The first decision tree in Figure 20 looks at production or development. If you produce make-to-stock, your best choice is usually a variant of kanban. If you produce make-to-order, you have the choice between CONWIP and POLCA. POLCA is a bit better in controlling the inventory, but is more cumbersome to implement and maintain. POLCA is also not designed for flow lines, but for job shops and networks of cells. CONWIP is easier to implement and maintain, but doesn't control the inventory in a job shop as nicely.

If you have a mixed system, you will need to choose two separate systems for the make-to-stock and the make-to-order items. Here, I recommend a combination of kanban and CONWIP.

Most systems are well suited for discrete production, where a card represents a fixed quantity. Even with continuous production, either the production or the sale is often in fixed quantities. However, with a truly continuous production, you cannot use cards for a fixed quantity of items. Here, it may be best to use reorder points for make-to-stock or CONWIP for make-to-order. However, many other systems can be adapted to continuous production with varying effort.

If you are producing make-to-stock, you have a few more decisions. First, if you are in the unfortunate situation to produce make-to-stock in a job shop, see if you can turn the job shop into a flow shop. If not, select a flow shop type pull system, although you additionally may have to take care of the routing of the items within the job shop.

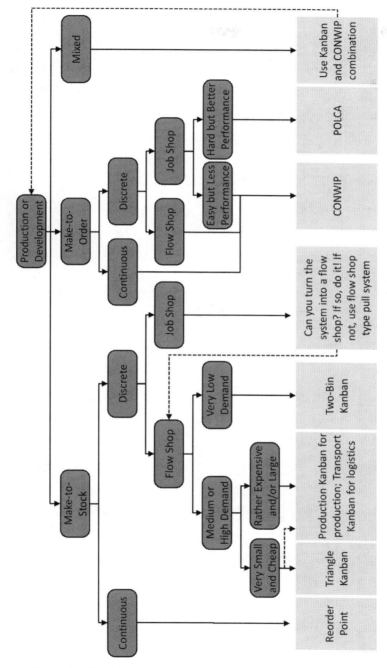

Figure 20: Decision tree to select pull system for production or development (Image Roser)

If you produce make-to-stock in a flow shop, you can now fine-tune the system. If the demand is low and the demand during the replenishment time is consistently less than the content of a single container, then you may need only a two-bin system. This is a kanban system with only two cards.

If the demand is higher, you may look at the value and size of the items. If they are a bit expensive or bulky, use a normal kanban system with production and transport kanban to minimize inventory and hence minimize tied-up capital and/or storage space.

If the items are very small and very cheap, you may use a triangle kanban to reduce the number of times you have to produce, although you still may choose a normal kanban to create smaller lot sizes and improve leveling.

The decision tree is easier for purchasing, shown in Figure 21. If you ship-to-order, you do not need a pull system at all. You just order all the items you need so they arrive on time when you need them. If the items are needed for your own production, the pull system of the production will decide when to produce what, and your ship-to-order items are derived from this make-to-order production system. Since you cannot produce before the parts arrive, the delivery times are part of the overall lead time for the customer order.

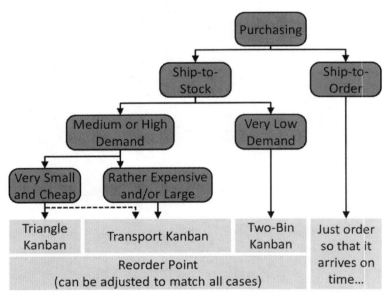

Figure 21: Decision tree to select pull system for purchasing (Image Roser)

If you order items to be on stock (ship-to-stock), the decision tree is similar to the make-to-order flow shops. If demand is very low, make sure you always have at least two items or batches. If one is consumed, order one more while the second item or batch ensures material availability.

If the demand is higher, you may use triangle kanban for very cheap and very small items, and transport kanban for larger or more expensive items. This is similar to the make-to-stock production. For all ship-to-stock methods, reorder systems are a valid alternative, as you can adjust the reorder points and reorder quantities to achieve a wide range of behaviors similar to the different kanban systems.

You may wonder which decisions you have to make to get to drum-buffer-rope, as none of the above decisions end up there. Drum-buffer-rope is in my view mostly inferior to kanban and CONWIP systems. Drum-buffer-rope requires the pull loop to end before the bottleneck, which in my view is a completely unnecessary restriction. If you ignore the restriction of the loop ending at the bottleneck, the system is actually very similar to CONWIP and quite workable.

There are real-world production systems that successfully use drum-buffer-rope. Hence, if your plant successfully uses drum-buffer-rope, has people skilled in it, and the method has the support of your people, by all means keep using it. I am fine with anything that works. Just don't artificially constrict yourself to end the loops at the bottleneck. If you have not yet done drum-buffer-rope, however, I recommend that you stick to kanban and CONWIP systems.

3.3 What Pull Systems Can Be Combined in the Same Loop?

Sometimes you may need only one type of pull system. In other situations, however, you may want to combine different types of pull systems for different part types in the same loop to fit your needs. Most commonly, you have a combination of make-to-stock products and make-to-order products. This would usually need two different pull systems to achieve a smooth production. Figure 22 shows a (again very subjective) compatibility of the different methods with each other within the same loop.

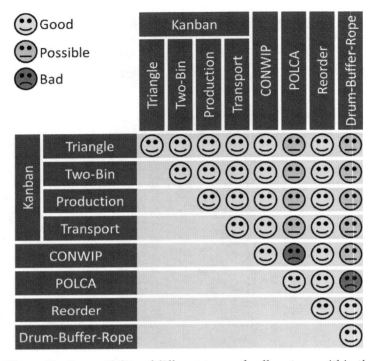

Figure 22: Compatibility of different types of pull systems within the same loop (Image Roser)

In general, any kanban system is compatible with any other kanban system. You merely change some information on the kanban. A CONWIP system is in its nature like a customizable kanban, and hence also very compatible with kanban. In general, **for a combination of make-to-stock and make-to-order, it is recommended to use a mix of kanban and CONWIP.**

Reorder systems are mostly used for purchasing, where you don't really need to worry about compatibility. The way you order one type of goods can be completely independent from the way you order another type of goods. You should worry only that you don't confuse your people with too many different systems.

It may be possible to combine pull systems with POLCA or drum-buffer-rope. However, the outcome may range from awkward to even more awkward. In general, the fewer different systems you have, the less confusing it will be for your operators. If you use different systems, make sure your first process in the loop has a good standard on which signal takes priority over which other signal, as shown in Figure 23.

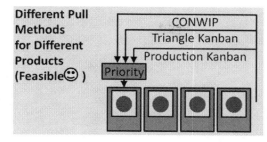

Figure 23: It is possible to have different pull systems for different parts within the same loop. Make sure the first process knows how to prioritize the different pull signals. (Image Roser)

Also, please note that this table applies to the pull system for **different** part or product types in the same pull loop. **Do not use different pull systems for the same part type in the same segment of your value stream.** It also does not apply to "overarching" nested pull systems, as shown in Figure 24. You can find these sometimes in literature, but I seriously doubt the benefit of such nested systems.

Figure 24: Nested pull loops are not advised. (Image Roser)

Chapter 4
FIFO and Other Limited-Buffer Inventories

An easy but usually only partial way to create a pull system is to limit the inventories in the processes, and especially between the processes. These are most commonly organized in a FIFO sequence. Other types of inventory management or even the complete lack thereof are also possible, as long as there is an upper inventory limit. However, **FIFO is not a complete pull system, since it lacks a good signal for reproduction**. Hence it is difficult to create pull only with FIFO.

Therefore, a limited-buffer inventory is rarely done on its own, and is usually only used as part of a larger pull system. Figure 25 shows a basic example where the buffer between stations is limited to a maximum of five spaces.

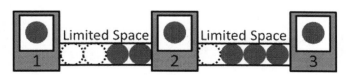

Figure 25: Basic limited-buffer inventory (Image Roser)

Such a simple system by itself is insufficient to manage the production. It lacks the crucial information on what to produce next for the first process in the sequence when a part leaves the system.

A production purely based on FIFO inventories between processes would probably be not a very workable solution. Your entire value chain from the beginning to the end would be one sequence of FIFO inventories. This is not manageable. Merging and splitting material flows, as for example in assembly, disassembly, or parallel processes, would be tricky to manage.

If the limited buffers are in a fixed sequence (for example FIFO, LIFO, or FEFO, see below), you would lose all flexibility in your value chain. The sequence of production jobs at the beginning of the value chain would flow down the chain with no changes. The first screw would already need to have been assigned to a completed car into which it will eventually go. All assembly locations would need components and parts in exactly the correct sequence. An end-to-end FIFO would be a logistical nightmare on a large scale. It also does not distinguish between part types, hence in make-to-stock productions you could have way too many of one part and way too few of another.

However, as part of an overarching pull loop, FIFO is very useful, powerful, and highly recommended. Figure 26 shows an example of a FIFO lane of people orderly waiting at a bus stop in Japan, although this example has no hard upper limit.

Figure 26: People waiting orderly in line at the bus stop is a FIFO sequence. Image was taken in Japan, where standing in line is almost an art form. (Image Roser)

Better approaches for pull production like kanban, CONWIP, POLCA, and so on break the value stream down into smaller, manageable sequences, and allow for more flexibility. Nevertheless, limited-buffer inventories are a crucial element of these more advanced pull systems. FIFO is recommended for kanban and CONWIP systems. A kanban loop that does not use FIFO throughout its loop is falling short of its potential. Hence, I would like to start my discussion of pull systems with limited-buffer inventories. They will be a crucial element of the later, more advanced pull systems, even if they are rarely used on their own.

4.1 Fundamentals

FIFO stands for First-In-First-Out and is an almost foolproof element of material flow. The first item that enters the inventory is also the first item that leaves the inventory. The items leave the inventory in the same sequence as they entered. FIFO is an important part of any lean material flow. It is a very simple way to define both the material flow and the information flow. Figure 27 shows a simple schematic example of a FIFO.

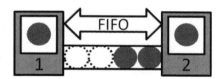

Figure 27: Schematic of a FIFO (Image Roser)

4.1.1 Reasons for FIFO: Decoupling

Different processes usually have different cycle times[27] to process parts. Even for a well-balanced line there are slight differences in the cycle time. Hence, processes have to wait for slower processes. In a world with no fluctuations or variations, this would never change, and the processes would always have to wait on the slowest process (i.e., the bottleneck). No amount of inventory in between would change that.

Imagine three static processes, as shown in Figure 28, where the middle process is always the slowest one. All inventories before are always full, and all the upstream processes are blocked after every part. Similarly, the entire inventory afterward is empty, and all processes downstream are

---

[27] Cycle time is often used in a different context. Here, cycle time is the time needed to process one part under ideal circumstances (i.e., without any losses or problems). If you include the average losses, it would be the takt time (i.e., the inverse of the number of parts produced per day).

starved for material after every part. Again, no amount of inventory or empty space in the FIFO between the processes will change that.

Figure 28: Schematic of two FIFO for a static system with no fluctuations (Image Roser)

However, in the real world, processes are not static but dynamic. Sometimes a process will take a longer or shorter time than average. In this case, any buffer type can improve utilization and throughput of the system by decoupling fluctuations. However, FIFO has quite some advantages over a general buffer. This will be shown below.

Ideally, the process with the slowest average speed should never have to wait on another process (either from lack of material or from being blocked). However, due to such fluctuations, the process may have to wait because another process is temporarily slower. This waiting can be avoided by having inventory. The long-term slowest process would fill into a buffer if the temporary slower process were afterward. If the temporary slower process were before, the long-term slowest process would take material from a buffer inventory.

Figure 29 below shows you the examples. In the first example, the last process is temporarily slower and the middle process fills the empty inventory slots. In the second example, the first process is temporarily slower and the middle process takes parts out of full inventory slots.

Figure 29: FIFO filling and emptying due to fluctuations (Image Roser)

Again, this works for any kind of buffer. A FIFO, however, has some advantages. But first I would like to talk about the rules that makes a FIFO a very special type of inventory storage.

4.1.2 FIFO Rule 1: No Overtaking

There are basically two rules important for FIFO. The first part that goes into the buffer is also the first part that comes out, hence the name FIFO for First-In-First-Out. The sequence of parts has to be maintained. No part can overtake another part in the FIFO. No part can squeeze in from the outside either. Overtaking, as illustrated in Figure 30, is not permitted.

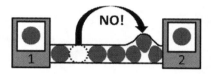

Figure 30: FIFO Rule 1: No overtaking in FIFO! (Image Roser)

This rule is important to avoid fluctuations in throughput time. One goal of lean manufacturing is to have a smooth material flow. If parts overtake each other, then the waiting time for the other parts will be longer. If this happens frequently, the waiting time could be potentially **much** longer. Eventually the delayed parts will be too late.

Imagine you're standing at the supermarket checkout, with ten people in line in front of you. While it may take some time, you can estimate how long it will take you to pay and leave. Now imagine someone with a VIP membership card cutting in line in front of you. Certainly, you will have to wait longer. Now imagine every third person cutting in line in front of you. Your waiting time can be very unpleasant. Finally imagine everybody but you being a VIP member, cutting in line in front of you. You will probably only get served when the store closes and no new customers enter.

While manufactured parts won't get upset if they wait in line longer, the customers waiting for the parts certainly will (as will your friends and family if you do not show up with the groceries from the supermarket). Hence, **it is important in FIFO to maintain the sequence**, although you sometimes can break the rules, as I will show you later on.

4.1.3 FIFO Rule 2: Clearly Defined Maximum Capacity

The second rule requires that **the FIFO must have a clearly defined maximum capacity**. There must be an inventory limit. **When the FIFO is**

full, the preceding process must stop. Overfilling, as shown in Figure 31, is not permitted. The reason for this rule is to avoid overproduction, which makes FIFO in particular and pull in general so much better than push.

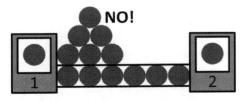

Figure 31: FIFO rule 2: No overfilling! (Image Roser)

By the way, there is no explicit rule for a minimum capacity. The minimum capacity of a FIFO is automatically zero. Since it is impossible to have fewer than zero parts in the FIFO, we need no extra rule to cover impossible cases. If there are no parts, the downstream process automatically stops due to lack of parts.

4.1.4 Breaking the Rules

As always, some rules can be bent and others can be broken. The two rules above turn a buffer into a FIFO. These rules make a lot of sense and should be followed. However, there may be rare cases when you can break the rules. Just be fully aware that by breaking these rules you will create some problems elsewhere that you cannot yet even see. The question is, is it worth it? Sometimes, the answer may be yes.

For example, assume you have different products in your FIFO and you are missing parts to process the next two products in the FIFO (they won't arrive until three days later). Now you have two options:

- Wait until the missing parts arrive three days later, while all processes are stopped.
- Take the products off the FIFO (and hence change the sequence).

Purists would say that you must not break the rules. Practice has taught me that sometimes it may be necessary to break the rules. In the example above, I would break sequence and take the two products that I cannot process off the line and continue with other products. After the missing parts arrive, I would put the products back in the FIFO, possibly even jumping ahead in the queue.

Let's be clear: I don't like it. However, I would like it even less to stop production for three days until the parts arrive.

At the same time, be careful not to make too many exceptions. Otherwise you mess up your system, you teach your employees that rules in general are only optional, and worst of all, you take pressure off the system to improve. Hence, avoid breaking the rules as much as you can.

4.2 Variants

There are a few variants similar to FIFO. They differ mostly in their sequencing rule. Let me give you an overview.

4.2.1 First-Expired-First-Out (FEFO) and Variants

FIFO is usually the inventory of choice for many pull systems. However, there are a few variants. In FIFO, the oldest part (first in the line) is removed first. In FEFO (first-expired-first-out), the part that is **first to expire** is removed first. This is especially important if the time between production and expiration may differ for different instances of the same product.

For example, if you make yogurt from very fresh milk, it lasts longer than if you use milk that, while still good, is no longer quite as fresh. However, you want to sell the yogurt with the earliest expiration date first. Hence, you would sell the yogurt from not-so-fresh milk earlier, even if it was produced later.

This approach may be used for perishable goods like many food products or some pharmaceuticals, as well as some chemical products with a short shelf life, like glues. However, this approach requires a lot more effort. The expiration date needs to be tracked for the entire stock of the particular item. Whenever an item is needed, the one with the earliest expiration date needs to be found and retrieved. Doing this on paper is difficult, as is finding the actual part. Usually an ERP or other computer system is used to keep track of the multitude of dates. Nevertheless, it is an additional effort.

It also requires a storage system where every part can be accessed at any time. For example, a queueing system similar to a FIFO would not work unless you can get a part out from the middle if it is the one that expires first. Normal storage shelves managed by computer systems are usually the way to go here.

Overall, avoid FEFO unless there is a significant advantage in doing so. Luckily, most industrial products have a much longer shelf life, and the sequence of production is also a good sequence for consumption.

There are similar and related approaches using other dates. Rather than the earliest expiration date, after which the product is no longer good, you can use the somewhat related **earliest best before date**, after which the product may still be good but it is not guaranteed.

In another variant particularly suitable for make-to-order, you can always remove the part that has the **earliest due date**. If job A is due in ten days and job B in eight, the job B due in eight days has priority over job A.

An even finer adjustment is to divide the remaining days until the due date by the remaining work content to determine the **highest percentage of work until the due date**. Using the example above, you need to put in 7 more days of work for job A and only 3 more days for job B. Hence, A has to be worked on 7/10 = 70% of the remaining days. Job B, however, needs only 3/8 = 37.5% of the remaining days to be worked on. In this case, job A would go first.

Closely related is the **smallest remaining time buffer until the due date**. Job A needs 7 days of work and is due in 10, hence the safety buffer is 3 days. Job B needs 3 days of work and is due in 8 days; hence, the buffer is a more comfortable 5 days. Here, too, job A would be processed first. The numeric examples are also shown in Table 1 below.

Job	Due in x Days	Remaining Work (days)	%Work in Remaining Time	Days Buffer
A	10	7	70%	3
B	8	3	37.5%	5

Table 1: Example data for FEFO variants

There are probably more possible variants depending on the dates used in your company for your products. **All of these approaches, however, are a larger effort than a FIFO, and should be used only if FIFO is not good enough.**

4.2.2 Last-In-First-Out (LIFO)

More for completeness' sake than as an actual recommendation, I would like to briefly introduce you to LIFO. In this method, the newest part is removed first and the oldest part is removed last. This is a very inferior approach as it risks old parts becoming even older and eventually expiring. **Your LIFO lead time will have very large fluctuations, even though the average lead time does not change compared to a FIFO.**

However, it is used sometimes because of limitations of the available storage. For example, if you use bulk goods like coal, iron ore, or wood chips, you may have a large pile of them. It is easiest to add and remove material from the top. However, in this case the most recently added material gets also removed first, as shown in Figure 32. Hence the storage uses LIFO.

Figure 32: Coal stockpiles added and removed from the top as an example of LIFO (Image Peabody Energy, Inc. under the CC-BY 3.0 license)

A better approach would be to use a silo where the material is added from the top and removed from the bottom. This would represent an approach closer to FIFO. However, this would require more expensive storage equipment.

Other examples for LIFO would be a bundle of CD or DVD disks on a central pole where the disks are added and removed from the top. Yet another example is a traditional potato storage, where the potatoes are merely shoveled into a basement storage. These are visualized in Figure 33.

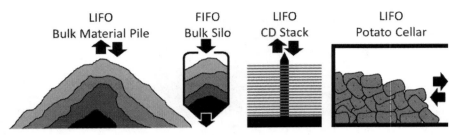

Figure 33: Example illustration of a pile of bulk material (LIFO) and a silo (FIFO) as well as a CD stack and a potato cellar. The illustrations have different scales. (Image Roser)

To avoid excessive aging of products, it is necessary to empty the entire storage occasionally. This can be done without interrupting the production if you have, for example, two piles, and you empty the first one completely before starting with the second one. Overall, **while LIFO is sometimes used in industry, it is best to avoid it if you can**.

4.2.3 Other Limited-Buffer Inventories

Finally, there is the option of having a buffer of limited size, but the rule for removing parts does not fit FIFO, FEFO, or LIFO, or there simply is no rule on the sequence at all. Since the buffer is limited in size, it can still be part of a pull system.

However, **you need to tell the shop floor in which order the products should be worked on**. If you have no such rule on the sequence, then the sequence will not be random but rather dependent on which jobs the operators like better than others. The unpopular jobs requiring a lot of effort, being dirty, or simply paying less than others will stay behind and (almost) be forgotten, while the popular jobs are rushed through.

There can be more elaborate rules depending on your needs. For example, POLCA uses a more sophisticated rule for job shops based on the due date of the next job and the availability of the subsequent processes. The important part is to limit the maximum inventory in order to help establish a good pull system. **Unless you have a specific reason for another limited-buffer inventory, I strongly recommend sticking with FIFO.**

4.3 Elements

The key element of a FIFO is an inventory. This has to follow the rules from above of **having a limited capacity and using a FIFO sequence**. Both could be established through rules. This is sometimes done with digital inventory management systems.

However, it is usually much easier and better to set up the FIFO in a way that you cannot break the rules easily. **Make it physically difficult to change sequence. Make it physically difficult to add more parts than intended.** Often this is done through a dedicated conveyor belt, slide, chute, or lane with limited space. For example, the beer bottling system shown in Figure 34 makes it hard to fit in more bottles than what the space allows, and also makes it cumbersome to change the sequence.

Figure 34: Beer bottling lane as an example of FIFO (Image mulderphoto with permission)

4.4 Calculations

One important factor is the size of your buffer. This is regardless of whether it is a FIFO, LIFO, FEFO, or other system. A buffer acts in two directions:

- An **empty space** means the preceding process can deliver its products into the buffer and continue with the next product. **If the buffer is full, the preceding process has to stop.**
- Material in the buffer means the subsequent process has material to continue working. If the buffer is empty, the next process will run out of material to work on and hence must stop.

For a static system with no random breakdowns or random changes in the cycle time, we would not need any buffers. If we would have buffers, all buffers in front of the bottleneck would be full and all buffers afterwards would be empty.

In reality, however, **every process has some random variations**. You may have breakdowns stopping a process for minutes, hours, or (hopefully not) even days. But you also may have smaller changes that you do not even notice. If an average part takes eight minutes, you will probably miss if one part takes three seconds longer and another part a fraction of a second less. Without buffers, each of these random fluctuations would influence the entire system. At any given time, the slowest process at that time would define the speed of the line. **Without buffers, your system would always run at its slowest possible speed.**

With buffers, however, you can... well... buffer these speed differences. If a process is temporarily faster than usual, the buffer before empties and the buffer afterwards fills up. If the process runs slower again, the buffer will change accordingly. This is visualized in Figure 35. If there would be no buffer, all the fluctuations would cause delays for the entire system. A buffer, therefore, can warn you of upcoming problems such as a process running slower than planned.

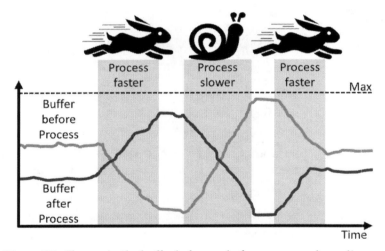

Figure 35: Change in the buffer before and after a process depending on the process speed (Image Roser)

The size of the buffer depends on how many of these fluctuations you want to buffer. **The larger the buffer, the more fluctuations are buffered, and the higher your utilization and your output.** However, **the larger the** buffer, the longer the lead time and the higher the inventory and expenses. Overall, the buffer size is a **trade-off between utilization and throughput on one hand and the lead time and inventory cost on the other hand**. In lean manufacturing, the tendency is clearly toward smaller buffers. If in doubt, go with the smaller buffer.

4.4.1 Mathematical Approach (Not Recommended)

There are mathematical ways to calculate or simulate a good buffer size. However, these are cumbersome and they require lots of data that you may not have. Do you know the standard deviation of your cycle time and of the breakdowns? Chances are you do not even know the mean time between breakdowns and the mean time to repair for your processes. Hence, I strongly recommend using a more practical approach. If you want to see the mathematical details, please check out my other publications.[28, 29]

4.4.2 Buffer Size Based on Buffered Duration

You can estimate the buffer size based on the breakdowns and interruptions you want to cover. For example, assume you want to cover at most a ten-minute stop of an adjacent process. If the adjacent process were upstream, the buffer would need to contain at least the equivalent of ten minutes' worth of parts. If the adjacent buffer is downstream, the buffer needs at least ten minutes' worth of empty space.

For example, if you produce one part per minute and want to buffer ten minutes, your buffer space would need ten parts. If, however, you produce one part every five seconds, ten minutes would require a buffer space of 120 parts. For fast cycle times and long buffer durations, the number of parts quickly spirals out of control. Please note that this does not guarantee

---

[28] Christoph Roser, *Determining the Size of Your FiFo Lane – The FiFo Formula*, in *Collected Blog Posts of AllAboutLean.Com 2014*, Collected Blog Posts of AllAboutLean.Com 2 Offenbach, Germany: AllAboutLean Publishing, 2020, 185–91, ISBN 978-3-96382-010-6.

[29] Christoph Roser, *The FiFo Calculator – Determining the Size of Your Buffers*, in *Collected Blog Posts of AllAboutLean.Com 2014*, Collected Blog Posts of AllAboutLean.Com 2 Offenbach, Germany: AllAboutLean Publishing, 2020, 209–12, ISBN 978-3-96382-010-6.

the desired coverage if the buffer upstream is already empty or the buffer downstream is already full. In this case, a stop of the adjacent process will no longer be covered.

There are many additional effects like the buffer being not completely empty or full when it is needed. Buffers farther upstream and downstream also influence the performance. Hence, this approach also includes some estimates.

4.4.3 Buffer Size Estimation

A similar approach is simply to take someone from the shop floor that is familiar with these or similar processes and have that person give an estimate of the buffer size. If possible, steer that person toward the lower end of the estimate range. Adjust if the observed behavior does not meet your expectations.

Yes, this is the current state-of-the-art for determining buffer sizes in factories: **an expert estimate** (which is nothing else than a wild guess by someone that is at least not totally clueless).

4.4.4 General Rules for Buffer Sizes

Here are a few more suggestions that may help you with placing your buffer capacities.

- Buffers are more important before and after the bottlenecks than they are around non-bottlenecks.
- If the cycle times of your processes are linked and all parts always move at the same time (e.g., as with a single conveyor belt or a pulsed line where the parts are all moved simultaneously), usually no buffers are needed.
- If the cycle times of your processes are not linked and different parts can move at different times, you should usually have at least a buffer capacity of one unit (a part or a box of parts) between processes.
- Manual stations may need slightly fewer buffers, because operators can and will speed up and slow down slightly if they feel that they are slowing others down or are slowed down by others, respectively.
- Buffers before the main bottleneck are usually full. Buffers after the main bottleneck are usually empty. Hence, buffers after the bottleneck

have a much smaller impact on inventory and lead time while having similar benefits as buffers before the bottleneck.

4.5 Advantages

A FIFO has quite a few advantages. First, **it is a clearly defined material flow**. The material between two processes is always limited to the FIFO capacity. You avoid clumping all your material in one spot as illustrated in Figure 36.

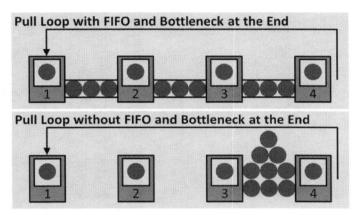

Figure 36: Comparison of a pull system with and without FIFO (Image Roser)

Furthermore, you cannot overfill the inventory between two processes, and so **you cannot overfill the entire system**. Hence, it is a lean material flow. Your system will still be able to react (relatively quickly) to changes in demand. Your total inventory is capped. Systematic defects will be detected earlier. All seven types of waste (of which overproduction is the worst) will be reduced.[30] Overall, it is more efficient.

It is also a **clearly defined information flow**. You do not need to tell the processes what to do except for the first process. They simply process whatever part comes down the FIFO. This makes it **easy to manage,** and it takes a lot of management overhead off your chest. You only need to control

---

[30] As a reminder, the seven types of waste are transport, movement, waiting, over-processing, defects, inventory, and (the worst one) over-production.

the first process in a FIFO system, possibly with a pull system; all the other processes manage themselves.

FIFO also **helps visual management**. It is usually easy to see if a FIFO is full or empty, giving you lots of clues on the status of the system, as for example the bottleneck. If you or your employees notice the FIFO getting rather full or unusually empty, you may investigate why and may be able to fix a problem before it becomes critical. Never underestimate the ability to go and see directly what is going on in your system.

4.6 Disadvantages

There are few disadvantages to FIFO. Usually, FIFO is recommended unless there is an explicit reason to use something else.

4.6.1 Minor Organizational Overhead

It may provide a bit less capacity than a simple pile of material. It may take a bit more effort to set up a FIFO compared to a simple pile of materials. But these disadvantages are usually minor compared to the benefits. A FIFO makes it a bit more difficult to change the sequence or to fit in more parts than intended... but that's the whole point of FIFO. If you frequently change the sequence, you may not need a FIFO.

4.6.2 Possible Block in Splitting Material Flows

However, there is one potential problem when working with FIFO. It can block other processes if the material flow splits. An example of such a block is shown in Figure 37. The material flow splits after process 1. All hexagons are processed at process 2. All circles are processed at process 3. Unfortunately, process 3 has a breakdown and the FIFO in front of process 3 is full. This in turn blocks process 1 from moving the already completed circle toward process 3. The sequence of hexagons waiting in front of process 1 will not move until the problem at process 3 is resolved, even though process 2 is starving for work. Such a block would usually need a manual intervention.

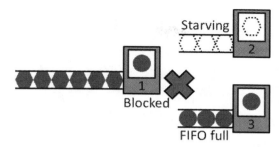

Figure 37: Example of a full FIFO at process 3 blocking the system with a splitting material flow into two FIFO (Image Roser)

The example shown in Figure 37 is very common in job shops, although usually with a higher part variety. In reality, of course, if such a block happens, the operators do a manual intervention. They shuffle things around and get the material flow going again. This usually breaks the FIFO sequence. However, this is usually the lesser evil here. To avoid such blocks in job shops completely, you would either need infinite buffers, which is impractical, or foresight to change the sequence before it happens. POLCA has by default an anti-block mechanism included.

A similar situation is shown in Figure 38, where there is only a single subsequent FIFO. Here, too, the circle in the first position of the subsequent FIFO cannot move to process 3. Since this is a FIFO, all other parts in the FIFO are blocked. This causes process 2 in this example to starve.

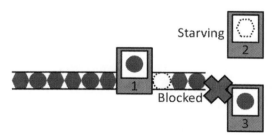

Figure 38: Example of a full FIFO at process 3 blocking the system with only one subsequent FIFO (Image Roser)

The situation in Figure 38 can easily be avoided by not using a FIFO after process 1. But this will not help the overall situation, as a non-FIFO inventory with a target limit still can fill up and block the first process. This is shown in Figure 39.

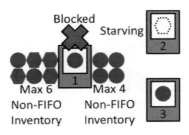

Figure 39: Example of a full inventory in front of process 3 blocking the system with a splitting material flow with an unstructured inventory (Image Roser)

Job shops with multiple overlapping material flows are especially susceptible to such blocks. One solution is **not to use inventories with a fixed upper limit**, albeit physically there will be a limit eventually. This is often combined with reassigning operators to processes that have the highest workload or number of jobs waiting. If there are multiple processes within a larger pull loop, the larger loop can still limit the inventory. However, in this case the individual processes downstream should be able to fit all parts of the larger pull loop in one inventory.

Another and probably better solution, used for example by POLCA, is to **start a job only if there is storage or process capacity available downstream** that can actually take the job. POLCA implements this by having a separate loop for every possible path in the material flow.

Usually, for a generic system, if there is no storage capacity downstream, the FIFO sequence is broken and the next available job with downstream capacity is started. In the example in Figure 37, this would mean not to start the last circle at process 1, and instead skip to the next hexagon, for which there is free capacity downstream. The last circle would wait in front of process 1 until there is downstream capacity at the FIFO for process 3.

In the example in Figure 39, this would require some consideration of the types of parts in the non-FIFO buffer. Process 1 should have produced a hexagon when the non-FIFO had only one slot left and was otherwise full with circles. This would also require either a non-FIFO inventory before the first process 1, or a supermarket before process 1. In any case, process 1 needs the ability to choose which parts to produce next based on the storage or process capacity downstream. In many job shops this is done by manual intervention, albeit some job shops have also a proper standard for this procedure.

4.7 Frequently Asked Questions

4.7.1 When Should I Not Use FIFO?

FIFO is very frequently used to manage buffers in pull production. However, all too often I hear people claim that all material flow MUST be FIFO. This is not true. There are situations where you should NOT use a FIFO.

4.7.1.1 Material in Batches, Bins, or Boxes

FIFO in its strictest sense is difficult to maintain if your material arrives in larger batches or boxes. This is visualized in Figure 40. If you are moving or processing your parts in boxes or batches, then it will be difficult to maintain a FIFO within the box. It is possible using some creative numbering scheme, but unless there is a compelling reason to do so, the effort is often not worth the benefit. Naturally, the boxes or crates themselves should be in FIFO if possible, only the parts within are in random order.

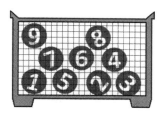

Figure 40: Illustration of a not-sequenced batch of material (Image Roser)

4.7.1.2 Prioritization and Other Sequencing Rules

Sometimes it makes sense to prioritize or sequence your production order. As police or an ambulance can overtake other cars in a traffic jam, so can parts overtake others in the production line. Sometimes, this may help your production.

For example, you may have high runners and rarely sold exotic parts. It may make sense for high runners to be built to stock. If your exotic parts are also built to stock, your inventory will go up disproportionately. You may choose to build exotic parts to order or try to reduce inventory. In this case, a faster throughput time for exotic parts may be helpful for customer satisfaction. By **prioritizing make-to-order parts** to cut in line, you may significantly improve delivery performance and inventory for exotics, while only marginally increasing inventory for high runners.

Another example may be when **something goes wrong with production or planning.** An order or part was forgotten, delayed, missed, messed up, or changed, etc., and now the key customer is screaming for parts. (Maybe you are familiar with such a scenario. I certainly am). In this case, it may also be possible to reduce pressure by allowing these jobs to cut in line. **The key for prioritizing is to do it sparingly.** Only one or two out of ten parts should be allowed to overtake the queue; otherwise the entire system may be thrown into chaos.

Yet another reason to break FIFO is **changeover optimization**. In many examples, it may be easier to change over your processes to a new process if the products come in a certain order. For example, in injection molding, it may be easier to start with a light color and gradually move to darker colors with the next batch. This way you will have to clean your machine less, since a speck of lighter-colored plastic left in the machine will be much less noticeable on darker-colored plastic. On the other hand, a speck of darker-colored plastic left in the machine may ruin clear or white parts. In such a case, it may be beneficial to break the sequence coming from the previous process and re-sequence the parts to reduced changeover time.

If different processes in your value stream have different ideal changeover sequences, you may break the sequence more than once. Overall, this will reduce changeover cost, although at the cost of a higher inventory and a wider range of lead times. Naturally, pure lean theory would be to optimize changeovers into nothingness and have a batch size of one with zero changeover time. However, until you have achieved this, you may opt to break FIFO to optimize your changeovers.

It boils down to a trade-off between the benefit of a part or job skipping the line and the effort to do so as well as the slightly increased chaos it creates. Changing the FIFO sequence should be an exception. If you change the sequence frequently, you may just go all the way and create a proper standard and rules for changing the sequence.

4.7.1.3 Parallel Lanes

Another example for breaking FIFO is when you have a longer FIFO but not enough space on the shop floor. Figure 41 illustrates an example. In this case, you may break the FIFO into different parallel lanes. The challenge here will be to maintain FIFO across multiple parallel lines. Both the source and the destination process need to follow rules when adding or removing parts to maintain FIFO across multiple lanes.

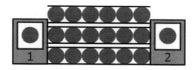

Figure 41: Illustration of three parallel FIFO lanes (Image Roser)

I have seen different approaches that try to wrestle control over such a system and signal the user when to add or remove parts. These may be elaborate digital signals, mechanical barriers, or even only cheap plastic flower pots on top of the goods. All of these required a lot of care when filling or emptying the FIFOs. Sometimes you may want to do this to maintain FIFO. In other situations, it may be easier to ignore FIFO and have both source and destination pick lanes at random. While this will not give you a strict FIFO sequence, it makes inventory handling easier. In all likelihood, unless your people can follow a standard to the letter, there will be hiccups in the sequence anyway.

However, be aware of the high risk of some products being in the lanes for an excessive time. This could happen either by chance or because they are more difficult and the destination process cherry-picks the easy work. Especially the latter happens frequently, trust me!

Another downside is that products may stay in the lanes for different periods, and that traceability in case of errors may no longer be available. For example, if the destination process notices an error, it will be more difficult to determine which parts in the parallel FIFO lanes have the same problem or what the cause at the source was.

I would do strict FIFO in parallel lanes only if there is a clear advantage by maintaining FIFO. This could be, for example, quickly aging products like milk or other food items, frequently updated products, or if FIFO really helps you track problems in your particular case.

However, I have in the past also broken FIFO in parallel lanes. The operators could add and remove randomly in whatever lane they chose. The random adding and removing is not quite FIFO, but in my situation, there was no system in place to track problems anyway—which by itself was another problem. The products also did not really age, nor was their design changed frequently. Only for a design change, special care had to be taken so as not to mix up the old and the new products. It was not a perfect solution, but at that time it was in my view the best option.

It all boils down to a trade-off: the effort of maintaining FIFO versus the benefits of having FIFO. I had situations when I chose to break FIFO. Of course, the best way would be to reduce inventory to have only a single FIFO within the available space; then the entire problem would be gone.

4.7.1.4 Variation in Storage Cost

Yet another example where it may make economic sense to break FIFO is for differences in storage cost. Assume, for example, that your warehouse is full and you have to rent space in an external warehouse. Your own warehouse is paid for, no matter how many products are in there. The external warehouse, however, may charge per storage slot and day.

In this case, it makes sense to fill up your own warehouse completely before adding to the external warehouse. Similarly, you should satisfy demand by delivering from the external warehouse first to reduce storage cost before emptying your own warehouse. Overall, the sequence will no longer be FIFO, but possibly more of a LIFO.

Again, there are some caveats. Make sure your products do not expire while sitting in your warehouse. And, of course, the best option may be improving your system so you can reduce your inventory altogether, although that is easier said than done.

4.7.1.5 Job Shops

A strict FIFO in job shops may lead to blocking, as shown in Chapter 4.6.2. A full FIFO may force everything else to wait until the process for which the next part is intended for can take it. This may require manual intervention.

You may have to break FIFO when the part flow is not identical for all parts. This may be, for example, with branching, looping, or skipping steps. In this case, the parts will leave the system in a different sequence than they entered. The more irregular your material flow is, the more the FIFO sequence will be messed up.

FIFO almost always gets broken for make-to-order goods in job shops. If the value stream is different for every part, then the sequence of the parts entering and leaving the system will be almost certainly different. Trying to establish FIFO rules for make-to-order goods in a job shop almost always asks for trouble. However, most job shops also have a supply of standard components like screws or standard-stock steel blanks. These could of course be managed through a FIFO.

4.7.2 Does FIFO Capacity Have to Match the Inventory Limit?

Let's assume you have a pull system that limits your inventory within the system to 100 parts. Does the total FIFO capacity have to match these 100 parts? Clearly, no. You can have less FIFO capacity than the maximum number of parts. Parts could wait in the supermarket, or wait for production.

You can also imagine a system where you have more FIFO capacity than your inventory limit. Larger FIFO generally increase process utilization. However, this is less common. To obtain a lean system, I would **avoid overly large FIFO**. In any case, the determination of the inventory limit for your pull system and the FIFO capacity are separate decisions.

Chapter 5
Kanban

Kanban is the best-known variant of pull systems. Often, kanban is even seen as a synonym for pull, although there are many ways to implement pull without kanban. This chapter focuses on kanban, but also explains many relations relevant to other pull systems. A kanban is attached to all parts in the pull loop. When the part leaves the loop, the kanban starts the replenishment of exactly this item.

5.1 Fundamentals

A kanban system is probably the easiest way to create pull production for make-to-stock items. You have an inventory at the end of your value stream segment. This inventory is called a supermarket. All items in the kanban loop, including the items in the supermarket, have a kanban attached. The kanban has information on the part type and quantity it is attached to.

Whenever the next process or customer takes an item out of the supermarket, the corresponding kanban is returned to the beginning of the kanban loop. This starts a reproduction or reorder of an item of the same type. The classical, well-known kanban system for production is also known as the **production kanban**, but kanban can also ship or reorder items. In this case, it would be called a **transport kanban**. Figure 42 shows a production kanban loop across four processes.

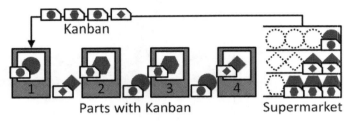

Figure 42: Schematic example of a production kanban loop. Every part has a kanban attached to it. (Image Roser)

Hence, a kanban is basically a bit of information attached to the parts in the kanban loop. It is often a printed piece of paper or a card, although it can take other forms including the container itself, digital, and more. One of the fundamental rules of kanban is that **every part has a kanban attached to the part or the container with the parts** (with the notable exception of triangle kanban systems).

Kanban systems are generally suitable only to replenish parts that you have in stock. The kanban describes exactly which part and how many it represents. Only this part is replenished. Fundamentally, kanbans are used to refill an inventory with make-to-stock parts or products. **Kanbans are not suitable for make-to-order products** that you produce only if there is a customer order.

A kanban represents at least one part. However, **a kanban can also represent multiple parts**. In this case, the kanban does not start the replenishment of one part but the replenishment of as many parts as indicated on the kanban.

The sum of parts represented by all kanbans of one part type is the target limit of the inventory for this part type. You can never have more parts than corresponding kanbans. The kanban also signals replenishment. Hence, it is a pull system. However, you can have fewer parts in the loop if some kanbans are waiting for reproduction, as shown in Figure 42. Determining the number of kanbans is a bit tricky, but **the goal is a trade-off between the minimum inventory and always having enough in the supermarket to satisfy the customer demand.**

5.2 Variants

There are a few variants besides the standard production kanban for reproducing parts. Let me show you the most common kanban variants.

5.2.1 Transport Kanban

The transport kanban is identical to the production kanban in all aspects except one. Rather than reproducing the consumed parts, they are merely resupplied from a previous inventory or the supplier. This is sometimes also known as the *transportation kanban, withdrawal kanban,* or *conveyance kanban*. Depending on the location in the value stream, it is also known as *supplier kanban* between the supplier and production, *finished-goods kanban* between production and the warehouse, and *customer kanban* between production and the customer. However, I think these additional distinctions add little value. An example of a basic transport kanban is illustrated in Figure 43.

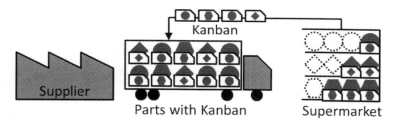

Figure 43: Simplified schematic example of a transport kanban system (Image Roser)

The main difference is that a production process usually has a limited capacity. If ten kanbans arrive at the same time, the production process has to process them one by one, which may cause a delay.

The supplying inventory, however, may supply multiple kanbans immediately. If ten kanbans arrive simultaneously, ten parts are simply taken out of the preceding supermarket inventory. Hence, the replenishment time is often much faster, limited only by the delay in sending the order and the time for the transport process. This assumes that the supplying inventory has the desired parts.

Such a transport kanban can be between inventories that are far apart, as for example your supplier and your own plant. These can also be closer together within your own plant. A **milk run** where material is delivered along a fixed route and with fixed time intervals is often implemented using transport kanbans.

You should **use a transport kanban system if the benefit of having a second supermarket close to the demand is worth the effort of installing and running a transport kanban system in between**. This may also include situations where the **original inventory is too large** to be put close to the subsequent process, and a smaller inventory at the process is supplied by a transport kanban. See Chapter 11.2.8 and 11.2.9 for details.

5.2.2 Two-Bin Kanban

Another variant of the kanban system is the two-bin kanban system. You have only two kanbans per part type. Instead of printed paper cards, these are often labels attached to the storage bins or boxes, hence the name two-bin kanban. Whenever a bin is empty, the bin is returned to be refilled. This is effectively a kanban system with two cards (bins). An example is illustrated in Figure 44.

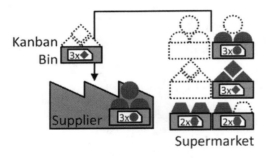

Figure 44: Example of a two-bin kanban system. As this works both with reproduction and reordering, a generic supplier icon is used as the source. A bin of circles is currently in delivery from the supplier; a bin of diamonds is ordered. (Image Roser)

This is used for parts when **the replenishment time of a bin is much shorter than the time to consume a bin** (i.e., the system can produce or order faster than the customer can consume). You need at least two kanbans; otherwise you risk running out of parts if the single bin is empty when you need another part. This can be avoided with two bins. Common examples are smaller parts with low consumption or spare parts. These are also used in hospital supply cabinets for occasionally needed medication.

Figure 45 shows a variant of such a two-bin kanban system used in a hospital.

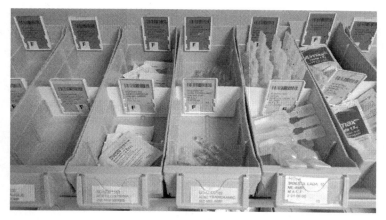

Figure 45: Variant of a two-bin kanban system in a hospital. If the front of the box is empty, the first white kanban is removed and the medication moved to the front. If the second box is also empty, the second red kanban signals high priority. System at the Consorci Sanitary Garraf near Barcelona. (Image Roser)

5.2.3 Triangle Kanban

The triangle kanban requires the least effort to move the kanbans, since there is only one kanban per part type, which reduces the frequency of replenishment. This is called a triangle kanban, since the kanban at Toyota was initially made from triangular metal scrap. You can cut triangular pieces easier from scrap than square ones. However, nowadays you can use any shape for the kanban you like, and rectangular paper also works just fine. At Toyota, this is also called a *signal kanban* (信号かんばん). The approach is actually very similar to the reorder point shown in Chapter 8.

While most kanban systems explicitly require a kanban attached to every part or group of parts, **the triangle kanban has only one kanban for every type of material**. This kanban is attached to one of the last parts in the available inventory. Parts are consumed normally. When you reach the triangle, it means that you have just enough material left to cover the replenishment time, including some safety. The triangle kanban is then used to reorder or reproduce a larger quantity of this type of material to refill the inventory. The card is then again attached to one of the last parts in the inventory, as specified on the card. An example is illustrated in Figure 46.

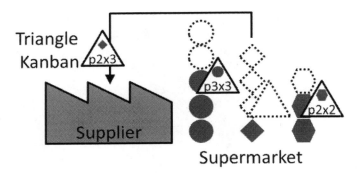

Figure 46: Example of a triangle kanban system. The kanban shows the position from the bottom p2 or p3 and the quantity 2 or 3. The diamonds triangle kanban is currently reordered or reproduced. (Image Roser)

A triangle kanban will order parts in larger batches. Rather than one normal kanban per used part (or group of parts), **you get one triangle kanban less frequently but with a larger quantity**. This goes against the basic idea of leveling (small quantities more frequently). Yet, if there is little or no capacity constraint or if the unleveled ordering is not a problem, it can be done to reduce the effort on ordering. A triangle kanban is also sometimes used if the changeover times are very large, as it can help to reduce the number of changeovers through larger batches. Nevertheless, reducing the changeover time directly through, for example, SMED (Single Minute Exchange of Die) is much preferred.

Figure 47 shows an example of a triangle kanban using a triangular shape, but it could also have any kanban shape you like (see Chapter 5.3.1.1). There is only one major difference from normal kanban. A triangle kanban needs to include the information to which part the card has to be attached. When the kanban returns to the inventory along with the fresh material, the inventory operators need to know which part they should attach the kanban to. If possible, maintain FIFO so that the oldest parts are used up first and the newly arriving parts are in the back of the inventory.

Triangle kanban work best for materials that you keep on stock, are small and of low value, and which you can resupply at large quantities without problems. It reduces the frequency of resupplying and hence avoids ordering effort. Effectively, **you reduce ordering effort or reproduction frequency at the cost of a higher inventory**.

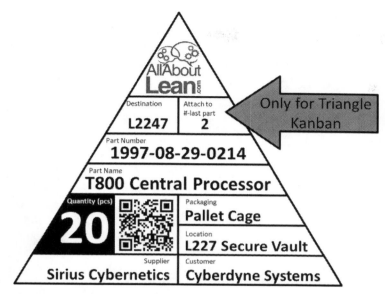

Figure 47: Example of a typical triangle kanban. Please note that the field with the position of the kanban is specific to triangle kanban. (Image Roser)

I have seen and used it frequently for office stationery supplies. You don't send out an order whenever someone takes a blue pen. Instead, when you open the last box of blue pens, you take the triangle kanban and reorder five more boxes of blue pens, which will last you for some time before you have to order again. There is also no problem when, by coincidence, you order five boxes each of blue, red, green, and black pens at the same time, as this "demand peak" won't overwhelm the capacity of the supplier to deliver.

It is also often used for restocking the office kitchen with coffee, milk, sugar, and other consumables. I use it to order A4 printer paper. When my wife or I open up the last pack of paper, we simply put the triangle kanban on my desk. I reorder more paper the next time I get around to it. The last pack of paper usually lasts till the next box of paper arrives. Figure 48 shows my very simple but working triangle kanban.

Another advantage of the triangle kanban and its use for office supplies is that this is an excellent pull system training opportunity for your people. Ensuring a steady supply of coffee is surely motivating for your people. It is a simple-enough system where you can have great results without the need to change your ERP system.

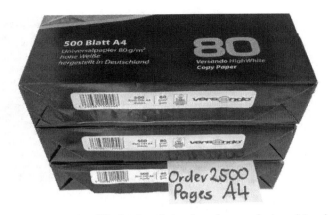

Figure 48: My simplified triangle kanban for reordering A4 printer paper. (Image Roser)

5.2.4 Kanban for Continuous Quantities

Most kanban systems count the quantity in items as the inventory limit. A kanban represents a certain number of products. However, there may be situations where you want to use a **continuous quantity** as the target limit. Instead of pieces, this could be measured in a continuous quantity like liters, kilograms, or cubic meters. It could also be measured as the **workload** within the system, although this makes less sense for kanban. Changing the measurement from a number of parts to a continuous value is easy. You just change the unit from "number of items" to whatever you need. The underlying calculations for the inventory limit remain the same.

You have fundamentally different options, however, for the kanban. The easier way is to set up the system where **one kanban represents a fixed quantity** and returning such a kanban to the first process means exactly this quantity is replenished. This is practical if your customer also orders the goods in certain fixed quantities. Imagine a crate of beer. One kanban represents a fixed number of crates of beer, and a returning kanban starts the reorder of this quantity of beer. However, you are effectively counting products again, which is just what a normal kanban does.

It becomes more difficult if the customer demands **varying fixed quantities**. Imagine a bottle, a crate, a barrel, and a tanker truck full of beer. You may use different kanbans for the different quantities, or decouple the kanban loops into separate loops when the continuous stream of beer gets filled into bottles, barrels, or tanker trucks.

It becomes most difficult if the customer does not have any fixed order sizes at all, but truly has a **continuous demand**. Imagine the water pipe from the water treatment plant to your house, where any quantity is possible, from a single drop to a swimming pool full of water. In this case, you can no longer use the traditional paper kanban, but would have to send a signal to replenish "any" quantity. You also can not really attach infinitesimally small kanban to the products.

You need some sort of tracking of the total quantity in production or in inventory and to always replenish the gap to the inventory limit. **A paper kanban is no longer the right tool for this continuous demand system.** It is doable on paper, although a digital system may be preferable. However, a reorder system would be much easier to use here.

We also have a continuous value if we limit the **workload** in the system. However, this makes no sense for kanban, as a normal kanban always represents a certain quantity of items. Reproducing these would have the same workload. Therefore, measuring kanbans by workload is an unnecessary additional effort. Both counting parts and measuring the workload for the same part type would work, but the latter requires much more effort. This will differ later when we discuss make-to-order systems like CONWIP.

5.3 Elements

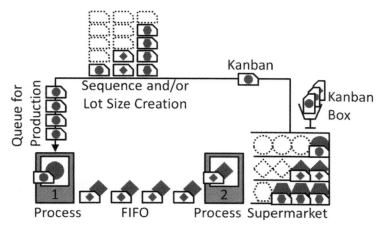

Figure 49: Overview of the elements of a kanban loop. The sequencing in this example generates lot sizes of five. (Image Roser)

FIFO and queues for production are common for all production systems. A typical kanban loop also includes—of course—kanbans, a supermarket, and a kanban box. It may also include a sequence or lot size creation. An overview is shown in Figure 49.

5.3.1 Kanban

A kanban is basically information to replenish parts. This could be a reproduction, a reorder, a logistic chain, or any kind of process that can provide you with more parts. Hence, in its most basic form it has to say "make me that quantity of this part" or "bring me that many of this part". While such very simple kanban systems are possible, usually it helps to include other information on the kanban. In this section I will go into great detail on how a kanban can look and what information should and can go onto the card. Usually, kanban include a lot of data.

However, there are also very simple kanban systems that have only the bare minimum of information, as for example the washer kanban in Chapter 5.3.1.1.5 or the kanban-less kanban system in Chapter 5.3.1.1.7. Also, less is more! Do not overload the kanban with data that are rarely needed or that change frequently. Figure 50 shows a typical production kanban.

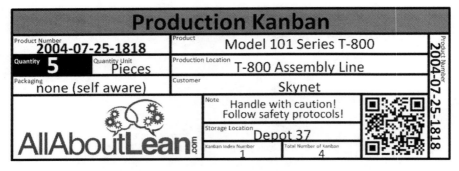

Figure 50: Example of the possible information on a kanban (Image Roser)

5.3.1.1 Physical (or Digital) Form of the Kanban

Kanbans contain information about the type and number of products to be produced. In some factories, a kanban is a simple sheet of paper. Unfortunately, in many factories, operators also have the habit of throwing out random sheets of paper found in material bins. In the often-confusing workplace, an important paper kanban may be thrown out like an unimportant sheet of scrap paper. Hence there will be no replenishment. **Losing kanbans will reduce replenishment and will mess up your system!**

In another example, one northern European plant laminated their kanbans in plastic covers. Unfortunately, these laminated kanbans made excellent ice scrapers for cars. Hence, every winter, kanbans disappeared quickly, since the employees used them to scrape the windows of their cars. Naturally, with missing kanbans, production performance suffered.

A kanban can have many different forms, including paper cards, paper in a protective folder, digital, a box or container, a piece of metal, or pretty much anything that goes with it. I usually prefer containers or metal pieces as kanbans, since they are less likely to get lost. They are also often easier to implement and visualize than digital ERP system kanbans. However, you have different options.

5.3.1.1.1 Digital Kanban

You can implement kanbans as part of your ERP system. Instead of reusing kanbans, the information is simply printed on a sheet of paper or displayed on a monitor. While this sounds like the easiest solution, it has the problem that both **the implementation and any subsequent changes to the system may need a programmer or ERP specialist.**

In my experience, these are usually in short supply, and waiting for these experts can delay the implementation quite a bit. Toyota actively tries to keep ERP away from shop floor control. Digital kanbans make the most sense for long-distance loops, as for example in supply chains. However, for systems located close to each other as on the shop floor, try to avoid digital-only systems. A compromise is often a paper card that is scanned at regular intervals and processed digitally. If there are discrepancies between paper and digital kanbans, clarify which system can overrule the other.

5.3.1.1.2 Paper Kanban

Very common are paper kanbans. These could be printed in an ERP system for single use. If the paper were to be used multiple times, then it would need some protection against wear and tear. It could be laminated or put in a plastic cover. The latter makes it easy to replace the paper inside. Such plastic covers are also available with hangers or holes to hang them to the part. You can also use glue strips to stick them permanently to a location, or magnetic strips to attach them temporarily to ferromagnetic metals like steel shelves or cast-iron parts. Examples are shown in Figure 51.

Figure 51: Selection of paper kanbans in covers of different sizes and colors. Pen for scale. (Image Roser)

5.3.1.1.3 Sturdy Plastic or Metal Kanban

I also have used sturdier kanbans made from plastic or sheet metal. While containing the same information as normal kanbans, the plastic or sheet metal makes the kanbans much heavier and sturdier. While paper may be thrown out by accident, a sturdy plate is much less likely to be thrown out. Hence, this reduces the risk of losing kanbans. In practice, this is still a printed paper kanban, but attached to a piece of plastic or sheet metal.

Figure 52: A very small kanban with dimensions approximately 3 by 5 cm. Made from plastic with a magnetic back. Used at the Consorci Sanitary Garraf near Barcelona. (Image Roser)

Figure 52 shows a small plastic kanban with a magnetic back used in a hospital to supply medication. Since the medication is often in small boxes, the kanban also has to be small, and a lot of additional information is omitted.

5.3.1.1.4 Kanban Bin, Box, or Container

The kanban information is permanently attached to a box or container, and the box becomes the kanban. The box has an appropriate size to hold all material related to the kanban. The two-bin kanban as described in Chapter 5.2.2 often uses such boxes as kanban. If the kanbans are permanently attached to the box, make sure that the box does not leave the pull system with the material, but goes back to the beginning of the pull loop for replenishment. Figure 53 shows an example of kanban boxes. On a shop floor, a kanban box is often easier and more intuitive to handle, since there is no separate card that needs to be moved. Regarding visual management, an empty box is also a clearer signal for a need of material than a card.

Figure 53: Examples of kanban boxes (Image Roser)

5.3.1.1.5 Any Clearly Identifiable Item Kanban

Depending on the complexity of the products in the kanban loop, you may not need all this information. Any item that can be clearly identified and associated with a part can convey the information on what to replenish. Toyota sometimes uses simply color-coded washers or balls to inform the preceding process on what to produce. An example is shown in Figure 54 below. A washer with a round hole means a round part, a washer with a hexangular hole means a hexangular part, and so on. This is suitable only for processes with few product variants and near each other. However, if the information is clear for the supplying process, then these systems also work. Figure 55 shows another very simple kanban used to restock water bottles in a hotel on Tenerife.

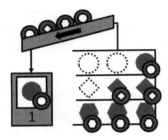

Figure 54: Example of a simple kanban system using washers (Image Roser)

Figure 55: A simple ring-shaped paper kanban for bottles from the Grand Tacande Hotel on Tenerife. (Image Roser)

5.3.1.1.6 Light Signal Kanban

The information can also be conveyed through light signals. Depending on which light goes on, the operator has to replenish a certain part. The lights may be a different shape or color, or a combination of multiple lights, as long as there is a clear relation between the light and the part. Fancier digital systems are easy to imagine.

5.3.1.1.7 Kanban-less Kanban

The absolutely easiest kanban is of course no kanban at all. If the supplying process and the supermarket are right next to each other and the product variety is small, the operator can simply be instructed to always fill up the supermarket. The operator would be starting with the part type that has the most free spaces or—if all part types have the same inventory limit—with the fewest parts. This is shown in Figure 56, where the operator sees that the biggest gap is round parts, and hence will reproduce one round part before checking again. It is still a kanban system, even though it has no actual kanbans anymore.

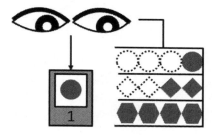

Figure 56: Example of an extremely simple kanban-less kanban system (Image Roser)

5.3.1.2   Information for Kanban

There is plenty of information that can go on a kanban. Some of it is quite useful, other is optional. Try to focus on the important parts, and reduce the optional elements as much as possible.

5.3.1.2.1   Part-Related Information

A kanban stands for one or more parts. Hence, first and foremost, you need information related to the part. In all the examples below, I assume you have a physical sheet (a card or a label on a box). For digital kanbans, the required data is similar, but now you can link it in your ERP system.

Part Number: Probably the most relevant information is the part number. In a proper modern manufacturing system, every part type has its unique part number, usually an alphanumeric string. It could look like, for example, 13261-74040. The computer can identify the part using this number. On a side note, Toyota also sometimes uses additional shorter 3-digit codes that are valid only within a certain part of the value stream. These three digits are easier to remember, and help users to identify the part within their own working area. If you plan to use a paper kanban that you stick sideways into slots, consider printing the part number sideways on the edge. This makes the part number visible if the card is inserted into a slot, as shown in Figure 57.

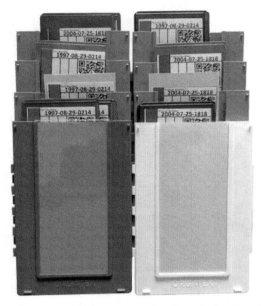

Figure 57: Text printed sideways on the edge of a kanban is visible in common kanban sorting systems. (Image Roser)

Part Name: Humans rarely know all the part numbers (although many of the people working with these numbers often know quite a lot of them). In any case, it helps to write out in plain language what the part is.

Quantity: This is the quantity of parts this kanban stands for. This is also sometimes called the number of parts per kanban (NPK). A kanban can represent exactly one part. However, if you have a lot of parts of this type in the system, it may make sense to use one card for a box or container with multiple parts. A kanban may stand, for example, for a box of twenty parts, or a pallet cage with two hundred. If you represent multiple parts with one kanban, I strongly recommend getting a container or box that fits this number of parts. This way it is easier to keep track of the parts if you take them out of the container one by one. If you have smaller packaging units in a larger pack (e.g., boxes on a pallet), you can also include this information (e.g., twenty packs of five pieces each). As this is a very important number, it may help to highlight these graphically. For example, in Figure 50 the color of the quantity is inverted and printed white on black. This prevents a mix-up with any other number on the card.

Unit: This is related to the quantity. If your kanban for screws says a quantity of twenty, does this mean twenty screws, or twenty packs with fifty screws each, or twenty kilograms of screws? Often, this may be obvious, but it is usually good practice to include the unit.

Picture: This is not very common, but you could include a picture of the part on the kanban. This may be helpful for humans to know what they're looking for, but it may be quite a bit of additional work to add the images to the kanban. Besides, a lot of your parts may look very similar. I usually avoid part images on kanban.

5.3.1.2.2 Material-Flow-Related Information

Kanban commonly also have information on the material flow. Where does the material come from? Where does it go to?

Type of Kanban: There are different types of kanbans. Most often, you distinguish between a production kanban and a transport kanban. A production kanban issues the reproduction of a new part. A transport kanban orders another part from a preceding inventory. Yet another option is a triangle kanban. It helps to write on the kanban if it is a production kanban, a transport kanban, or a triangle kanban so you don't mix them up and accidentally produce a part instead of delivering it. You may even think about using different colors to distinguish the different types. Also, depending on the type, the following information may differ.

Lot Size: In the easiest case, you produce in lot sizes of exactly one kanban. However, due to, for example, time-consuming changeovers, you may choose a larger lot size comprising multiple kanbans. Here it may help to write the lot size in number of parts or number of kanbans onto the kanban. Clarify the unit. Also clarify if this is a minimum lot size and the lot can include more kanbans, or if the lot needs to be exactly of this size, not one more or less. However, a change in the lot size would require reprinting all kanbans. It may be easier not to include this lot size on the kanban.

Packaging: A kanban can also include packaging information. Is it a pallet, a pallet cage box, a cardboard box, a standard-size industry plastic box, etc.? This helps you to know how to ship the goods.

Source: Where the material comes from. For a transport kanban, this may be the warehouse or inventory where the material is taken out. For a production kanban, this may be the production line that reproduces this part. This information can also be set up in different levels. You could indicate the source as it is known to the operators (e.g., "housing line" or "inbound warehouse"). You could also use the ERP numbering system for the inventories or systems (e.g., "L23-5" or "I225/4"). For loops between plants, you could add not only the line or inventory but also, if necessary, the plant or warehouse (e.g., "Detroit East" or "Kentucky II"). You could also add the ERP code for these locations.

Destination: Similarly, where the material goes. Since it is a kanban, the destination should be a supermarket. Again, write on the card where the material goes. This can be in human-readable form or using an ERP code, possibly also including the plant location.

5.3.1.2.3 Information-Flow-Related Information

After the part and material-flow-related information, we now look at the information flow.

Index Number: First, it is really helpful to number your kanbans. If you have twenty kanbans for a single part type, you could number them from one to twenty. This helps if you want to check for lost kanbans. For example, if all kanbans but #13 are repeatedly passing through the supermarket as part of their loop, then it is possible that kanban #13 got lost and needs to be replaced. However, if you print a new #13 kanban, and then the previous #13 kanban comes back from wherever it was hiding, then you will now have **two** #13 kanbans. This can lead to confusion. Sometimes the **date of the printing** of the kanban is also included on the kanban. A **kanban serial number** could also avoid this problem. On the other hand, a single unique kanban serial number requires more number management effort. If your kanbans are managed by an ERP system, such a kanban serial number is often used.

Total Number of Kanbans: How many kanbans are in the loop for this part number. This may be helpful information for anyone checking or trying to understand the system. On the other hand, in a kanban system it is often good practice to experiment by adding and removing kanbans to improve the number of kanbans. In this case, you would have to either exchange all kanbans in the loop to update this number or have a wrong total number of kanbans on some kanbans. Alternatively, you could just skip this information altogether.

Kanban Loop: You may have a name and/or number for the kanban loop to uniquely identify the kanban loop where the card belongs. This is not always used but may be helpful depending on your situation.

Lead Time: Some cards include additional data like lead time or replenishment time. Personally, I find this less helpful, as the lead time can change quite a bit over time. Also, I wouldn't need this on a kanban. Still, some people like it that way. You decide if it is helpful for you or not.

Contact Person/Department: The kanban may also include a contact name of the person or department that issued the cards and handles the upkeep of the kanban. This is also not common, and may not be necessary.

Printing Date and Due Date: This is possible for kanbans that are printed from an ERP system, where the paper printout is thrown away and reprinted whenever the kanban leaves the supermarket. In this case you can include the additional information for the order printing date and/or time or the due date and/or time for this cycle of the kanban through the kanban loop. However, this information is cumbersome if you reuse the kanban. On the other hand, this information is helpful if it is a closely related CONWIP card for made-to-order goods.

Location in the Stack (Triangle Kanbans Only): For triangle kanbans only, you also need to know at which part or location in the stack, queue, or pile you should add the triangle kanban. Should the card go to the last part, second-to-last part, or third-to-last part, and so on.

5.3.1.2.4   Other Information

The kanban can be read by humans, but nowadays it is often useful to have it also in a machine-readable form.

1D/2D Barcode: A digital code in either the classical barcode form or a 2D code that can store more information. Here, a simple handheld laser scanner will make it much easier to transfer information from the card into your ERP system. But do not underestimate the effort to implement the software for this type of system. A 2D code can store much more information, and may be more future-proof compared to a barcode. At one point, Toyota needed nine different barcodes on a kanban which was becoming very cumbersome. Subsequently, Denso, a company of the

Toyota group, developed the 2D QR code in 1994. It was designed to be resistant to dirt. This single QR code replaced nine different barcodes on a Toyota kanban. Figure 58 shows an example barcode and a 2D QR code.

https://www.allaboutlean.com/

Figure 58: Example of a 1D barcode and a 2D QR code (Image Roser)

RFID: Another option is to include an RFID (radio frequency identification) chip. Rather than with a laser scanner, RFID gets the information from the card through wireless communication with a small antenna embedded on the card. While this also works if the code is dirty or not in the line of sight, this approach has other issues (e.g., with shielding by metal parts). An RFID chip also costs more than a barcode, which often has almost no additional cost if they are part of a printed kanban.

Company Logo: Often, kanbans include a logo or name of the company. Strictly speaking, this is not necessary, but it is something companies often like to do.

5.3.1.3   Good Practice for Kanban Card Design

There are a few things to keep in mind when adding data to the kanban.

Priorities: Which information you really need. You have limited space, so use it for the information that is necessary and don't overload the kanban. Some information on the card is more important than others. For example, the **part name, part number, quantity**, and **barcode** or **2D code** are probably the most important information. This is closely followed by the **source** and **destination**. Mixing these up will lead to lots of problems downstream. On the other hand, the index number of the kanban is needed less frequently. This should influence the size of the text. Some information may not be needed at all. Also, keep in mind that information may change. If you add, for example, the lot size, the total number of kanbans, or the lead time, you will have to exchange all kanbans whenever these values change.

Readability: Print the important information using a larger font. Keep in mind that not all of your employees have 20/20 vision. At least the critical information should be easy to read. If you stick your paper kanban into slots, you may print your part number sideways on the edge. This way your people can read the part number without removing the kanban, as shown in Figure 57.

Labels: This should be obvious, but do label the fields or boxes. If you have a box with the number "20", it helps to know if this is the quantity, the packaging type, or the ERP code for the source. Sometimes you may also include units (e.g., "1000 pieces" or "250 liters").

Colors: You can use kanbans in different colors. This may help your people. You could, for example, distinguish production and transport kanbans by color. You could also distinguish high runners from exotic parts, indicate source or destination, or use color to create priorities. For paper kanbans, you can use colored paper, colored plastic sleeves, or combinations thereof. Just don't overload the color combinations to confuse the operators.

Clarity: Avoid choices or options for the operators. For example, if a transport kanban could get parts either from "Warehouse A" or "Warehouse B", it will lead to confusion and waste. The same goes for "If... then..." kind of information. Instructions like "If Warehouse A has more parts than Warehouse B, use Warehouse A" is a sign of an ill-designed kanban system that leads to waste. Luckily, those kinds of thing seem to be very rare (or I just have not yet gone to places that do this).

Overall, the actual design of the kanban is not quite as easy, and a few things can be considered. Please take the time to think about this when designing kanban. Just because you have the information does not mean it is necessary on the kanban. **Less is more!**

5.3.1.4 Example: A Toyota Transport Kanban

Figure 59 shows a photo of a Toyota kanban. I got permission to take the image during one of Toyota's plant tours. The paper is about 210 mm wide and around 100 mm high, like an A4 paper cut into three parts. In a Toyota factory, such simple printouts are attached to boxes using clips or added into folders attached to the material. Especially for supplier shipments, these cards are printed new each time they are used. Let's dig deeper into the card.

Figure 59: Toyota transport kanban (Image Roser)

The card contains several elements. I have translated the different areas of the card and explained them. Figure 60 below shows the translation of the general areas of the card corresponding to Figure 59, with the detailed explanation following below.

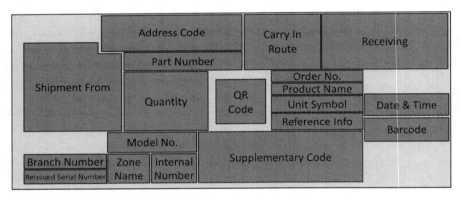

Figure 60: Toyota transport kanban with English text for selected fields (Image Roser)

5.3.1.4.1 Product-Related Information

- **Part Number** (品番; *Hinban*): The part number of the product. In this example *42450-12200-0* stands for a Toyota rear wheel hub.
- **Product Name** (品名; *Hinmei*): The product represented by this kanban is an *axle hub and bearing* (RR アクスルハブ&ベアリン; *RR akusuru habu & bearin*). This is a similar product as shown in Figure 61, although this part is for an Opel Vectra.

Figure 61: Wheel hub assembly of an Opel Vectra (Image Cschirp under the CC-BY 3.0 License)

- **Reference Information** (参考情報; *Sankō jōhō*): Additional information on the product, here *142L*. This is a Toyota internal code for a Toyota ZR engine used in the Toyota Auris, Yaris, Corolla, and others, as shown in Figure 62.

Figure 62: Toyota 2ZR-FE engine (Image Ypy31 in public domain)

- **Model No.** (型番; *Kataban*): The model number is *3DACF027F-11NS*, which is the model number for the *angular contact ball bearings hub unit*.
- **Quantity** (収容数; *Shūyō-sū*): *Eight containers, each including four parts.* Notice how this highly crucial information is not only printed very large but also white on black to make it stand out even more.
- **Unit Symbol** (ユニット記号; *Unitto kigo*): Place to add a unit (e.g., liter or kilogram). This is left blank here, since the unit is in pieces.

5.3.1.4.2　Source Information

- **Shipment from** (出荷場; *Shukkaba*): The items seem to be shipped from the *Kokubu plant* of the automotive supplier *JTEKT*, part of the Toyota Keiretsu (conglomerate) (7372-A ジェイテクト国分名張; *7372-A JTEKT Kokubu Nabari*). They provide, for example, in-steering systems and driveline components. The Kokubu plant is near Osaka, which means it is at least a three-hour drive to the Takaoka plant. This is quite far away by Toyota standards. The code underneath the shipment, *7372-0423-04 18:34*, contains the date April 23, which matches the date on the right-hand side of the card.
- **Branch Number** (枝番; *Edaban*): *8314* is an internal code for the location within the JTEKT plant.

5.3.1.4.3　Destination Information

- **Receiving** (受入; *Ukei*): The destination of the card is the *Takaoka plant of the Toyota Motor Corporation location 1000-K 07* (トヨタ自動車 高岡工 受人; *Toyotajidōsha, Takaoka Ko Shunin*). Note how this important information is printed white on black to make it stand out more.
- **Carry In Route** (搬入コース; *Han'nyū kōsu*): Here *G 09*, a Toyota internal route code.
- **Address Code** (所番地; *Tokoro banchi*): The exact destination where the part has to go, here *7SN-27-4*. Notice how this important information is printed very large.

5.3.1.4.4　Kanban-Related Information

- **Reissued Serial Number** (再発行連番; *Sai hakkō renban*): The serial number of the kanban, *1-96578*.
- **Order Number** (オーダー No; *Order No.*): The order number is *2013/04/23-15*, indicating that it was ordered on April 23 in 2013, and probably was the 15th order on that day for the supplier JTEKT.
- **Date and Time** (4月23日 04便 7372 00:25; *4 gatsu 23 nichi 04 ben*): The date and time for the card, stating *April 23rd, 00:25 AM*. There are additional service numbers *04* and *7372*, which you can also find again on the "shipment from" section.

5.3.1.4.5　Additional Information

- **QR Code**: Internal code for scanning within Toyota. If anyone is interested, the code here contains 152 bytes and says *JT7372AKOB 1000K07 10042304092013042315 Z5760 8424501220000000040FTP342*

83147SN -27-4 2. You can find a lot of the other information again here in this QR code.

- **Barcode**: The barcode here does not contain any information. Maybe a historic leftover?
- **Zone Name** (ゾーン名; *Zōn-mei*): Unused label for a zone name.
- **Company Internal Number** (社内背番号; *Shanai sebangō*): More information to be used within Toyota. The internal number is *65*.
- **Supplementary Code** (補助コード; *Hojo kōdo*): This is a supplementary code *FGPO/OORQK 010/010*.

5.3.1.5 Example of a Triangle Kanban

Figure 63 shows an older Toyota triangle kanban in situ at a stamping press used for production. This is an older model without a barcode, on display in the Toyota Commemorative Museum of Industry and Technology in Nagoya. It contains less information but still works as a kanban. Let's go through it from top to bottom.

Figure 63: Example of a sheet metal triangle kanban at the Toyota Commemorative Museum of Industry and Technology, Nagoya, Japan (Image Roser)

- **Part Number** (品番; *Hinban*): The part number of the product, here *13261-74040*. The first character of the text is not visible in Figure 63, as the kanban hangs behind a pipe, but it is the same as in the modern kanban above. They refer to stamped steel parts.
- **Quantity** (収容数; *Shūyō-sū*): There are to be *500* pieces per container.

- **Reference Number** (基準数; *Kijun-sū*): When the inventory has reached this level, a reproduction is started using the kanban. The number 2 stands here for two containers, or 1000 parts. When the remaining inventory reaches this quantity, a reorder is issued using the triangle kanban. This information is unique to triangle kanban and not found on other types of kanban. At Toyota, this is sometimes also called *ordering point* (発注点; *Hotsuchuu-ten*). When the production run is completed, this number also defines the position where the triangle kanban is attached. In this example, the kanban is attached to the second last container.
- **Lot** (ロット; *Rotto*): The production quantity is *4000* pieces. When the triangle kanban signals reproduction, 4000 pieces, the equivalent of eight containers, are to be made.
- **Line** (ライン; *Rain*): This kanban is for the machine *ER2500*.

In Figure 64, you can see the kanban again at the bottom left, and the two receiving material supplies in the back for two different part types (13261-74040 for 500 connecting rods and 41314-20020 for 60 flanges). Both are to be made on the ER2500 machine.

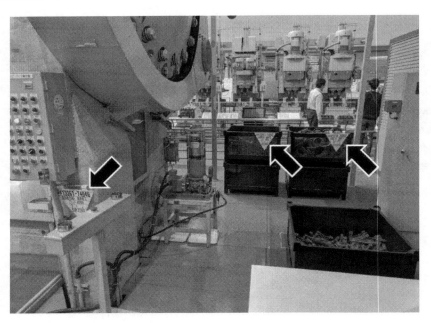

Figure 64: Usage of the sheet metal triangle kanban at the Toyota Commemorative Museum of Industry and Technology, Nagoya, Japan. The kanbans are highlighted with arrows. (Image Roser)

5.3.2 Supermarket

Simply said, supermarkets are inventories at the end of a kanban loop. As supermarkets are part of kanban systems, they are only useful for make-to-stock items that you have... well... on stock in the supermarket. However, not every inventory is a supermarket.

5.3.2.1 What Makes an Inventory a Supermarket

A supermarket is not just any inventory. A supermarket is an inventory organized according to some rules. The three primary conditions that define a supermarket are:

1) **The products are split by part type**: In a supermarket, parts are stored in groups according to their part type. Ideally, they are stored in physical groups, which allows easy observation of the current state. This helps with visual management. Alternatively, they could also be merely digitally grouped within an ERP system, although in this case you would need to dig through the data to see if you are running out of stock.

2) **FIFO is maintained**: The first part of one type that went in the supermarket is also the first part that is taken out if that part type is required. The FIFO principle ensures that the oldest part is always used first. Alternatively, it could also be FEFO (first-expired-first-out) or similar approaches. See Chapter 4.2 for details.

3) **A part leaving the supermarket gives a signal for reproduction or delivery**: The requirement for pull production is that any part leaving the last inventory (the supermarket) gives a signal (the kanban) to replenish the parts. If the supermarket is at the end of a production line, the signal is to produce more. If the supermarket is at the end of a logistic chain, the signal is to order more. It is essential for a functioning supermarket to give such a signal. Since this signal is crucial, it is highly recommended that the supermarket is owned and managed by the processes that receive the signal. Hence, the supermarket is always managed by the preceding processes. Only having a part-type-specific FIFO (the first two conditions) is not a supermarket, but merely a nice inventory.

5.3.2.2 The Minimum Limit (Optional)

Some practitioners, including Toyota, also add a part-specific **minimum limit** to the supermarket (also known as *minimum level* or *warning level*). This is a warning signal of an imminent stock-out. Using such a minimum is not only possible but often recommended. You should use a minimum level in the supermarket whenever it can help you prevent stock-outs. I believe it is beneficial in many kanban systems, especially larger ones where the operators do not always have a full picture of what is going on. In a small kanban loop, the operators often have a good grasp of the situation. Hence, they may automatically react if they are running low. In larger and difficult-to-understand pull systems, they may not. In any case, the minimum level is optional. Also, please note that the minimum is part of the total inventory limit represented by all kanbans for this part type, not in addition to the total.

It is quite possible to establish kanban supermarkets without minimum levels. A minimum can be added later anytime if you find out that you need one. Quite a few kanban systems I have seen did not have a minimum, and those that had one did not always use it.

A supermarket inventory of completed goods of a part type below the minimum level shows something is going wrong. The supermarket is in danger of running out of parts. If your supermarket falls below this minimum, check if more parts of this type are in the pipeline. If there are no parts in the pipeline that will become available shortly, you may have to act and reprioritize production to avoid stock-outs.

Please do not confuse a minimum level with an inventory that cannot be touched. If you need the parts, use them, even if your inventory falls below the minimum level. But find out and hopefully fix why you are running out of parts before you run out of parts.

The minimum in a supermarket is very similar to the fuel gauge in your car, as shown in Figure 65. If your car is low on fuel, a warning light blinks and maybe there is also a warning sound. This gives you time to refuel before you are stranded.

Figure 65: The fuel gauge in a car also has a minimum warning. (Image Roser)

However, if the warning light goes off when you have only three kilometers' worth of fuel left, then it is probably way too late. Hence, your minimum is too low. On the other hand, if the warning goes off when there is still half a tank of fuel, then it will be more annoying than helpful. In this case, your minimum is too high. Finally, if your warning limit is set at 25% but blinks five times a day, then your fuel tank is too small! The same goes for supermarkets.

Some people get really excited with adding a minimum and want to do more. Sometimes they also add a yellow area to indicate a pre-warning and a green area to indicate everything is fine. Frankly, I would advise against that. It may be a case of too much labeling, or too much 5S. Again, take your fuel gauge as an example. Do you really need a warning that there is "only 75%" of fuel left? Do you really need a yellow and a green area? If you have too many green, yellow, and red colors, as in Figure 66, it confuses the message and makes people ignore warnings. In any case, don't expect shop floor people to pay attention.

Figure 66: Too many different color levels have little use and will only confuse operators. (Image Roser)

Sometimes there is even a discussion to use a **maximum level** in the supermarket that forces the supplying system to stop. This is unnecessary, redundant, and dangerous! **Only a lack of kanbans should bring processes to a stop.** If a supermarket full of one type of parts would stop the preceding processes, you either have to mess with the FIFO sequence or risk running out of parts for the other part types.

Anyway, a minimum level in a kanban supermarket is a useful warning signal that you are about to run out of stock. This will give you time to react and prevent an actual stock-out. Usually this involves some degree of emergency firefighting. Even though I don't like firefighting much, it may be the lesser evil here.

If you reach the minimum, then you have too few kanbans with material of this part type in the supermarket. There are many possible reasons for that. Maybe you cannot produce due to **lack of raw material**. In this case, the issue should have been escalated already, but now is a good time to escalate again with even more urgency.

Another possibility is that the **critical kanbans are merely delayed due to other kanbans being in front of them**. This is much easier to fix. Simply fast-track the needed kanban to the front of the queue for production. Make sure to allow enough time for logistics to transport the material! Depending on the urgency, you may also escalate with logistics to accelerate the material delivery for these urgent kanbans. If you have a prioritized queue for production anyway, put the urgent kanbans in the queue for prioritized parts. Figure 70 shows an example. The balls are below their minimum. As part of the escalation, one of the corresponding kanban is moved to the front of the queue for production.

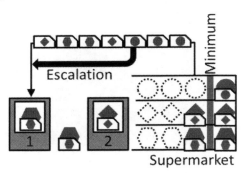

Figure 67: Example escalation upon reaching the minimum by moving a kanban to the front in the queue for production (Image Roser)

In the best case, you find that **the needed parts are already in production** and will arrive in the supermarket shortly anyway. Here, you probably don't have to do anything. The problem is already solved, and material will arrive before you run out. In the example in Figure 68, the balls also have reached their minimum. However, there are already multiple balls in production, and no action is necessary.

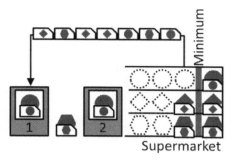

Figure 68: If critical products will be completed soon anyway, no escalation may be necessary. (Image Roser)

There is a complication for **kanban systems with a very long lead time**. In such kanban systems, most kanbans will be under replenishment at any given time. Depending on your minimum level, moving a kanban to the front of the queue for production may not be enough. It may be necessary to escalate by prioritizing products already in production. It may be necessary to move parts in production to the front of their respective queues. An example is shown in Figure 69, where a ball already in production is moved ahead in the FIFO to prevent a stock-out.

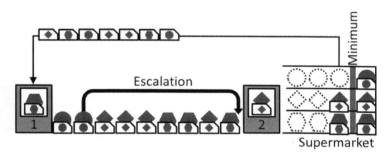

Figure 69: For long lead times, it may be necessary to re-sequence parts already in production. (Image Roser)

Moving parts already in production will allow lower minimum limits. This may even be necessary for systems with very long replenishment times to avoid overly large minimums, which would cause too many minimum warnings. However, if you can, avoid moving material already in production. Depending on your system, **this can increase chaos and can**

cause subsequent problems. It is also much more effort than merely moving a kanban card.

The minimum level in a kanban supermarket depends on what emergency measures you are willing to take to **accelerate the replenishment time** in order to prevent a stock-out. The minimum level should be large enough that you still have time to act before you run out of parts. **Accelerating the information** flow by prioritizing the critical parts is almost always possible. **Accelerating the material flow** is also possible, but may require much more effort and is potentially much more chaotic.

The minimum level should represent the customer demand during such an accelerated replenishment time. How many parts will the customer demand while you fast-track the replenishment? This should include the time needed to notice that you have reached the minimum and to start the countermeasures. You may also include a small safety margin for unforeseen events.

Implementing the minimum can be as simple as a colored area in the supermarket. If the inventory falls below this level, you have reached the minimum. It could also be a light signal or similar, or part of a digital system. The harder part is training the operators to understand the minimum and to actually react if they reach the minimum. A minimum level won't help if it is ignored by the operators.

You may find out that you still run out of stock frequently despite emergency escalations. Especially for a newly implemented minimum level, keep track of how often you reach it, and how often it actually resulted in escalations. If you lack raw materials, then it is a supplier issue. **If it is an internal problem and you can't react fast enough, then your minimum is too low.** You do not have enough time to counteract the problem. In this case you may increase the minimum. Alternatively, you may change the escalation procedure and accelerate the replenishment time even more. On the other hand, if your reaction frequently leaves you with ample time, then your minimum may be too large.

If you reach the minimum too often, you may have too few kanbans or a too-large minimum. A higher inventory limit (i.e., more kanbans) would make it less likely to reach the minimum. If you never reach the minimum, you may have too many kanbans... although this may be the lesser evil. Overall, like with many lean methods, **the fine-tuning is based on observing the system and adjusting as needed**.

Please note that the reorder point of the reorder point method shown in Chapter 8 is sometimes also known as a minimum inventory level. However, its function is totally different. The minimum level in the reorder point method is a signal to replenish. This reorder point is reached regularly. The minimum (the reorder point) should be large enough to replenish comfortably using the normal replenishment process. This is very different from a minimum level in a kanban supermarket. The latter is a warning signal, and the replenishment uses non-standard emergency actions. It should be reached only seldom. Please do not confuse these two, even though they have a similar name.

5.3.2.3 Physical Form of the Supermarket

The supermarket can have different physical forms. The most common ones are **rolling or sliding lanes**, where a container is added from the rear and slides or rolls forward until it bumps into the next part or the front of the slide. Figure 70 shows such a rolling rack for small boxes. Some of these racks even have brakes at the end, so pallets slow down before they bump into the end stop. This prevents parts from falling out during an abrupt stop.

Figure 70: A small supermarket on rolling racks at the Karlsruhe University of Applied Sciences, front and detail of back (Image Roser)

Such racks are available for containers in different sizes, ranging from pallets down to small boxes. They may use rollers across the entire width of the lane, or a smaller set of rollers on each side, or even a simple slide. Gravity causes the container to roll or slide forward slowly toward the exit of the lane. Small containers can also be pushed by hand along a horizontal slide.

You may even have a simple shelf, and the operators **organize the FIFO sequence by hand**. An example from a hospital is shown in Figure 71. However, this is additional effort and has the risk of breaking a FIFO sequence.

Figure 71: Detail of a medical supermarket in a hospital using a normal shelf at the Consorci Sanitary Garraf near Barcelona (Image Roser)

For a smaller number of pallets, it is also possible to use two simple **rails on the floor** about 5 cm high and a generous pallet width apart. The forklift driver puts the pallet in at one end and then pushes forward until the first pallet in the row reaches the exit of the rails. This is cheaper than a set of rollers, but requires additional effort from the forklift driver, possibly additional walking by the person taking material out, and causes more wear on the floor and the pallets. I certainly prefer the rolling lanes.

The entire system can also be built **digitally**. A computer or ERP system tracks the location of each pallet or box in a normal warehouse. Whenever material is needed, the computer determines the oldest material of that type in the warehouse and releases this material. Hence, the logic in the computer maintains FIFO within each material type. This has the advantage that the warehouse or storage area can be used more efficiently and can store more material. The inventory of a part is not limited by the length of a lane. However, it is more effort in programming, more difficult to change or update, and less robust than a single rolling lane. Most of all, it lacks the easy visualization. In a rolling lane you can quickly see how much material you have. In a digital system, you have to look up the information on a computer.

5.3.3 Kanban Box

A kanban box (sometimes also called a "kanban post") is a simple box at the supermarket. Whenever material is consumed, the kanban should return to the beginning of the loop. However, the person picking up the material rarely has the time (or interest) to return the kanban. To simplify the process, a small box is often attached to the supermarket where the kanbans are dropped. In regular intervals (thirty minutes, one hour, two hours, etc.) a person responsible for the supermarket comes, picks up the cards from this box, and moves it to the next step in the information flow. Figure 72 shows two examples of such kanban boxes, one using a plastic box, another using magnetic rails.

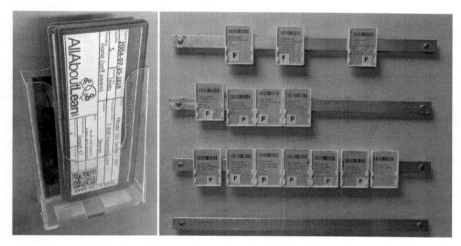

Figure 72: On the left, a common design of a simple plastic kanban box with magnetic strips that can be attached to a steel shelf. The kanban box at the right uses magnetic kanbans at the Consorci Sanitary Garraf Hospital near Barcelona. (Image Roser)

This person then brings the kanbans upstream to the next step in the kanban loop to continue the information flow. This next step may be the queue for production, a lot size generation, or another type of step where the kanbans are sequenced.

For visual management you could install a simple light that turns on after a predetermined time interval. This is the signal to check for kanban and to transport the kanbans from the kanban box back upstream. A reset button turns off the light until the next time interval is up. This can help to maintain your regular standard for transporting kanbans from the kanban box.

If the kanbans are maintained by an ERP system, the person responsible for the supermarket may take the kanbans out of the box and scan or type the information into the ERP system. This is necessary for the system to know what has been consumed and what needs to be replenished. This also should happen either immediately or at regular intervals.

5.3.4 Sequence Creation

The simplest kanban systems use no explicit sequencing at all. All returning kanbans are simply added into the queue for production in first-come-first-serve sequence. This is in effect a FIFO. However, often there may be reasons to create a sequence to make it easier for the production system. At Toyota, this sequencing is crucial for leveling. Sequencing is much less common for transport kanbans, as they simply take whatever they need from the preceding inventory.

Below, I will show you some of the most common reasons for sequencing. These can also appear in combinations (e.g., both changeover sequencing and lot size creation). Figure 73 shows examples of a kanban board and a kanban arrangement system to help with arranging the sequence of your kanbans. Similar systems are also often called a *"heijunka* box", based on the Japanese term for leveling, *heijunka*.

Figure 73: Examples of card-sorting tools to help with sequencing or lot creation of kanbans (Image Roser)

5.3.4.1   Lot Size Formation

One of the most common reasons to create a sequence is to create lot sizes. While in lean manufacturing the ideal lot size is one, you may not yet have reached this level of godliness. Hence, at one point in the flow of kanbans back to the beginning of the loop, someone collects kanbans and releases them only if they represent at least the required minimum lot size.

Shop floor personnel often prefer to make the lot sizes as large as possible to reduce the changeover effort. However, this will increase the replenishment time and hence your inventory, as we will see later. Make sure your people do not fall into this temptation. Also, for a lean system, try to make the lot size as small as feasibly possible.[31]

5.3.4.2   Changeover Sequencing

Similarly, there may be a sequence to create easier changeovers. For example, in processes that add or use colors like injection molding, it is common to go from light to dark. Injection molding of the same shape (i.e., the same tool) in multiple color starts with the lightest-color clear or white, followed by increasing darker colors until it ends with the darkest-color black. A tiny fleck of white material is not really noticeable in a yellow part, whereas a yellow spot on a white part can be a noticeable defect.

Other examples include parts where one changeover requires only an adjustment of the tool, whereas another changeover requires the exchange of a tool or even exchanging multiple tools. Creating a good changeover sequence is a bit of an art, and I won't go into detail here. Just be aware that creating such a sequence requires the rearrangement of the kanbans before they are released into the production queue. This in turn increases the replenishment time.

Similar to the lot size formation you may be tempted to create an elaborate changeover sequence to squeeze the last bit of time out of the changeover. Be wary, however, that in this case kanbans may have to wait for longer and longer until they fit into the sequence. This will increase the

---

[31]   Christoph Roser, *How to Determine Your Lot Size – Part 1*, in *Collected Blog Posts of AllAboutLean.Com 2017*, Collected Blog Posts of AllAboutLean.Com 5 Offenbach, Germany: AllAboutLean Publishing, 2020, 12–16, ISBN 978-3-96382-019-9.

replenishment time and requires either a larger supermarket with more kanbans, or risks running out of material in the supermarket.[32]

5.3.4.3 Workload Balancing

For very small lot sizes, the sequence may also be adjusted to create an even workload. For example, in automotive, installing four doors takes longer than installing two doors. Hence, if there are a lot of four-door models coming down the line, the door assembly may be overloaded. If afterwards there are many two-door models, this station may be idling. However, if you alternate two- and four-door models, the door assembly takes a bit longer for the four doors, but this is canceled out by the next two-door model. Such a sequencing approach is also more of an art than a science, and I won't go into detail here. Yet this also can be included in the kanban sequencing.[33, 34, 35, 36] However, this also increases your required inventory.

5.3.4.4 Leveling

Leveling is the idea that the production sequence should be as uniformly repeating and evenly distributed as possible. This is a very popular topic—

[32] Christoph Roser, *Changeover Sequencing – Part 1*, in *Collected Blog Posts of AllAboutLean.Com 2017*, Collected Blog Posts of AllAboutLean.Com 5 Offenbach, Germany: AllAboutLean Publishing, 2020, 149–54, ISBN 978-3-96382-019-9.

[33] Christoph Roser, *Mixed Model Sequencing – Introduction*, in *Collected Blog Posts of AllAboutLean.Com 2019*, Collected Blog Posts of AllAboutLean.Com 7 Offenbach, Germany: AllAboutLean Publishing, 2020, 128–32, ISBN 978-3-96382-025-0.

[34] Christoph Roser, *Mixed Model Sequencing – Basic Example Introduction*, in *Collected Blog Posts of AllAboutLean.Com 2019*, Collected Blog Posts of AllAboutLean.Com 7 Offenbach, Germany: AllAboutLean Publishing, 2020, 143–47, ISBN 978-3-96382-025-0.

[35] Christoph Roser, *Mixed Model Sequencing – Complex Example Introduction*, in *Collected Blog Posts of AllAboutLean.Com 2019*, Collected Blog Posts of AllAboutLean.Com 7 Offenbach, Germany: AllAboutLean Publishing, 2020, 159–64, ISBN 978-3-96382-025-0.

[36] Christoph Roser, *Mixed Model Sequencing – Summary*, in *Collected Blog Posts of AllAboutLean.Com 2019*, Collected Blog Posts of AllAboutLean.Com 7 Offenbach, Germany: AllAboutLean Publishing, 2020, 189–93, ISBN 978-3-96382-025-0.

at least with management in larger companies. It is full with buzzwords like *EPEI* (Every Part Every Interval), *PFEP* (Plan for Every Part), and *heijunka* ("leveling" in Japanese). The operators on the shop floor, however, often feel very differently. They are often much less enthusiastic on leveling than management. Leveling can help significantly with your production system. Unfortunately, most implementations I have seen outside of Toyota were flawed attempts at highly advanced leveling that increased chaos instead of reducing it.

There are different types of leveling. Some variants of leveling are quite doable, while others are more advanced and difficult techniques in manufacturing that most companies simply cannot do (yet). In general, you can **level for volume** (same quantity every day across all parts) and **level for variety** (mix up your part types as much as possible using as small lot sizes as possible).

Using the smallest feasible lot size is always beneficial, and doable for all companies. Trying to **distribute the small lot sizes evenly by product type throughout the day** is also quite possible. Both are highly beneficial for pull systems. It is often even argued that these are prerequisites for pull. I believe, however, that they are not quite a prerequisite, but rather a way to reduce your inventory and therefore make it easier to set up a pull system. Hence, I recommend using small lot sizes and level daily quantities before or while you implement pull.

But **stay away from longer leveling sequences like a two-week pattern**. These are highly advanced and require maturity of your production system. If you can't even reliably produce tomorrow what you planned today, a multi-week pattern will increase chaos and create havoc with your shop floor. At best, attempting such a longer pattern leveling will show you that your system is not as good as you thought. In this case, you should go back to the basics of establishing flow, stabilize flow using standards, implement pull, reduce lot sizes and other fluctuations, and create a daily mix.

Overall, leveling can help you with pull systems, but it is not a prerequisite. My advice is to reduce your lot sizes as much as possible, stick to the basics of leveling including small lot sizes and a daily sequence if you can, and try to get a good kanban system up and running. Doing longer patterns is highly advanced and to be avoided for most companies.

5.3.5 Queue for Production

The next common element after sequencing is the queue for production. This applies mostly to production kanbans (i.e., if the pull loop covers a production system). It is less common for transport kanbans that resupply from another inventory. Overall, if you don't have enough capacity to serve every arriving kanban immediately, you need a queue for production.

The production sequence is a line of jobs waiting to be started. In its easiest form, this is a simple queue with no prioritization. But here you can also include prioritization of jobs. You could have one queue for normal jobs, and one queue for urgent jobs. Resist the temptation to have more than two queues for prioritization [37], unless you are prioritizing patients in the emergency room of a hospital.

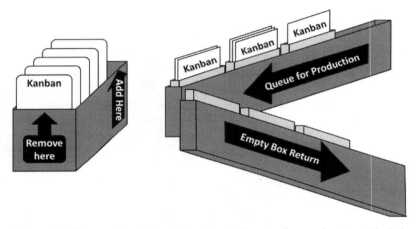

Figure 74: Two options to create a physical queue for production. The left image shows a box where kanbans are added from the back and removed from the front. The right image shows metal boxes with kanbans sliding down a chute and returning on another chute. (Image Roser)

Such queues for production can have different forms. They could be a list in a computer. They could be a sequence of kanbans in a stack where you have to always make sure that the oldest kanban is removed on one side

---

[37] Christoph Roser, *How to Prioritize Your Work Orders – Basics*, in *Collected Blog Posts of AllAboutLean.Com 2016*, Collected Blog Posts of AllAboutLean.Com 4 Offenbach, Germany: AllAboutLean Publishing, 2020, 156–59, ISBN 978-3-96382-016-8.

and the newest is added from the other side. Another variant common at Toyota is a sliding chute containing small metal boxes, each of which contains one or more kanbans. There is one chute with boxes filled with one or more kanbans, and a return chute with empty boxes to be refilled if a new kanban comes along. Having multiple kanbans in a chute allows easier management of kanban lots. This is visualized in Figure 74.

5.4 Calculations

One frequent and tricky question when designing a kanban system is to determine your inventory limit represented by a number of kanbans. There are two possible approaches. You can calculate the number of kanbans using a kanban formula. This is rather complex, imprecise, and far from foolproof. Alternatively, you can estimate the number of kanbans. The latter approach is usually easier. In any case, you should adjust the system as it is running.

Of course, a major assumption for the kanban system is that **the system can deliver parts faster than the customer needs them**. If your system is too slow and has not enough capacity, no amount of kanbans will fix your lack of capacity. A second assumption is that **raw materials for the kanban system are always available**, although here a larger number of kanbans can buffer short-term supply issues.

5.4.1 Fundamentals for Kanban Calculation

For your understanding, I will develop how the formula comes together instead of presenting the full formula outright. In any case, there is not a single "right" kanban formula, just different variants to estimate the number of kanbans. This subchapter also contains fundamental information for the calculation of other pull production systems.

5.4.1.1 On the Precision of the Kanban Calculation

Kanban formula, kanban calculation… it sounds like physics or science, it all sounds so precise. But let me be very clear on one point: **kanban calculation is not precise!** The kanban calculation is nothing more than a formula for a very rough estimate using many assumptions. Slightly different but equally valid assumptions may easily change the number of kanbans by 30% or more. I will point out the assumptions and their effects below to show you the level of precision of the kanban formula.

The number of kanbans defines the performance of a pull system. If you use too few, you will have constant problems with interruptions and missed deliveries or idle operators and processes. If you use too many, you waste space and money for inventory. Of course, if you have the choice between missed deliveries and idle operators or slightly more inventory on the shop floor, I would go for slightly more inventory. Hence, in kanban calculations, it is customary to err on the conservative side. Make-to-stock is generally a trade-off between finished-goods material availability and the inventory. The availability usually has a higher priority. **In case of doubt, use more kanbans, and adjust later when the system is running.** Luckily, pull systems are very robust, and minor differences in the number of kanbans do not have a huge impact on the performance.

Below are the mathematical calculations (estimations!) to determine the number of kanbans. I will develop the kanban formula step by step to make the underlying relations more transparent. Important: **You need to calculate this separately for every part number that you want to put in your kanban stock.** Do not calculate this only once for the sum of all product types and then split the kanbans according to the volume of the product types. This will not work! If you calculate the number of kanbans only once for the sum of all product types, then chances are you may have some part in stock when you need some. However, these will probably be the wrong part type.

5.4.1.2   The Basis—The Customer Takt

The demand on our pull system is set by customer demand in relation to the available production time. The average time between parts ordered by the customer is the basis for calculating the number of kanbans, or any other inventory limit of a pull system. This is the **customer takt**. *Takt* is a German word for tact, pulse, or timing. This word made it from Junkers Aircraft manufacturing in Germany to Mitsubishi Zero manufacturing in Japan during World War II, to Toyota, and from there to lean manufacturing.

To calculate the customer takt for a part type, you first need to decide which time period you want to look at. This could be, for example, a week or a month. Then you need to estimate the **working time period, which is** the time your system is actually operating during this time period. Next, you need to estimate the **demand for this part type during this time period**. This is the total number of parts for this part type that you expect to be ordered by the customer during this time period. **The customer takt for a part type is now simply the total available working time of your system, divided by the total customer demand for that part type during that period.** This is shown in Equation 1. The customer takt is the average time between the demand for a single product within your working time, measured as a time per part. The inverse would be the demand frequency for that part type, measured in parts or quantity per time.

$$TT_n = \frac{TW}{D_n} = \frac{1}{DF_n}$$

Equation 1: Customer takt for part type n

The variables for Equation 1 and Equation 2 are as follows. A list of all variables used in this book can be found in the appendix.

D_n Demand of part type n during a given time period (quantity)
DF_n Demand frequency for part type n (quantity per time)
Q_n Produced quantity of part type n (quantity)
TL_n Line takt for part type n (time per quantity)
TP_n Throughput for part type n (quantity per time)
TT_n Customer takt for part type n (time per quantity)
TW Working time period of a system (time)

The **working time period** needs a bit more discussion. The usual approach is to use the working time of your system. If your line works 5 days per week with 7 hours per day, then you have a total working time of 35 hours per week. If your total demand is 2100 parts per week, then your customer takt is 35 hours divided by 2100 parts or 1 minute per part.

This is easy to understand if your loop has the same working time throughout the loop. However, especially with logistics, different parts of the pull loop may work with different schedules. The supplier may have a 5-day work week, but the trucker also drives on weekends and late at night. You have to take the working time period that best represents your pull loop. This could even be an around-the-clock time period of 7 days with 24 hours per day.

Similar to the customer takt, there is the **line takt**. The customer takt is the average time between a demand for one product. The line takt is the average time between the completions of a good product. Make sure to count only good parts and exclude defects and scrapped parts. Equation 2 shows the calculation of the line takt for a part type based on the produced quantity of this part type n.

$$TL_n = \frac{TW}{Q_n} = \frac{1}{TP_n} \approx TT_n$$

Equation 2: Line takt for part type n

This line takt is also the inverse of the production frequency, which is more commonly known as the throughput. There are some almost philosophical discussions when you should use the customer takt and when the line takt, or similarly the demand frequency or the throughput. In reality, this usually makes little difference.

For a good production system, the customer takt is very similar to the line takt. For a normal production system, the average number of goods you produce and the average number of products you need to produce should be very close to each other. If the customer orders too few items, the working time for this system is reduced until the line takt again equals approximately the customer takt. Similarly, if the customer demands more overtime and extra shifts increase, the work time until the customer and the line takt are again similar. I prefer using the customer takt for the calculation of the number of kanbans, but feel free to use the line takt instead if you feel more comfortable with it.

Please make sure to distinguish between the customer or line takt of **one part type** and the combined customer or line takt for **all part types**! The latter is sometimes called a **compound takt time**. For the kanban calculation, you will most likely need both. For example, you need the customer takt for your current part type to convert a time into a number of kanbans, as shown in Equation 11. However, you also need the customer takt for all parts when calculating the time in the queue for production. **Make sure you don't mix up the different takt times!**

Equation 3 shows you how to combine the customer takt times for multiple part types. Equation 4 calculates the combined demand frequency. However, it may be easier to change Equation 1 using the total demand across all part types. This is shown in Equation 5, where the combined demand is simply the sum of the individual demands, as shown in Equation 6.

$$TT_{All} = \frac{1}{\sum_{n=1}^{m} \frac{1}{TT_n}}$$

Equation 3: Combined customer takt for m different part types

$$DF_{All} = \sum_{n=1}^{m} DF_n$$

Equation 4: Combined demand frequency for m different part types

$$TT_{All} = \frac{TW}{D_{All}} = \frac{1}{DF_{All}}$$

Equation 5: Customer takt across all part types

$$D_{All} = \sum_{n=1}^{m} D_n$$

Equation 6: Joint demand across all part types

The variables for Equation 3 to Equation 6 are as follows:

D_n	Demand of part type n during a given time period (quantity)
D_{All}	Demand for all part types during a given time period (quantity)
DF_n	Demand frequency for part type n (quantity per time)
DF_{All}	Demand frequency across all part types (quantity per time)
m	Count of all part types in the pull loop (no unit)
n	Generic referrer to a part type (no unit)
TT_n	Customer takt for part type n (time per quantity)
TT_{All}	Customer takt across all part types (time per quantity)
TW	Working time period of a system (time)

If you have multiple kanban loops in sequence, the relevant customer takt is always the working time of the kanban loop divided by the demand of the subsequent process or customer. This accounts for increases in demand along the value stream due to quality losses. The takt also changes with the number of subcomponents. If your customer takt for one car is 60 seconds per car, then the customer takt for your wheels is 15 seconds, since you need four wheels for one car. Anyway, in most cases the takt for the next segment in the value stream should be pretty close to the end customer takt, adjusted only for the number of subcomponents and working time.

5.4.1.3 Converting Parts to Cards to Time and Back

The goal of the kanban formula is to calculate an upper inventory limit. It is possible to express this as a quantity of items. It is also possible to express this as a number of kanbans. Finally, it is also possible to express this as a time.

Some variables needed for the kanban calculation will be times, which have to be converted into a production quantity and then into a number of kanbans. This could be, for example, a setup time. **Other variables for the calculation are quantities**, which would also have to be converted into a number of kanbans. This could be, for example, the inventory in the production system. Finally, **some variables for the calculation are easiest to get as a number of kanbans**, and no conversion is necessary. This is, for example, the lot size.

Transforming one type of unit to another is therefore important for the kanban calculation. To transform a time unit into a number of parts, you need the customer takt or the demand frequency. This can be done across all part types, or only for a specific part type, or for a group of part types.

Dividing your time by the customer takt or multiplying it with the demand frequency gives you the quantity that can or should be produced during this time, as shown in Equation 7. The reverse of converting a quantity into a time is shown in Equation 8.

Equation 8 is actually a famous equation called Little's law. Little's law was known for a long time and simply assumed to be true, before being scientifically proven by John Little.[38] The law gives the relation between the waiting or production time, the number of items in the system, and the customer takt or demand frequency.[39] The law is quite simple, rather precise, and in my view quite beautiful.

---

[38] John D. C. Little, *A Proof for the Queuing Formula: L = ΛW, Operations Research 9*, no. 3 June 1961: 383–87.

[39] In the original literature, the nomenclature is usually called the waiting time, the inventory, and the throughput. I have changed this here to fit better with the theme of the book.

$$Q = \frac{T}{TT} = T \cdot DF$$

Equation 7: Transforming a time into a quantity

$$T = Q \cdot TT = \frac{Q}{DF}$$

Equation 8: Transforming a quantity into a time

The variables for Equation 7 to Equation 12 in this section are as follows:

DF	Demand frequency (quantity per time)
DF_n	Demand frequency for part type n (quantity per time)
$NC_{Kanban,n}$	Number of kanbans for part type n (card quantity)
NPC_n	Number of parts per kanban for part type n (quantity per card)
Q	Quantity in general (quantity)
Q_n	Produced quantity of part type n (quantity)
T	Time in general (time)
TT	Customer takt (time per quantity)
TT_n	Customer takt for part type n (time per quantity)

You can also convert a quantity into a number of kanbans. Often, a kanban represents exactly one item. In this case, the number of parts per kanban for this part type is one, and the quantity for this part type equals the number of kanbans. However, if a kanban represents a larger quantity, then you need to divide the quantity by the number of parts per kanban for this part type to get the number of kanbans, as shown in Equation 9. The reverse of converting a number of kanbans into a quantity is shown in Equation 10.

$$NC_{Kanban,n} = \frac{Q_n}{NPC_n}$$

Equation 9: Transforming a quantity into a number of kanbans

$$Q_n = NC_{Kanban,n} \cdot NPC_n$$

Equation 10: Transforming a number of kanbans into a quantity

Combining Equation 7 and Equation 9, you can convert a time into a number of kanbans, as shown in Equation 11. The reverse of converting a number of kanbans into a time is shown in Equation 12.

$$NC_{Kanban,n} = \frac{T}{TT_n \cdot NPC_n} = \frac{T \cdot DF_n}{NPC_n}$$

Equation 11: Transforming a time into a number of kanbans

$$T = NC_{Kanban,n} \cdot TT_n \cdot NPC_n = \frac{NC_{Kanban,n} \cdot NPC_n}{DF_n}$$

Equation 12: Transforming a number of kanbans into a time

5.4.1.4   The Fundamental Kanban Formula

Equation 11 can be used for the kanban calculation if the time is the replenishment time. Therefore, the underlying fundamental formula to calculate the number of kanbans, or the inventory limit for pretty much any pull system, is shown in Equation 13. But don't use this yet, as there are many complications in its calculation, especially in the handling of fluctuations.

$$NC_{Kanban,n} = \frac{RT_n}{TT_n \cdot NPC_n} = \frac{RT_n \cdot DF_n}{NPC_n}$$

Equation 13: Underlying fundamental formula to calculate the number of kanbans. Please do not use as is, as the formula does not account for fluctuations.

The variables for Equation 13 are as follows:

DF_n Demand frequency for part type n (quantity per time)
$NC_{Kanban,n}$ Number of kanbans for part type n (card quantity)
NPC_n Number of parts per kanban for part type n (quantity per card)
RT_n Replenishment time for part type n (time)
TT_n Customer takt for part type n (time per quantity)

The challenges here are how to calculate the replenishment time, and — even more difficult — which fluctuations to include. In general, **a make-to-stock pull system needs to be conservative and include most fluctuations in the inventory limit**, which is represented here by the number of kanbans. This ensures a high delivery performance. For make-to-order systems, the delivery performance depends mostly on the lead time, and average values can frequently be used to determine the inventory limit.

Hence, this Equation 13 is difficult to use directly. I will show you the main factors influencing the number of kanbans below before going into more detail on my approach on how to calculate the different elements for the different types of kanban systems.

5.4.1.5 Factors Influencing the Number of Kanbans

The number of kanbans in particular or the inventory limit for a pull system in general depends on two main factors. These are the replenishment time and the customer demand. Let me give you a bit more theory before finally showing you (my version of) the kanban formula.

5.4.1.5.1 The Replenishment Time

The replenishment time is the time needed for one kanban to make a complete circle. If a part is taken out of the supermarket, the kanban is sent back for replenishment. The time between the kanban leaving the supermarket and the kanban coming back to the supermarket attached to a new part is hence known as the **replenishment time**. For our kanban calculations, this replenishment time is needed to estimate the number of kanbans to supply the customer while the supermarket is restocked. This is visualized in Figure 75 for production and transport kanban.

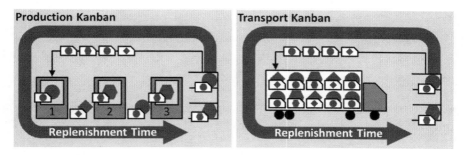

Figure 75: Visualization of the replenishment time and customer demand for a production kanban and a transport kanban (Image Roser)

You need enough kanbans to cover this replenishment time for this part type. This time can be converted into a quantity and hence into a number of kanbans, as per Equation 11. To have enough kanbans representing the average replenishment time ensures that there is on average at least one item in the supermarket. For an unrealistic perfectly stable production system and a perfectly regular customer having no fluctuations whatsoever, the number of kanbans is simply a representation of the average replenishment time, as shown in Equation 14. But again, this is not realistic. Note that the customer takt must be the customer takt for **this specific part type**.

$$NC_{Kanban,n} = \frac{RT_{\varnothing,n}}{TT_n \cdot NPC_n} = \frac{RT_{\varnothing,n} \cdot DF_n}{NPC_n}$$

Equation 14: Calculation of the number of kanbans for a perfectly stable system with no fluctuations, neither in the production system nor with the customer

The variables for Equation 14 and Equation 15 are as follows:

DF_n Demand frequency for part type n (quantity per time)
$NC_{Kanban,n}$ Number of kanbans for part type n (card quantity)
NPC_n Number of parts per kanban for part type n (quantity per card)
$RT_{Max,n}$ Maximum considered replenishment time for part type n (time)
$RT_{\varnothing,n}$ Average replenishment time for part type n (time)
S Safety factor (card quantity)
TT_n Customer takt for part type n (time per quantity)

However, perfectly stable systems exist only in theory, and never in reality. No matter what, you will have fluctuations. Both the replenishment time and the customer fluctuate. For the production systems, fluctuations can be due to a temporary lack of material, breakdowns, maintenance, changeovers, changes in the product mix, and a multitude of other reasons. Using the average replenishment time in Equation 14 would mean that you have on average one part in the supermarket… which means that half of your time you would be out of stock. If the customers would wait until they get their part, your delivery performance would approach zero as your queue of customers approaches infinity.

Yet, a kanban system wants to provide a high delivery performance. There should be material in the supermarket for the subsequent processes, even under adverse circumstances. To reflect the fluctuations in the production system, it is highly advisable to use a **very conservative estimate of the replenishment time** to ensure that there are no stock-outs. This is shown in Equation 15, where the customer takt is again for the specific part type. We also added a safety factor.

$$NC_{Kanban,n} = \frac{RT_{Max,n}}{TT_n \cdot NPC_n} + S = \frac{RT_{Max,n} \cdot DF_n}{NPC_n} + S$$

Equation 15: Number of kanbans of part type n for a fluctuating production system, but still with a perfectly stable customer, using a conservative replenishment time

Please note that this conservative estimate is highly recommended only for make-to-stock or ship-to-stock systems, as the goal of these systems is a high material availability. This is very different in make-to-order systems, where production can only start after an order by the customer. Hence, any customer automatically has to wait for the order. A make-to-order system therefore has very different goals from a make-to-stock system. Rather than a high material availability, the goal for make-to-order is a trade-off between a short lead time and a good process utilization. Hence, for make-to-order systems it is feasible to use the average replenishment time, as we will see in Chapter 6.4.1.

5.4.1.5.2 The Customer Demand

One source of fluctuation is the production system. The second source of fluctuation is the customer demand. If the customer demand would be perfectly stable with an order size of one kanban, Equation 15 would be perfectly adequate to calculate the number of kanbans. However, the customer demand also fluctuates.

There are two main factors. First, your customer may order quantities larger than one. If your replenishment system guarantees one item in the supermarket, then a customer ordering two at a time will have to wait. Hence, **larger customer orders** have to be factored in the kanban calculation.

Second, even with smaller lot sizes, your customer may have a **peak demand.** They may temporarily order more than usual. If your customers order on average 100 items per month, you don't want to disappoint them if they order 130 items in one month. To cover for this peak demand, you would need additional kanbans representing these extra 30 parts. Therefore, these two factors also increase the number of kanbans, as we will see later in Chapters 5.4.2.1.8 and 5.4.2.1.9.

5.4.2 The Kanban Formula for Production Kanban

Let me start with the kanban formula for production kanban. The main difficulty here is to determine the replenishment time, as there are lots of different elements that may or may not contribute to the replenishment time and its fluctuations. Also, this calculation is just one possible way to calculate the number of kanbans. There are many different variants of the kanban formula out there. I do not expect you to follow this formula to the letter. Instead, understand the factors that influence the number of kanbans and how they could be calculated.

5.4.2.1 Elements of the Production Kanban Calculation

The replenishment time is easy to define as the time between a kanban leaving the supermarket and the replenished part with the same kanban returning into the supermarket. However, it is much more difficult to measure. Similarly, the peak customer demand is also difficult to determine exactly. Figure 76 shows the possible elements that contribute to the number of kanbans. There are many different ways for how to determine these values, or even which ones to include. Depending on your preferences, the kanban formula may look quite different, and also have slightly different results.

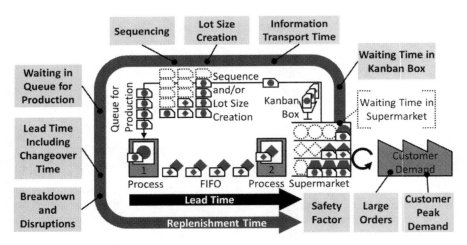

Figure 76: Elements influencing the number of production kanban. The waiting time in the supermarket in dotted brackets is not relevant. (Image Roser)

Please note that **the waiting time in the supermarket is NOT part of the replenishment time**. After a part is consumed, we want to get its replacement parts back into the supermarket. The supermarket is our buffer against fluctuations in make-to-stock production. As the goal of make-to-stock production systems is a good material availability and subsequently a good delivery performance, this supermarket inventory is needed to decouple the fluctuations. Since the cards in the supermarket are already "ready" for the customer, they are not part of the replenishment time. Hence, the waiting time in the supermarket is of no concern. This will be one of the major differences for make-to-order production systems later, as these have different goals, and the replenishment time has different start and end points.

5.4.2.1.1 Waiting Time in the Kanban Box

The first element is the waiting time of the kanban at the supermarket in the kanban box after a part has been taken out of the supermarket. This applies both for physical kanban and digital kanban, which may have a waiting time until they are scanned or processed. Here it is advisable not to use the average, but to use a reasonable worst-case assumption to ensure material availability in the supermarket.

Please note that it is very helpful to have a clear and concise standard for the transport or scanning of the kanbans. If the standard is not followed, or there is no standard and the team leaders move the cards *whenever they feel like it*, then it is much more difficult to estimate this waiting time. If you do not have a good standard, you would have to take a more conservative estimate of the waiting time, which may be much longer than a standard time. This increases your fluctuations, and hence the required inventory limit to buffer these.

If a team leader brings the kanban from the collection box at the supermarket to the production every hour, the average waiting time of a kanban at the supermarket would be 30 minutes. However, a kanban can wait up to 60 minutes if a part was taken out of the supermarket just after the team leader collected the cards. Nevertheless, the kanban system still has to work. Hence, we take the time between pickups as the maximum waiting time at the supermarket. In this example, this worst-case waiting time in the kanban box would be 60 minutes.

5.4.2.1.2 Information Transport Time

The kanban has to be transported from the kanban box back to the sequencing and lot size creating process and from there onward to the queue for production. For digital systems, this transport time is a magnitude of milliseconds, and even for physical kanbans it is rarely more than a few minutes. Hence, this information transport time is usually much smaller than the other elements of the replenishment time. **Most times, this information transport time can safely be ignored**, as it won't make much difference. You should include the information transport time in the calculations only if it is very long.

5.4.2.1.3 Waiting Time for Lot Size Formation

The number of kanbans also depends on the waiting time of your kanban for lot size formation. Here we have to distinguish between the lot size measured in parts, and the lot size measured in kanban. To determine the waiting time, the lot size measured in kanban is relevant.

If your lot size is 100 parts, but your kanban represents 100 parts, your lot size is a single kanban. This would also be the easiest case, since a lot size of one kanban does not have to wait at all. If your lot size is a single kanban, you do not have additional waiting time for lot size formation. In this case, you can **ignore this waiting time for lot size formation if your lot size is one kanban**.

However, if your lot size is multiple kanbans, the first kanban in a lot has to wait for more kanbans to arrive until the lot is complete. For example, if your lot size is 7 kanbans, the first kanban has to wait for 6 more, the second for 5 more, the third for 4 more, and so on. With a lot size of 7 kanbans, the average kanban has to wait for 3 more kanbans until the lot is completed. However, when measuring the waiting times, we do not want to take the averages, but the worst case. Hence, in this example with a lot size of 7, a kanban would have to wait, in the worst case, for 6 more kanbans. Or more generally, **a kanban would have to wait at most for an entire lot size in kanbans minus one**. This would again lead to a waiting time of zero if the lot size is one kanban.

Larger lot sizes will lead to larger waiting times for lot size creation. However, they will lead to even larger waiting times later in the production queue! **The large effect of the lot size onto the number of kanbans and**

subsequently on the overall inventory and the lead time is one reason why lean aims to reduce lot sizes if possible.

We could now convert the waiting time measured in kanbans into an actual waiting time as per Equation 12, as the replenishment time is measured in time units. However, later in the kanban formula we want to convert the replenishment time back into a number of kanbans as per Equation 11. I recommend avoiding this back-and-forth calculation and just representing the waiting time for lot size formation as a number of kanbans. This makes subsequent calculations easier.

5.4.2.1.4 Waiting Time for Sequencing

There may also be a waiting time due to additional sequencing rules. This waiting time, however, depends heavily on your sequencing rules. This could be a changeover sequence, a prioritization sequence, etc. It is difficult to generalize this calculation. I can only say for sure that **if you don't have any sequencing, then you can ignore the waiting time for sequencing**.

If you have sequencing, determine how much this adds to your replenishment time. For example, if your standard is to always collect 10 lots of kanbans before you create a changeover sequence, then a kanban would have to wait for 9 more lots in the worst case. Please note that this is **9 lot sizes** of kanbans, not necessarily nine kanbans.

This sounds similar to the waiting time for lot size formation, but there is one crucial difference. When waiting for lot size formation, a kanban has to wait for more kanbans of exactly the same part type, and we can simply use this number of kanbans directly as part of the replenishment time. When waiting for sequencing, a single lot of kanbans has to wait for more lots of kanbans of **any part number**.

Hence, you cannot substitute the number of kanbans directly into the kanban formula. Instead, you actually have to convert the number of kanbans into a time unit using the **customer takt for all parts combined**, similar to Equation 12. Later you have to convert this waiting time back into a number of kanbans, similar to Equation 11, but now with the **customer takt for this specific part type**. Make sure you do not mix up the combined customer takt for all part types with the customer takt of a specific part type! Furthermore, do not mix up a kanban with a lot size of kanbans.

5.4.2.1.5 Waiting in Production Queue

A sequenced lot size may not be processed immediately. There already may be other lots waiting for processing. We have to include the **waiting time in the production queue**. This is usually a major part of the replenishment time, and can easily be 50% of the entire replenishment time. Unfortunately, this is also very hard to estimate. I have emphasized above that the kanban calculation is only a very rough estimate. This part here is the kicker in terms of imprecision. The waiting time for other lots can fluctuate wildly. You also have to distinguish if you have only one queue for production, or if you have multiple queues. The latter case may be a prioritization of exotic parts, or a combination with a CONWIP system.

Let's start with the slightly simpler case of a **single queue for production**. It is possible to measure this waiting time using Little's law, but it is difficult to determine this theoretically.

What I usually do is to **assume that for every lot, one lot size of each other high-runner product (which may be multiple kanbans) is waiting in front of the latest lot**.[40] For example, assume you have 10 types of product, 3 of which are frequent high runners, and each of them has a lot size of 4 kanbans. Here, the latest lot of high-runner kanbans arriving may wait for 2 other high-runner lot sizes representing a total of 8 kanbans. An exotic low-runner kanban has to wait for all 3 high-runner lot sizes representing 12 kanbans. This is illustrated in Figure 77. But again, this is only the roughest of the very rough estimate.

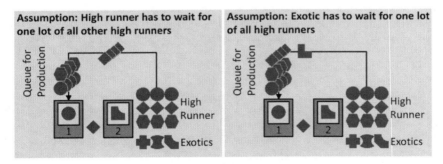

Figure 77: Illustration of the waiting time in the queue for production for high runners and exotics (Image Roser)

---

[40] Many thanks to Holger Friebe for teaching me this trick (and many others).

Here ±30% is easily possible depending on your assumptions. Determining all other factors of the kanban formula in high precision is a waste since this waiting time in the production queue estimate negates all other precision. **It is almost impossible to get precise data here, but you can't ignore it since it is a big part of the replenishment time!**

As for the lot size above, the waiting time for other lots can be expressed in kanbans. However, similar to sequencing, we cannot simply add these to the number of kanbans for our part type, since this queue for production may contain kanbans for all parts that are produced in the system. Hence, we must convert this waiting time in the production queue from a number of kanbans to an actual waiting time using the **combined customer takt for all part types**. Later we will have to convert it back into a number of kanbans, but now using the **customer takt for this specific part type**. This calculation must also **be done for every part type separately**. Different lot sizes for different part types may give different results.

Be careful so as not to mix up the customer takt times. If you start to get nervous about how complex the kanban calculation is going to be, rest assured that I also usually prefer an estimation over this rather complex calculation. (More on the estimation later.)

This approach also applies to a mixed kanban and CONWIP system as explained in 6.2.3, although under two conditions. First, they must use the same queue. Second, the number of CONWIP cards must be significantly less than the number of kanbans.

It gets even more complex if you have **more than one queue for production**. A common example is to use kanban for the make-to-stock items, and CONWIP for the make-to-order items. In other words, in separate production queues, a make-to-order CONWIP card may have priority over a make-to-stock kanban to provide faster deliveries of CONWIP products to the customer. I will explain such mixed systems in more detail in Chapter 6.2.4. A card arriving for the queue with higher priority will have a much shorter waiting time than a card arriving for the queue with lower priority. The benefit or delay depends heavily on the number of prioritized kanban or CONWIP cards.

If the share of prioritized cards is below 20%, it is easy. You can assume that the waiting time in the prioritized queue for production is close to zero, and that the increase in waiting time for the non-prioritized cards is negligible.[41] Figure 78 shows an example of the changes in waiting times for prioritized and non-prioritized parts depending on the share of prioritized parts based on the work by my master's student Yannic Jäger.[42, 43] Up to around 20% to 30% of prioritized production parts or workload, you can set the waiting time for prioritized parts often to zero, and the waiting time for non-prioritized parts based on the estimation explained above. Of course, an actual measurement would be preferred.

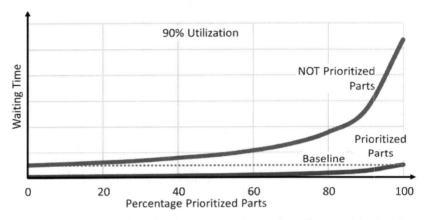

Figure 78: Example of the changes in waiting times for prioritized and non-prioritized parts depending on the share of prioritized parts (Image Roser)

If the share of prioritized cards increases, the waiting time benefit for the prioritized cards will decrease, and the waiting times for the non-prioritized cards will become problematic. The exact effect depends

[41] Christoph Roser, *Effect of Prioritization on Waiting Times*, in *Collected Blog Posts of AllAboutLean.Com 2018*, Collected Blog Posts of AllAboutLean.Com 6 Offenbach, Germany: AllAboutLean Publishing, 2020, 113–20, ISBN 978-3-96382-022-9.

[42] Yannic Jäger and Christoph Roser, *Effect of Prioritization on the Waiting Time*, in *Proceedings of the International Conference on the Advances in Production Management System* International Conference on the Advances in Production Management System, Seoul, Korea, 2018.

[43] Yannic Jäger, *Einfluss von Priorisierung auf das Verhalten eines Produktionssystems* Master Thesis, Karlsruhe, Germany, Karlsruhe University of Applied Sciences, 2017.

significantly on your system and is hard to generalize. If you worry about where to get this number, let me remind you that the kanban formula is nothing more than a guesswork construct with a hint of math. Just take your best guess of the changes in the waiting time and adjust the number of kanbans later when the system is running. In any case, such additional waiting times would have to be estimated and added to the kanban calculation. Please include this in the waiting time if you have multiple queues for production.

5.4.2.1.6 Lead Time (Including Changeover Time)

If you produce different product types, you have changeovers. If you are fortunate, this changeover time is very small and can be ignored. If your changeover times are larger, you may have to consider these for the kanban calculation. However, I find it easiest to simply include the changeover times in the lead time calculation.

The **lead time** is the time from the beginning of the actual processing at the first process until the part with the kanban comes back to the supermarket. This includes the changeover time. The equation to calculate this lead time is Little's law and shown in Equation 8. The lead time is illustrated for production and transport systems in Figure 79.

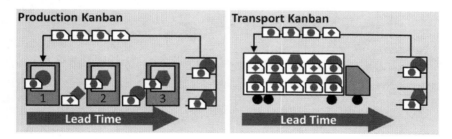

Figure 79: Illustration of the lead time in a production system and a transport system (Image Roser)

For example, assume you have an inventory of 150 parts in the system and the throughput states that there are 5 parts leaving per hour. In this case, the total lead time is 30 hours (150 parts divided by 5 parts per hour). A good example is waiting in a supermarket line. If there are 15 people in front of you and, on average, the checkout staff serves 3 people per minute, then you will have to wait 15/3 = 5 minutes.

Little's law is widely valid and quite precise. Unfortunately, the imprecision comes from getting the data, which adds more fluffiness to our very rough kanban estimate. What number to use for the parts in your system? Of course, you can count them now, but will this still be valid tomorrow? With respect for kanban calculations, I recommend a conservative approach. Take the maximum number of parts that fit in your system (i.e., assume all your FIFO are full and all your processes are loaded to capacity). It may or may not happen, but you still want your kanban system to work when it happens.

Second, how fast are your parts leaving the system? Here we need to use the **customer takt across all parts**. This has the benefit that it also includes the average losses of the system, including the changeover time.

Of course, if your lead time includes delays for bulk processing or shipment, you have to take this into account too. For example, if your kanban loop includes shipping from China, then the ship takes two months, including customs, no matter how many parts are on the ship. In this case, the lead time would be two months. Similarly, if your changeover time is very large only for the specific part that you are calculating, you may also have to add this to the lead time.

5.4.2.1.7 Breakdown and Other Disruptions

The system delivering the new products will also fluctuate. Not everything will go according to plan, and sometimes there will be delays. The lead time we calculated above is somewhat of an average, even though we made conservative assumptions. When calculating how fast the parts were leaving the system, we used the average customer takt of the system. Hence, we **already included long-term average losses**.

What we did not include were **short-term problems**. For example, assume your system has technical problems and is down for two hours. You may choose to have enough kanbans in the system to cover these two hours until the system can catch up again. Similarly, if you want to cover breakdowns of up to four hours' duration, you will need four more hours' worth of kanbans.

Unfortunately, no matter what disruption you plan to cover, you can easily imagine a problem that would be longer than the covered time, however unlikely. Here you have to decide what you want to cover. You need to

decide at what point you would rather take the bullet and run out of stock rather than keep insane amounts of stock available all the time.

This decision should be based on previous experience with the reliability of your system. It is also based on the amount of problems your company gets if a customer delivery is delayed. Keep in mind that so far we have always used conservative estimates for other factors. It is unlikely that all possible worst-case fluctuations will happen at the same time. Kanbans added to cover one type of fluctuation can also cover another type of fluctuation as long as they don't happen at the same time. This coverage for breakdown and disruptions is often given as a time, which will be later converted into a number of kanbans in the kanban formula.

5.4.2.1.8 Large Customer Order

The customer order is probably also fluctuating. Ordering less is usually not a problem for the production system, as the inventory simply fills up, although this is not good for the company. Ordering more than average, however, may be tricky. We have two factors to consider.

You will probably have **larger orders** sometimes. Not all customers order their products one by one. It is more common for a customer to order multiple parts at the same time. A customer may pool all needed items into one order per week or even per month.

However, the kanban system as calculated above so far only ensures that you have one kanban worth of parts in your system at any given time. If your customer wants more than one kanban worth of parts in one order, you need to add more kanbans. Please keep in mind that a kanban may represent more than one part. You calculate this by taking the largest order that you reasonably expect, and transforming it into a number of kanbans using Equation 9. Next you subtract one kanban, since this should be already in the supermarket due to the normal kanban loop behavior. The resulting extra kanbans should not be less than zero.

For example, assume your customer usually orders up to 200 parts at once. With 20 parts per kanban, this represents 10 kanbans. Reducing by 1 kanban, which should be in the supermarket anyway, you get 9 kanbans. Hence, you need to add 9 additional kanbans to your total number of kanbans.

5.4.2.1.9 Customer Peak Demand

Second, your customer may sometimes have a higher **peak demand** than the average. This may be a problem, even if the orders themselves are rather small. Ordering less is usually not an immediate problem. However, if the customer orders more, you may need additional kanbans.

You need to estimate what a possible additional peak demand within a replenishment time could be. You could do this as a percentage, but it will be easier later on if you do it as a quantity.

You first need to estimate how many parts your customer orders normally during the replenishment time. Second, you need to estimate what the maximum number of parts could be that the customer orders during the replenishment time. To be more precise, what maximum number of parts do you want to cover? **The gap between the "normal" demand and the "maximum" demand during a replenishment time is the peak demand**, which you need to add to the inventory limit.

This is also a fudgy part of the calculation. You may know neither your replenishment time nor your customer peak demand with any accuracy. This peak demand also overlaps sometimes, but not always with the large customer order. But don't worry too much about the accuracy; just take your best guess.

If it is a **seasonal demand** that you know beforehand, you may alternatively add extra kanbans before the season starts and remove them again after the season is over. However, you may also need to cover random excess demands, for example due to weather, fashion change, a media hype, etc.

5.4.2.1.10 Safety Factor

The last thing to add would be the safety factor. Technically, since we use conservative values for most other elements, this is usually not needed. The kanban calculations above—for all their uncertainty—are usually quite conservative. You may get away with even fewer kanbans. However, in many plants, shop floor personnel or lower management previously had negative experiences with upper management cutting margins too thin, hurting plant performance, and therefore creating problems, especially for the people on the shop floor. Plus, your problems may be bigger than you think they are. Therefore, a safety factor may be helpful.

The safety factor is a way of giving additional safety to people who worry if the numbers match or if there will be a mess on the shop floor afterwards. I actually prefer to add the safety factor after calculating the number of kanbans without the safety factor. Having a number of kanbans without safety gives me a better feel for how much safety would be appropriate.

The safety factor is either a number of kanbans, or a percentage that is added on top of the kanban calculation. For a small number of kanbans, it may also be enough to simply round up to the next integer. Strictly speaking, the safety is unnecessary, but the few extra kanbans are usually worth the peace on the shop floor.

5.4.2.1.11 Other Elements

The above entries are the most common and also some less common elements that go into the kanban formula. However, depending on your production system, in rare cases there may be more. For example, if your sequencing process is done by a manager who has time only once per week, then you may have an additional delay until the kanbans are sequenced. You would need more kanbans to cover this delay, or your queue for production may run empty until the manager has time to sequence again.

Another example would be a mixed system using both kanban and CONWIP. In this case, the additional delay for kanban due to CONWIP cards may have to be included into the kanban calculation.

Other unusual elements in your system may also cause a delay in the replenishment time. Or there may be special factors in your customer's behavior that you would have to include in the calculation. Try to find out if these are a significant contribution to your number of kanbans. If not, ignore them. If they make a difference, don't worry too much about precision but take your best guess.

5.4.2.2   Calculating the Number of Production Kanbans

Now we have everything together to estimate the number of kanbans. Table 2 gives you an overview of the different elements, including the units, the relevance, and if the values are usually different for different parts. This also includes the unit of the element.

Group	Element	Unit	Usually Part Specific?	Usually Relevant?	Variable
Replenishment Time	Waiting Time in Kanban Box	Time	No	Yes	WB
	Information Transport Time	Time	No	Rarely	TI
	Lot Size Formation	Kanban	Yes	If lot size > 1 kanban	KL
	Waiting Time for Sequencing	Time	Maybe	Only when sequencing	WQ
	Waiting in Production Queue	Time	Yes	Yes	WP
	Lead Time	Time	No	Yes	LT
	Breakdown and Disruptions	Time	Rarely	Yes	BD
Customer	Large Customer Order	Quantity	Yes	Yes	OS
	Peak Customer Demand	Quantity	Yes	Yes	PD
Other	Safety Factor	Kanban	Often	Yes	S
	Other Elements	???	???	No	n/a

Table 2: Overview of variables contributing to the number of production kanban

To determine your number of kanbans for the selected product type in the kanban loop, you merely have to convert the elements in Table 2 into kanban and sum them up. Some elements are already measured in kanbans and can simply be added. Times and quantities need to be converted into kanbans using Equation 11 and Equation 9.

It is also likely that you have to calculate the number of kanbans for multiple part types in your system. Remember, **every part in your kanban loop needs to have its number of kanbans calculated separately**. Some elements that go into the kanban formula are specific to the part type. Other elements may be the same for any part type in your system. Table 2 also shows where you may have to recalculate an element separately for every part type.

Some of these elements appear in almost every system, while others are only relevant sometimes. Here, too, Table 2 gives you a hint on which element you have to consider. Finally, I also included the variables I use for the equations in this book.

The safety factor should be added at the end, as it may be based on the number of kanbans without the safety factor. This safety factor is also often used to round the resulting number of kanbans to the next largest integer. The complete kanban formula for production kanban is shown in Equation 16.

$$NC_{Kanban,n} = \frac{WB + TI + WQ_n + WP_n + LT + BD}{TT_n \cdot NPC_n} +$$

$$+ \left(\frac{OS_{Max,n}}{NPC_n} - 1\right) + (KL_n - 1) + \frac{PD_n}{NPC_n} + S$$

Equation 16: The kanban formula for production kanban

The variables for Equation 16 are as follows:

BD	Additional time to cover breakdowns and disruptions (time)
KL_n	Lot size as a number of kanbans for part type n (card quantity)
LT	Lead time (time)
$NC_{Kanban,n}$	Number of kanbans for part type n (card quantity)
NPC_n	Number of parts per kanban for part type n (quantity per card)
$OS_{Max,n}$	Largest expected order size for part type n (quantity)
PD_n	Peak customer demand for part type n (quantity)
S	Safety factor (card quantity)
TI	Time for the transport of information (time)
TT_n	Customer takt for part type n (time per quantity)
WB	Waiting time at (kanban, CONWIP…) box (time)
WP_n	Waiting time in queue for production for part type n (time)
WQ_n	Waiting time for sequence creation of part type n (time)

Here is a small trick for any complex calculations. I thoroughly label the units and include all units in the calculation. At the end, there should be only the unit left that I want to calculate. If not, then there is probably a mistake. This is recommended also for Equation 16. For example, if your result is measured in "kanban hours per second", then you may have mixed up your time units. While this trick won't prevent all mistakes, it will catch quite a few.

Just keep in mind that this is only a very rough estimate. Furthermore, this is not the only possible way to calculate the number of kanbans. Many different flavors of the formula exist, often with different inputs and assumptions. Again, such kanban formulas are not like physics, where there is only one valid equation; they are an estimation only. Therefore, rather than the calculation, I prefer an estimation approach. You will find a calculation example in Chapter 5.4.2.4.

5.4.2.3 The Toyota Formula

Equation 16 is one way to calculate the number of kanbans. But again, despite the appearance of mathematical accuracy, it is only an estimate. It is also by far not the only formula out there to determine the number of kanbans. As an alternative, let me show you the Toyota formula [44] in Equation 17, to show you that there are more formulas out there. There is no single correct kanban formula; all of them are just different approaches to an estimation. They differ mostly in the way to calculate the replenishment time and how to include uncertainties and fluctuations.

$$NC_{Kanban,n} = \frac{TWT_n + PT_n}{TT_n \cdot NPC_n} \cdot (1 + \alpha)$$

Equation 17: The "Toyota formula" for the number of production kanban

The variables here are as follows:

$NC_{Kanban,n}$	Number of kanbans for part type n (card quantity)
NPC_n	Number of parts per kanban for part type n (quantity per card)
PT_n	Sum of all process times for part type n (time)
TT_n	Customer takt for part type n (time per quantity)
TWT_n	Sum of all transport and waiting times for part type n (time)
α	Safety factor (percent)

If you compare Equation 17 with Equation 16, you will see many similarities. Like pretty much all kanban formulas, it is the replenishment time divided by the customer takt and the number of parts per kanban. The replenishment time is determined in less detail. Toyota uses the waiting and information transport times as one variable, and the sum of the process

---

[44] Koichi Shimokawa et al., *The Birth of Lean* Cambridge, Massachusetts: Lean Enterprise Institute, Inc., 2009, ISBN 1-934109-22-3.

times as another. Together they also give you the replenishment time. Toyota lets you figure out how to obtain these times on your own, whereas my Equation 16 gives you some guidance on how to determine the individual values that make up the replenishment time.

For the safety factor, Toyota uses a percentage rather than an absolute value, but the effect is the same. When Ohno and his team were developing this formula, Ohno insisted on including this safety factor α to allow human sensibility to enter the equation. This safety factor is considered very important at Toyota.

However, the Toyota formula is missing all the elements related to fluctuations. This includes the fluctuations of the replenishment time, the largest customer orders, and the peak demand of the customer that we want to cover within our replenishment time. This is not an oversight, but due to the particular approach used by Toyota to manage its production.

Let's start with the **fluctuations of the replenishment time**. Even though Toyota does quite a good job at keeping these fluctuations down, they do have fluctuations like unplanned stops, defects, or slow-downs. However, at Toyota in Japan they cover these fluctuations not with inventory (i.e., kanban), but with capacity. A shift at Toyota in Japan does not end when the time is up. The shift ends when the target production is reached. Hence, if problems cause a delay in production, the shift is simply extended up to a maximum of 2 hours. Similarly, but less common, if fewer problems happen, the operators can go home earlier.

Since they can decouple production fluctuations with capacity, they do not need to decouple it with inventory (i.e., kanban). Please be aware that in many parts of the world the unions would rip your head off if you would try that. If you like your head on your shoulders, decouple these fluctuations with inventory rather than capacity, and plan the number of kanbans accordingly.

Furthermore, Toyota does not need to cover the customer demand fluctuations, both the **largest customer orders** and the **peak demand** of the customer. Toyota manages to have an extremely stable production system throughout most of its supply chain. I have visited Tier 3 suppliers of Toyota, and they showed me their production plan for the month. Every day had exactly the same quantity for the same parts. There was no deviation. If Toyota makes 637 cars per day every day of the month, then the supplier will make 637 steering wheels every day, and the sub-supplier will make 637 steering wheel covers every day. This daily quota may be changed by the end of the month, but only with advanced notice and strict limits on how much to change (i.e., with thirty days' notice, the quantity cannot change more than 10%).

Hence, the Toyota supply chain does not really have customer fluctuations. The fluctuations of the end customer are decoupled with inventory at their sales location and with time that the customer has to wait for the car. Therefore, Toyota does not need to include customer fluctuations in their Toyota formula. However, chances are your shop floor is not quite as leveled as Toyota. Depending on your level of customer fluctuations, you would be better off including extra kanbans to cover these.

5.4.2.4 Example Production Kanban Calculation

In the following, I will give you an example for the calculation of the number of production kanbans. I will first give you all the parameters and information on the system. Thereafter I will calculate the number of kanbans step by step.

For optimal learning, you may first try to calculate this yourself, and then compare your calculations with the example given here. As there will be quite a few assumptions, your result may differ somewhat from mine depending on these assumptions. Try to understand these differences, and see if these are based on different assumptions or an actual error somewhere. Hopefully, you will get a similar number of kanbans.

5.4.2.4.1 The Production System Data

Figure 80: The example system produces yellow, red, and blue toy cars. (Image Roser)

The example make-to-stock production system produces wooden toy cars in three different colors, red, blue, and yellow, as shown in Figure 80. Red and blue are very popular, but yellow is an exotic product with a very low demand. Since the demand differs, they also have different lot sizes and different number of parts per kanban.

Production planning estimated the expected monthly demand for the upcoming months for each of these products, as well as the largest expected single orders and the peak demand. An overview of this data including the lot size and the number of parts per kanban is given in Table 3.

Color	Lot Size (Cars)	Number of Parts per Kanban	Expected Monthly Demand (Cars)	Largest Orders (Cars)	Peak Demand (Cars)
Red	560	80	10 000	200	650
Blue	300	50	4000	120	420
Yellow	30	10	200	60	80
Total	n/a	n/a	14 200	n/a	n/a

Table 3: Overview of parameters for example calculation of production kanban

The production system itself is very simple. A milling process cuts the car shape out of a wooden board. In a second process, the car is painted. In the final assembly, the wheels are attached, and the car is complete. Between the three processes are FIFO with a maximum capacity of 100 cars, even though on average there are only 50 cars in each FIFO. Each process can hold at most one car at a time. The basic value stream is shown in Figure 81.

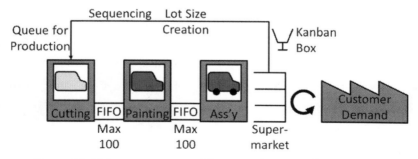

Figure 81: Value stream map of the example system (Image Roser)

The production system works for 20 days per month, with one shift of 7 hours each. The supervisor picks up the kanbans from the kanban box every hour and brings them to the lot size formation. Walking from the kanban box to the lot sizing takes about 3 minutes. After there are enough kanbans of one car type for a lot size, the kanbans for this part type move to sequencing.

To reduce changeover time, the paint process requires a color sequence from yellow to red to blue. The sequencing always waits until at least 1000 cars are ready for sequencing from the lot size formation and then releases them in sequence to the queue for production. Management has decided that they want to cover 2 hours of breakdowns and other disruptions. Any more than that, and they would rather have a stock-out than a permanent excess inventory.

5.4.2.4.2 Calculation of the Elements

An important variable for many of the subsequent calculations is the **customer takt**. We have the expected monthly demand from Table 3. The total working time is 20 days per month with 1 shift per day and seven hours per shift, for a total of 140 working hours per month. Dividing the working time by the demand would give the customer takt. However, in our example, if you measure it in hours per piece, it would be a pretty small number. Hence, we multiply the 140 hours by 3600 seconds per hour to get 504 000 seconds of working time per month. Now we can calculate the customer takt for all parts separately and also as a combined customer takt across all parts. The calculation of the customer takt for the red cars is shown in Equation 18. An overview is given in Table 4.

$$TT_{Red} = \frac{TW}{D_{Red}} =$$

$$= \frac{20d \cdot 7\frac{h}{d}}{10\,000 \text{ pieces}} = \frac{140h}{10\,000\text{pieces}} = \frac{504\,000s}{10\,000\text{pieces}} = 50.4\frac{s}{\text{piece}}$$

Equation 18: Customer takt calculation for the red car

Color	Expected Monthly Demand (Cars)	Customer Takt (Second/Car)
Red	10 000	50.4
Blue	4000	126.0
Yellow	200	2520
Total	14 200	35.5

Table 4: Customer takt times for the production kanban example

In order to determine the number of kanbans, we would need to determine the different elements for the number of kanbans. Following the sequence as in Chapter 5.4.2.1, we start with the **waiting time in the kanban box**. Since the supervisor picks up the kanbans in the box every hour, the maximum waiting time is 1 hour. Please note that we go for the maximum of 1 hour rather than the average of 30 minutes. This time is the same for any of the three product types.

The **information transport time** is also already given in the description as 3 minutes. Since this is quite small compared to the other values, I would normally ignore it, but for educational purposes let's keep it in the equation.

The **waiting time for the lot size formation** depends on the lot size. Since this differs for every product type, we need to determine this separately for every product type. The easiest way is to take the lot size in pieces, divide it by the number of parts per kanban, and you get the lot size as a number of kanbans. We could now calculate the average waiting time. However, since this is a make-to-stock production, we need the maximum waiting time, which is the number of kanbans in a lot minus one. Hence, red cars with a lot size of 7 kanbans need to wait at most for 6 other kanbans, blue cars for 5, and yellow cars for 2 before the respective lot is complete. An overview of the data is given in Table 5.

Color	Lot Size (Cars)	Number of Parts per Kanban	Lot Size (Kanban)
Red	560	80	7
Blue	300	50	6
Yellow	30	10	3

Table 5: Waiting time for lot size formation example

The tricky part is the **waiting time for sequencing**. This is at best a guesstimate, and depending on how you approach this, your number may look different. Keep in mind that the whole kanban equation is only an estimation, and slight differences do not matter. The standard requires at least the equivalent of 1000 parts ready for sequencing before the sequence is created. It would be possible to determine a more precise average waiting time using queueing theory or simulation data, but these are too complex for most kanban calculations. Hence, here I simply use the time needed for 1000 parts to accumulate. Since these parts could be of any color, I have to use the overall customer takt across all part types of 35.5 seconds per part from Table 4. Multiplying 1000 parts with 35.5 seconds per part gives a waiting time in the sequencing of 35 493 seconds or roughly 9 hours 52 minutes. This is the same for all part types.

You probably can already see quite a few "holes" in this approach. The first lot from the lot size formation would have to wait less than the last lot. However, our lot sizes differ by product type. We could have decided which lot size to use when and deducted this one lot from the total, but this would open up other questions. Overall, there is no perfect answer to the question of the waiting time for sequencing besides actually measuring it or using advanced mathematics and simulations, which is difficult. However, let's take a mental note that this waiting time is probably a bit of an overestimation. Maybe you could also make the safety factor a bit smaller later on.

The **waiting time in the production queue** is also a messy calculation. In Chapter 5.4.2.1.5 I presented my approach, albeit with little claim for scientific accuracy. Every lot may wait on one lot of each other high runner. Hence, red parts would have to wait for one lot of blue parts, blue parts for one lot of red parts, and yellow for a lot of red and a lot of blue parts. The waiting time for one lot of a certain part type is the lot size in pieces multiplied by the customer takt for this part type.

For example, it takes 560 times the takt of 50.4 seconds or 28 224 seconds until one lot of red cars arrive. Red waits for one lot of blue, blue waits for one lot of red, and yellow waits for the sum of a lot of red and blue each. Hence, this waiting time is different for every product type. The overview is shown in Table 6.

Color	Lot Size (Cars)	Customer Takt (Second/Car)	Lot Size (Seconds)	Waiting Time in Queue for Production (Seconds)
Red	560	50.4	28 224	37 800 (Blue)
Blue	300	126.0	37 800	28 224 (Red)
Yellow	30	2520	75 600	66 024 (Red + Blue)

Table 6: Waiting time in production queue example

The **lead time** can be determined using Little's law. We have on average 50 parts in the FIFO, plus one in each process, for a total of 103 parts in the system on average. However, we don't want to have material in the supermarket on average, but pretty much all the time. Hence, we have to take the worst case. This would be two full FIFO with 100 parts each and a part in each process for a total of 203 parts. Multiplying this with the **customer takt across all parts** of 35.5 seconds per part gives us a total worst-case lead time of 7205 seconds. This is the same for all part types.

The additional time to cover for **breakdown and disruptions** was determined by management to be 2 hours. This is simply included later in the kanban calculation.

The **largest expected customer** order in Table 3 is the largest expected order in excess of one kanban, which should be in the supermarket anyway. Later in the kanban formula we will convert the quantity into a number of kanbans and subtract the equivalent of one kanban from the largest order to determine the additional kanbans needed to cover this largest order.

The **peak demand** is also already given in Table 3. Please note that this is specific to the part type. Furthermore, note that high runners often fluctuate less, and exotic parts fluctuate more relative to the total quantity, as is the case here too.

The **safety factor** will be added later, as we first want to calculate the number of kanbans without the safety factor. We do not have any **other elements** that we want to include in the calculation of the number of kanbans.

5.4.2.4.3 Example Calculation Results

Table 7 shows an overview of the elements for the number of production kanbans that we have determined so far. Please note that they are quite different units.

Element	Unit	Red Cars	Blue Cars	Yellow Cars	Variable
Waiting Time in Kanban Box	Hours (Seconds)	1 (3600)	1 (3600)	1 (3600)	WB
Information Transport Time	Minutes (Seconds)	3 (180)	3 (180)	3 (180)	TI
Lot Size	Kanban	7	6	3	KL
Waiting Time for Sequencing	Seconds	35 493	35 493	35 493	WQ
Waiting in Production Queue	Seconds	37 800	28 224	66 024	WP
Lead Time	Seconds	7205	7205	7205	LT
Breakdown and Disruptions	Hours (Seconds)	2 (7200)	2 (7200)	2 (7200)	BD
Large Customer Order	Cars	200	120	60	OS
Peak Customer Demand	Cars	650	420	80	PD

Table 7: Elements for the number of production kanban, not yet including safety

For subsequent calculations, we would need to convert the times into consistent units. We convert all times to seconds, since our customer takt is also measured in seconds per part. These we can enter now into the calculation of our number of production kanbans from Equation 16. The calculation with numbers for the red car is shown in Equation 19, including the corresponding units. Make sure all your units cancel each other out and you get only "kanban" at the end.

If at this point you get worried about the complexity of the calculation, let me remind you about the estimation approach that I will talk about later. Anyway, without the safety, we get a total of 38.3 kanbans for the red car. Similar calculations would give 27.8 kanbans for blue cars and 19.8 kanbans for yellow cars.

$$NC_{Kanban,Red} = \frac{WB + TI + WQ_{Red} + WP_{Red} + LT + BD}{TT_{Red} \cdot NPC_{Red}} +$$

$$+ \left(\frac{OS_{Max,Red}}{NPC_{Red}} - 1\right) + (KL_{Red} - 1) + \frac{PD_{Red}}{NPC_{Red}} + S=$$

$$= \frac{3600s + 180s + 35\,493s + 37\,800s + 7205s + 7200s}{50.4\,\frac{s}{part} \cdot 80\,\frac{parts}{kanban}} +$$

$$+ \left(\frac{200\,parts}{80\,\frac{parts}{kanban}} - 1\,kanban\right) + (7\,kanban - 1\,kanban) + \frac{650\,parts}{80\,\frac{parts}{kanban}} + S$$

$$= 38.3\,kanban + S$$

Equation 19: The kanban formula for production kanban for the red car example

Now we can add the safety. Since we already had a very conservative estimate for the waiting time for sequencing, we probably need little safety, and I would simply round up the number of kanbans to the nearest integer. However, if you feel uncomfortable with this, you could also add more. The safety is also often expressed as a percentage, and 10% or even more are added.

If we simply round up generously, we could end up with 40 kanbans for the red cars, 30 kanbans for the blue cars, and 22 kanbans for the yellow cars, as shown in Table 8. The safety factor hence would be between 4% and 10% of the total number of kanbans, with the largest percentage for the highest fluctuating exotic yellow car. If you did the calculation on your own, you should be somewhere near this number, although 30% difference is quite possible with slightly different assumptions.

Color	Number of Kanbans without Safety	Safety (Kanban)	Number of Kanbans with Safety	Safety (Percent)
Red	38.3	1.7	40	4.2%
Blue	27.8	2.2	30	7.3%
Yellow	19.8	2.2	22	10%

Table 8: Number of kanbans without and with safety for the production kanban example

It is also possible to determine the individual contributions to the number of kanbans. The visual representation of this in the form of a waterfall diagram is shown in Figure 82 for the red car example. Here, the largest factors are the production queue, the sequencing, and the effect of the peak demand. If you want to reduce your inventory, you will have to reduce the lot size. This would reduce your sequencing, your waiting time in the production queue, and the time for lot size formation. It could also reduce the peak demand. Reducing all lot sizes by half would reduce the number of kanbans and hence the total inventory by 30%. The information transport time on the other hand could have been safely ignored.

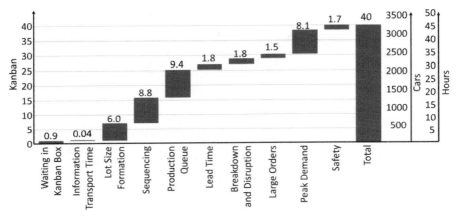

Figure 82: Waterfall diagram for the red car example (Image Roser)

Figure 82 shows primarily the number of kanbans. However, since this can easily be transformed into parts or times, the axes for the number of cars and the time in hours are also given. Figure 83 shows the similar graph for the blue car where the peak demand has the largest effect, followed by the sequencing and the lot size formation. Figure 84 shows the same graph for the yellow car. As it is common with exotics, fluctuations like large orders and peak demand have the largest effect on the number of kanbans for the low-volume yellow car.

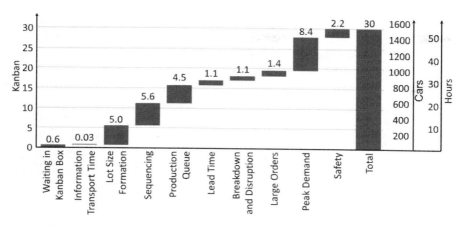

Figure 83: Waterfall diagram for the blue car example (Image Roser)

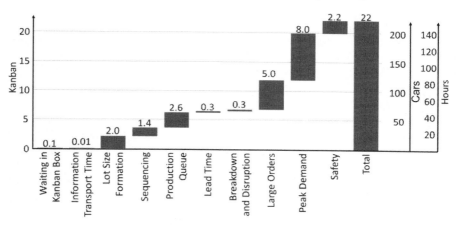

Figure 84: Waterfall diagram for the yellow car example (Image Roser)

5.4.3 The Kanban Formula for Transport Kanban

The calculation for the transport kanban is very similar to the calculation of the production kanban above, but easier. Since you do not need to reproduce the items, the entire replenishment time calculation is much simplified. One major difference, however, is that your customer takt may be based on a different time period than your production system. Use the time period that best represents your system. Furthermore, similar to production kanban, it is sensible to **use conservative values to ensure a high material availability**.

5.4.3.1 Elements of the Transport Kanban Calculation

Figure 85 gives you an overview of the elements for the transport kanban calculation. This is adjusted from Figure 76 for the specifics of the transport kanban.

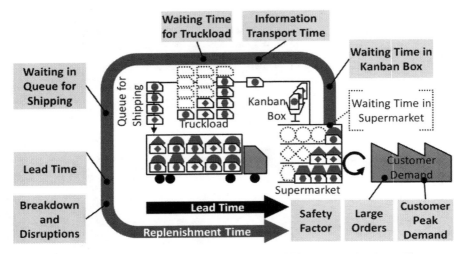

Figure 85: Elements influencing the number of transport kanban. The waiting time in the supermarket in dotted brackets is not relevant. (Image Roser)

Much of these are either identical or very similar to production kanban, and sometimes much simpler to calculate. The **waiting time in the supermarket** is irrelevant here too. Absent is also the **time for the sequencing** of the kanban lots, since usually shipping does not require a certain sequence of products.

The **lot size creation** is also usually no longer needed and instead replaced by the waiting time for a truckload. There may be exceptions, as for example a ship-to-line and just-in-sequence delivery where the items are shipped directly to the production line in sequence. In this case, you would need to include the sequencing into the replenishment time. But even then, it is much easier to calculate, since it usually only involves picking the goods out of the preceding inventories in the correct sequence.

5.4.3.1.1 Waiting Time in the Kanban Box

The waiting time in the kanban box is identical to the production kanban. If there is a regular pickup, the relevant time is the interval between pickups. This accounts for the worst case if a kanban is added to the box just after the pickup left.

5.4.3.1.2 Information Transport Time

The information transport time for transporting the kanbans is simply the time needed to transport the kanbans. For production kanban, this may be negligible. For digital transport kanban you can ignore this microsecond delay. For physical transport kanban, however, it may be a quite relevant delay if you physically have to transport the kanbans back to the beginning of the loop.

5.4.3.1.3 Waiting Time for Truck Load Creation

A waiting time for truck load creation may apply. Most times, companies want to ship only full loads of a truck, shipping container, or similar. Hence, they wait until they have enough orders to fill up a truck to minimize the shipping cost. This, however, will increase your overall inventory, and Toyota prefers smaller trucks more frequently and also quite regularly. The calculation of this time depends on the behavior of your system.

It is recommended to use a more conservative approach and to go with the larger number of kanbans. Usually, this is measured as a time unit, unlike the lot size formation of production kanban that can be measured in kanbans. If you have a regularly scheduled truck, the waiting time should include this worst-case delay between two trucks.

5.4.3.1.4 Waiting Time in the Queue for Shipping

The waiting time in the queue for shipping is somewhat similar to the waiting time in the queue for production, but much simpler to calculate. How long does an order have to wait until a truck is ready and can be loaded? This may include, for example, the sequence creation for a just-in-sequence delivery. It may also overlap with waiting times for a truckload. Hence, most times this may also be negligible.

This may also include other delays as for example a delay due to a missing driver or due to moving the departure to the next day if the truck won't make it before its destination closes. Whether you want to include it will depend on your system.

5.4.3.1.5 Lead Time

The lead time is simply the time it takes for the goods to be loaded and moved to the destination. This could also be called the shipping time. As such, it is similar to the lead time, but usually much easier to calculate. You probably should take a more conservative measure, as this lead time should also cover shipping during rush hour.

5.4.3.1.6 Breakdowns and Disruptions

Depending on how conservative your estimations are so far, you may add additional time for breakdowns and disruptions, similar to the production kanban. For example, there may be an accident, and even if it did not involve your truck, it may still be stuck in the traffic jam. Here, too, you won't be able to cover all eventualities, and you should not let the inventory escalate for the rare chance that you actually need it.

5.4.3.1.7 Large Customer Order

The estimation of the effect of large orders is identical to the production kanban. This is the largest reasonably expected order converted into kanbans minus one kanban. It is entirely possible that the largest customer order is also the same as the average customer order. This often happens if the customer is, for example, a production system that forwards any demand without delay.

5.4.3.1.8 Customer Peak Demand

Similarly, the system has to cover for peak demand. What is the largest additional demand by the customer that you expect within a replenishment time? The difference between the average and the largest demand is the peak demand. This number of parts has to be converted into a number of kanbans and added to the total.

5.4.3.1.9 Safety Factor

On top of this, you may add a safety factor as an absolute number of kanbans or as a percentage. Depending on how conservative your other estimates are, you may have a larger or smaller safety factor. Similar to production kanban, this is also a feel-good factor for the people on the shop floor or in logistics.

5.4.3.1.10 Other Elements

Similar to the production kanban, there also may be other unusual elements that influence your replenishment time or customer demand fluctuations. However, these are rare and probably will not apply to your system.

5.4.3.2 Calculating the Number of Transport Kanbans

The elements shown here cover most cases, but if your transport kanban system has additional delays or fluctuations, please include them in the calculation. Table 9 gives you an overview of these elements.

Group	Element	Unit	Usually Part Specific?	Usually Relevant?	Variable
Replenishment Time	Waiting Time in Kanban Box	Time	No	Maybe	WB
	Information Transport Time	Time	No	No	TI
	Waiting Time for Truckload	Time	No	Maybe	WT
	Waiting in Shipping Queue	Time	No	Maybe	WS
	Lead Time	Time	No	Yes	LT
	Breakdown and Disruptions	Time	No	Yes	BD
Customer	Large Customer Order	Quantity	Yes	Yes	OS
	Peak Customer Demand	Quantity	Yes	Yes	PD
Other	Safety Factor	Kanban	Often	Yes	S
	Other Elements	???	???	No	n/a

Table 9: Overview of variables contributing to the number of transport kanban

Based on these elements, you can calculate the number of transport kanbans. Elements that are times or quantities would have to be converted into a representative number of kanbans using Equation 11 and Equation 9. The complete kanban formula for transport kanban is shown in Equation 20. Similar to the production kanban in Equation 16, I recommend using and checking units throughout the calculation.

$$NC_{Kanban,n} = \frac{WB + TI + WT + WS + LT + BD}{TT_n \cdot NPC_n} +$$

$$+ \left(\frac{OS_{Max,n}}{NPC_n} - 1\right) + \frac{PD_n}{NPC_n} + S$$

Equation 20: The kanban formula for transport kanban

The variables for Equation 20 are as follows:

BD   Additional time to cover breakdowns and disruptions (time)
LT   Lead time (time)
$NC_{Kanban,n}$ Number of kanbans for part type n (card quantity)
NPC_n Number of parts per kanban for part type n (quantity per card)
$OS_{Max,n}$ Largest expected order size for part type n (quantity)
PD_n Peak customer demand for part type n (quantity)
S   Safety factor (card quantity)
TI   Time for the transport of information (time)
TT_n Customer takt for part type n (time per quantity)
WB   Waiting time at (kanban, CONWIP...) box (time)
WS   Waiting time in shipping queue (time)
WT   Waiting time for a truckload (time)

5.4.3.3   Example Transport Kanban Calculation

As with the production kanban, I will give you a detailed example calculation for the transport kanban. I will provide you with all the necessary parameters, so you can try the calculation on your own before looking at my example solution. As there will be quite a few assumptions, your result may differ somewhat from mine depending on these assumptions. Try to understand these differences, and see if these are based on different assumptions or an actual error somewhere.

5.4.3.3.1   The Transport System Data

The example for the transport kanban follows the example of the production kanban in producing toy cars in three different colors. The wheels for the toy cars are purchased from a supplier and are transported to the manufacturing location for the final assembly. A set of four wheels with yellow, red, or blue hubcaps is needed to assemble a car in the corresponding color. The wheels and the final products are shown in Figure 86.

Figure 86: The example system transports the wheels for the toy cars with yellow, red, and blue hubs. (Image Roser)

The customer demand overall stays the same, but every car needs four wheels. Hence, the demand by the assembly line on wheels is exactly four times the demand of completed cars on the assembly line. Here we assume that our defects and scrapped parts are negligible.

Our transport system can handle any lot size, and hence we do not need to create larger lots. Therefore, our default lot size is one kanban. The number of parts per kanban is also needed. Management decided for simplicity reasons that a kanban of wheels should match a kanban of cars. Since a car has four wheels, the number of parts per kanban for the wheels is four times the number of parts per kanban of the cars for the respective color. Table 10 summarizes this data.

Color	Number of Parts per Kanban	Expected Monthly Demand (Wheels)	Peak Demand (Wheels)
Red	320	40 000	1300
Blue	200	16 000	680
Yellow	40	800	70
Total	n/a	56 800	n/a

Table 10: Overview of parameters for the example calculation of the transport kanban

The production system continuously removes wheels from the inventory. As soon as a new kanban quantity is started, the kanban is returned to the supplier. Hence, we do not have any large orders, as the standard order size is one kanban. However, we do have a peak demand. The fluctuations of the end customer are buffered by the production system to some extent. Therefore, the fluctuations for the supplier in this example are smaller than for the production system.

Note, however, that this is not always the case, and a bullwhip effect can lead to increasing fluctuations as you go back along the supply chain. In any case, the peak demand here is estimated to be less for the wheels than for the final products. This is adjusted for having four wheels per car. The overall expected demand is also given in Table 10.

Figure 87 shows the value stream map for the transport kanban system. The kanbans are scanned once every hour. Afterwards, the ERP system sends the order digitally to the supplier. The supplier will ship the goods once there is a full truck of 10 000 wheels. The truck itself needs on average around five hours for the trip, including loading and unloading. However, this can take significantly longer during rush hour or if there is an accident. Management decided that they want to cover an additional three hours for shipping for these disruptions. Both the customer and the supplier warehouses are open for 16 hours per day, with approximately 20 workdays per month. However, the truckers in our example won't leave if they can't make it during the same day. If there is less than 6 hours left to the end of the day, the truck will wait until the next day.

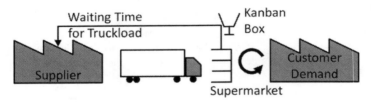

Figure 87: Value stream map for the transport kanban loop (Image Roser)

5.4.3.3.2 Calculation of the Elements

As for the production kanban, probably one of the first things we need to calculate is the **customer takt**. However, compared to the customer takt of the production kanban, there are two major differences. The first one I already mentioned: we need four times as many wheels as we need cars. The second one is that the time period is also different from the production kanban. Both the supplier and the customer can send and receive trucks for 16 hours per day, with roughly 20 days per month. The truckers also drive only during these hours, since they won't be able to offload their goods otherwise. Hence, our time period is 20 days, with 16 hours per day, or 320 hours. Dividing this time by the demand, we get the customer takt for the respective color and also for all parts combined, as shown in Table 11.

Color	Expected Monthly Demand (Wheels)	Customer Takt (Second/Wheel)
Red	40 000	28.8
Blue	16 000	72.0
Yellow	800	1440
Total	56 800	20.3

Table 11: Customer takt times for the transport kanban example

The kanbans in the kanban box are scanned every hour, and therefore the **waiting time in the kanban box** is at most one hour. To be on the safe side, we use the worst case rather than the average. After scanning, the kanbans are sent out digitally by the ERP system, and hence the **information transport time** is close to zero and can be safely ignored.

The **waiting time for truckload creation**, however, is more significant. The truck runs only if there are 10 000 parts. Multiplying this with the customer takt across all part types of 20.3 seconds per wheel of any color, we get a waiting time for truckload creation of 202 817 seconds, or 56 hours and 20 minutes.

Most of this time overlaps with the **waiting time in queue for shipping**. However, if there are only 6 hours left in the workday, the truck won't leave until the next morning, since they won't make it before the receiving plant closes its door at the end of the day. To ensure a stable supply of material, this maximum possible waiting time of 6 hours in the queue for shipping should be included. You can easily see that the more you go into the details of the kanban calculation, the more what-ifs and if/thens pop up, which will make a precise calculation impossible. Don't try to achieve perfect precision, because that is almost impossible for real-life systems. Eventually you have to take your best guess and go with it. Always adjust the number of kanbans later when the system is running.

The **lead time** was already given as 5 hours, as was the time for additional **breakdowns and disruptions** with 3 hours. Due to the constant demand of a production system, we do not have any **large customer orders**, and our "largest order" is one kanban. Since we have one kanban in the supermarket by design anyway, the additional impact on the calculation is zero. Nevertheless, for educational reasons, I keep this in the equation here. The **peak demand** is also already given in Table 10. Please note that this is specific to the part type. The **safety factor** will be added later, as we first want to calculate the number of kanbans without the safety factor. We do not have any **other elements** that we want to include in the calculation of the number of kanbans.

5.4.3.3 Example Calculation Results

Table 12 shows an overview of the elements for the number of production kanbans that we have determined so far. Please note that some of these values have different units.

Element	Unit	Red Wheels	Blue Wheels	Yellow Wheels	Variable
Waiting Time in Kanban Box	Hours (Seconds)	1 (3600)	1 (3600)	1 (3600)	WB
Information Transport Time	Time	0	0	0	TI
Waiting Time for Truckload	Seconds	202 817	202 817	202 817	WT
Waiting in Shipping Queue	Hours (Seconds)	6 (21 600)	6 (21 600)	6 (21 600)	WS
Lead Time	Hours (Seconds)	5 (18 000)	5 (18 000)	5 (18 000)	LT
Breakdown and Disruptions	Hours (Seconds)	3 (10 800)	3 (10 800)	3 (10 800)	BD
Large Customer Orders	Wheels	320	200	40	OS
Peak Customer Demand	Wheels	1300	680	70	PD

Table 12: Elements for the number of transport kanbans, not yet including safety

For subsequent calculations, we would need to convert the times into consistent units. We convert these into seconds, since our customer takt is also measured in seconds per part. These we can enter now into the calculation of our number of transport kanbans from Equation 20.

We can drop the information transport time TI since it is zero. We can also eliminate the element for the large orders since we don't have any orders larger than one lot size. The calculation with numbers using the remaining elements for the red wheels is shown in Equation 21, including the corresponding units. Make sure all your units cancel each other out and you get only "kanban" at the end.

$$NC_{Kanban,Red} = \frac{WB + TI + WT + WS + LT + BD}{TT_{Red} \cdot NPC_{Red}} +$$

$$+ \left(\frac{OS_{Max,Red}}{NPC_{Red}} - 1\right) + \frac{PD_{Red}}{NPC_{Red}} + S =$$

$$= \frac{3600s + 0 + 202\,817s + 21\,600s + 18\,000s + 10\,800s}{28.8\,\frac{s}{piece} \cdot 320\,\frac{pieces}{kanban}} +$$

$$+ \left(\frac{320\ pieces}{320\,\frac{pieces}{kanban}} - 1kanban\right) + \frac{1300\ pieces}{320\,\frac{pieces}{kanban}} + S =$$

$$= 31.9\ kanban + S$$

Equation 21: The kanban formula for transport kanban for the red wheel example

We get a total of 31.9 kanbans for the red wheel with no safety factor. For the production kanban, my gut feeling told me that it included a lot of conservative measures, and hence I had only a small safety factor. Here for the transport kanban I feel a bit less confident and hence take a slightly larger safety factor. The number of kanbans for all wheel colors without and with safety is shown in Table 13. The percentage safety is based on the total number of kanbans, including safety. If you did the calculation independently on your own, you should arrive at somewhat similar numbers, although differences of 30% are quite possible.

Color	Number of Kanbans without Safety	Safety (Kanban)	Number of Kanbans with Safety	Safety (Percent)
Red	31.9	3.1	35	8.8%
Blue	21.2	3.8	25	15.1%
Yellow	6.2	1.8	8	22.4%

Table 13: Number of kanbans without and with safety for the transport kanban example

This formula can also analyze the main effects on your number of kanbans, and hence your inventory. Figure 88 shows the waterfall diagram of the number of kanbans for the red wheel. Such a waterfall diagram visualizes the magnitude of the different factors influencing the number of kanbans. This in turn allows focusing on the larger factors if you want to reduce the number of kanbans and hence your inventory.

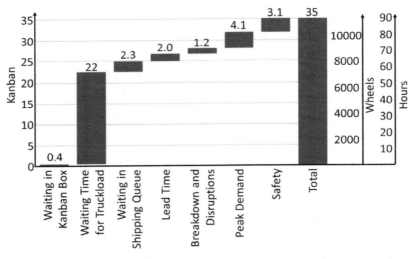

Figure 88: Waterfall diagram for the red wheel example (Image Roser)

Since only the peak demand and the safety differ between the product types, the waterfall diagrams would look very similar for the different part types in this example. Hence, only one diagram is shown here. The scale, however, would be different due to the different takt times and number of parts per kanban. Figure 88 also has the axes measured in pieces and in hours.

The primary contributor to the number of kanbans and hence to the inventory is the waiting time for the truckload. This represents two-thirds of all kanbans. Hence, if you would like to reduce the number of kanbans, use smaller trucks more frequently or even run trucks that are not completely full. Toyota often prefers to use smaller trucks more frequently for the same reason.

5.4.4 The Kanban Formula for Two-Bin Kanban

The calculation here is identical to the calculation of the production or transport kanban, with the caveat that you can have only two kanbans, representing two bins. Hence, you would have to massage the numbers to get two kanbans. If you have fewer, simply round up. If you have more, you may increase the number of parts per kanban. **If you can't get the number of kanbans down to two, then this part in your system is not suited for a two-bin kanban.**

The same applies for the estimation approach. If you can reasonably estimate that a system with two kanbans would work, then you can use the two-bin kanban system. If not, adjust the number of parts per kanban. If you can't get down to two kanbans, then this part in your system is not suited for a two-bin kanban.

5.4.5 The Kanban Formula for Triangle Kanban

The triangle kanban differs from other kanban calculations. Not only does it need an upper limit like all other kanban systems, but you also need a lower limit on where to place the single kanban. In its nature, this is identical to the reordering system. The minimum quantity needs to be enough to cover the replenishment time. The maximum depends on a trade-off between the efforts of issuing an order versus the inventory cost.

This is effectively the paper version of a reorder point system. Please see Chapter 8 and especially Chapter 8.4 for the calculation of the reorder point system. Make sure, however, that the estimate of the delivery lead time is feasible for your production system. See the corresponding elements of the production kanban calculation for inspiration. And, as always, with the general lack of precision of kanban calculations, you may just estimate these values.

5.4.6 The Kanban Formula for Continuous Quantities

The kanban formula for continuous quantities like volumes or mass is similar to the formula for "normal" production or transport kanban in Equation 16 and Equation 20. Your kanban simply represents a continuous quantity instead of a number of parts. In fact, if a kanban always represents the same fixed quantity, the equations are identical. This quantity could be a final packing unit, like a crate or barrel. It could also represent a batch size if you produce in batches. In this case, it is actually unnecessary to use continuous quantities, and merely counting pieces or batches is much easier.

If the consumption is in different quantities, it will still work with kanban systems. For a box of material, the kanban is released either with the first item or the last item consumed as discussed in Chapter 5.7.1. Similarly, a continuous quantity kanban could be released if the first or last of the continuous quantity represented by the kanban is consumed. This then starts a replenishment of this quantity. Here, too, a discrete "piece-based" kanban is usually sufficient and much easier to handle.

5.4.7 The Alternative: Kanban Estimation

Above, I described how to calculate the number of kanbans. However, this calculation is complex, and the result is nothing more than a very rough estimate. Hence, my preferred method for determining the number of kanbans is, broadly speaking, "just take enough, and see if you can reduce them later".

When determining the number of kanbans, rather than going through the calculations, you could simply estimate the number of kanbans. For this you need a bit of experience, but it is doable. I also recommend not doing it alone. Instead, do this as part of a group that includes a supervisor or team leader from the affected shop floor. If you feel uncertain, you can use the kanban formula for guidance and estimate the different factors in the kanban formula.

Of course, this estimation is also not very precise. I usually go for a conservative number, where I believe I'll definitely have enough kanbans. Having many parts instead of a few is better than missing deliveries or idling operators.

"But isn't lean all about reducing material?" Not all, but yes, it is one aspect of lean. Already during implementation, verify if the number of kanbans fit the system, and adjust up or down as needed.

5.5 Advantages

The advantage of kanban is very similar to the advantages of pull in general. It keeps the inventory under control and simplifies and speeds up the replenishment of items. As for pull production, kanban is **one of the easiest and most intuitive pull systems**. It can easily apply to many make-to-stock production systems. This makes it also **easy to manage**, taking less valuable time from the shop floor supervisors and managers.

Kanban can **help to highlight problems**. It is easy to see if material is about to run out in a supermarket, and countermeasures can be taken. A good kanban system also often has many beneficial aspects of visual management. Overall, kanban is an excellent approach for make-to-stock production.

5.6 Disadvantages

Kanban is a quite versatile system. Its major limitation is that **kanban is suited only to replenish items to stock**. It is absolutely **incompatible with make-to-order or ship-to-order products**. If the make-to-order product is created using standard parts, however, kanban can of course be used to manage these ship-to-stock or make-to-stock parts.

Kanban also has **problems with large fluctuations**. If your demand for one part is 10 this month, 2000 next month, and 300 the month afterwards, you have two options. You either have to change the system regularly if you know the fluctuations beforehand or, if you don't know the fluctuations beforehand, set up the kanban system for the largest expected demand. This results in having lots of material on stock, even though you need it only very infrequently. Due to this relation between fluctuations and inventory, leveling is often recommended for kanban systems.

But then, most systems have problems with large fluctuations and would benefit from leveling. Kanbans are often adjusted every few months, especially to cover seasonality, but are rarely adjusted more than once per month. Otherwise, kanbans are a great tool, and I am a big fan of kanban for make-to-stock.

5.7 Frequently Asked Questions

5.7.1 Move the Kanban After the First or Last Part in a Box?

If your kanban represents only one part, the kanban is moved to the kanban box or to scanning immediately after this single part is removed from the supermarket. If, however, your kanban represents multiple parts, the kanban can be moved with the removal of the first part, or with the removal of the last part, or with the removal of any part in between, as shown in Figure 89.

Figure 89: It is possible to move the kanban with the first part or with the last part, but avoid moving with any part in between. (Image Roser)

All of these are workable. If you **move the kanban with the first part**, the information of the consumption of one part is forwarded faster. Toyota prefers this approach. However, now you have material in your supermarket with no kanban attached to it.

If you **move the kanban with the last part**, all your material always has a kanban attached, although the quantity does not quite match. The information flow is also delayed by almost one kanban. Hence, if you move your kanban with the last part, you simply have one more kanban in the system to cover this situation. On the other hand, it allows you to permanently attach the kanban to a box. Both moving the kanban with the first part or moving it with the last part are feasible options. However, I prefer the latter as it always keeps a kanban with material, even if it is not a full box of parts.

Moving the kanban with any part in between is not so good, as this will confuse people. Is a box with one part left missing a kanban, or has it been moved already? Sometimes the information will flow faster, sometimes slower. Hence, do avoid these in-between kanban moves.

In some cases, there is an obvious answer for the question on when to move the kanban. **If the kanban is permanently attached to a box or other type of container, it makes sense to move the box only after the last part when the box is empty.** It would be difficult to move the box with the kanban while keeping the remaining parts without the box still in the supermarket.

Note that sometimes when a box is almost empty, operators put the remaining parts in the next box and send back the empty box. This would be similar to moving the kanban with any parts in between. Not ideal, but the effort in creating and enforcing a rule forbidding that is not worth the benefit.

Therefore, if you use boxes or containers as kanban, move the kanban (the container) with the last part. Otherwise, I recommend moving it with the last part anyway to always have a kanban with material and to be compatible with kanban boxes. However, it is also possible to move the kanban with the first part, but do not mix these systems on the same shop floor, as this will confuse the operators.

5.7.2 Should You Use Physical or Digital Kanban?

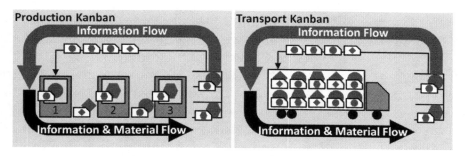

Figure 90: Illustration of the information flow and the information and material flow for production and transport kanban (Image Roser)

The kanban goes around the kanban loop repeatedly. Information on an arriving (digital or physical) kanban signals the start of production. The information then travels with the part through the production process and the corresponding inventories. When the part leaves the loop, the information is returned to the beginning, and the process starts anew. This is illustrated in Figure 90.

For the outward leg (downstream), the information is attached to the part and moves with the part. Hence, on the downstream path the information cannot be faster than the part. Regardless of whether it is physical information or digital information, the speed is the same as the corresponding part. Therefore, for the material flow we cannot influence the speed through our choice of digital or physical kanban.

On the return leg, however, the information is on its own. Therefore, on the way back, the (physical or digital) information should go as quickly as possible. The faster the movement of the information, the shorter the replenishment time and the faster the turnaround time. Once the information is back in the production queue, the information has to wait and the speed is no longer relevant.

Digital information can move much faster than physical information. Hence, the digital information will always be faster — once the information is in the system. The picture may be more mixed, however, if we take the surrounding actions into consideration. Regardless of whether the system is physical or digital, the information flow starts with the removal of the part. Usually the cards are collected at a kanban box. Physical cards are transported back to the first process at regular intervals.

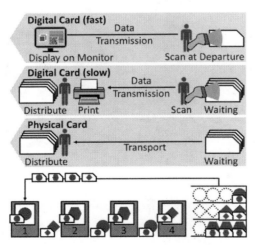

Figure 91: Comparison of the speed and complexity of digital kanban transfer with physical cards (Image Roser)

For digital systems, this would require the additional work of scanning (barcode, RFID chips, or similar) or otherwise entering the data into the system. This may happen while the part is taken out of the inventory, or shortly afterwards for multiple removed parts as a batch. Once the data is back in cyberspace, the speed can be (almost) lightning fast. On the other end, it may appear on a monitor. If it is a printout, it again would have to be transported. Figure 91 illustrates some possible choices.

Depending on how the collection and distribution of this digital information is managed, the digital information may be even slower than physical information. In any case, on short distances there won't be much difference. A physical card may take one or two hours. Digital information may also take thirty minutes to two hours for scanning and processing the data. This does not have a large impact on a replenishment time that may take days.

This becomes very different, however, on longer distances. Here the electronic transmission of data significantly outpaces that of physical data. Assuming you are receiving your goods in America by ship from a supplier in China, would you send the reorder information by postal mail? By ship, this would add weeks to the replenishment time. By air, it would still add days. A digital transmission, on the other hand, would be almost instantaneous, and even with handling will take only minutes or hours.

Hence, there is a strong case to use digital transmissions for long distances. It does not have to be as far apart as America and China; even if your supplier sits in the next town, a digital transmission may be beneficial. But before you decide based on the speed of the information flow alone, please note that there are more things to take into consideration.

Another important factor is the ability to understand the current situation. Which jobs or cards are where? Here it is important to distinguish between the manager's view from the office and the operator's view from the shop floor.

The manager likes to click on the computer and see the current situation in the ERP system. Digital kanbans are very well suited for use with computers. This works anywhere in the world as long as the manager has access to the database. This is often even the preferred way for a manager to access data, and many shop-floor-related managers spend way too little time on the shop floor.

The operators, on the other hand, want to see the situation on the shop floor without having to log into a system that they may or may not be familiar with, or may not even have access rights for. Hence, they prefer the physical version of information, as shown in Figure 92.

Figure 92: Example of the typical but very different ways a manager and an operator accesses data (Images by Thomas Karol in public domain and style-photographs with permission)

Managers (and many others) often see the world only from their point of view. They think if it is good for them, it will be good for everybody. Unfortunately, this is not necessarily true. Especially with shop-floor-related data, the people on the shop floor have a much more frequent and urgent need to understand the situation than a manager who may not even look at the data at all while insisting that it must be accessible.

In sum, a physical representation of data is often much more beneficial for the shop floor, where the operators frequently need to know the upcoming orders to provide material and plan the manning of the processes. This ties in very closely with visual management.

On the other hand, if there is no shop floor but only logistics, then this is somewhat less relevant. The truck driver will not open the truck to check what is loaded but rather refer to the loading papers. Hence, if you are not on a shop floor, then there is much less benefit of physical data.

Lean lives and breathes continuous improvement. The ability to do continuous improvement is much, *much* easier in physical systems. Changing the handling of information is much easier if it is a paper card than if it is a digital system. Verifying your workload and inventory levels to adjust the manning or the number of cards is also much easier in physical systems.

Of course, this can also be done in digital systems. However, here you need a programmer or specialist for changes to the digital system. And programmers are always in much higher demand than they are in supply. You have to get the programmers, convey to them what you want them to do, and then hope that they understood what you actually wanted. Even if they got you what you wanted, you may not be able to use trial and error to try things out. Usually, continuous improvement grinds to a standstill if computer systems are involved. In any case, the choice between a physical and a digital kanban is not always easy.

You may think, *If both physical and digital systems have advantages, could I do both systems and get the advantages of both?* **Don't!**

Seriously, don't do it. Obviously, you will have twice the work by creating two systems. But the much bigger problem is that these two systems will eventually have differences. The digital system says A and the physical system says B. What do you do? The operator on the shop floor needs a single clear signal, not two conflicting messages. While everything works in theory, the practical situation will be much more chaotic. Do your people a favor and do not have cards on top of a digital system.

It is fine to print out paper versions of the digital system, however. It is also possible to scan cards to update the digital system. But only one can be the master of the data. Either the cards are just a dumb copy of the digital world, or the digital world is just a dumb counter of the physical cards. If there are differences between the systems, one of them has to give way to the other — and the physical information is more likely to be the correct one.

So, what should you do? My recommendation is to use digital information for longer distances (across different plants). This will give you a faster replenishment time, and since it is probably not a production line but a logistics process, the visual management is not quite as critical. However, for your information flow within the plant, physical information may be much easier to understand and improve. On the other hand, it may be difficult to break free from the ERP system that handles everything else.

5.7.3 How Big Should the Supermarket Be?

The question of the size of the supermarket is tricky. Ideally, it should be **able to fit all the material represented by kanbans** (i.e., it should be able to hold all the inventory that is permissible in the system). Hence, in a best-case scenario you have a supermarket that is big enough to fit all your kanbans.

However, in a normal system many of the kanbans wait for processing or are currently in processing. Your supermarket may not be completely full. Often, half of the kanbans across all product variants are not in the supermarket, and the supermarket overall is only half full. Hence, reserving all the space for inventory that you rarely need may also be wasteful. However, it is entirely possible that all parts of one part type are in the supermarket, eventually.

The main factor influencing the likelihood of all parts of one part type being in the supermarket is the replenishment time. The following figures show the histogram of the supermarket inventory for three examples. All three examples had a utilization of 90%, comparable fluctuations, and a 99.9% delivery performance. The only difference was the duration of the replenishment time and the corresponding inventory limit.

Figure 93 shows the supermarket inventory histogram of an example with a very short replenishment time. The replenishment time was only about two cycle times. As a result, most of the inventory limit is always in the supermarket. The supermarket for this part type is sometimes even 100% full. The mean inventory fill level was around 76% of the inventory limit.

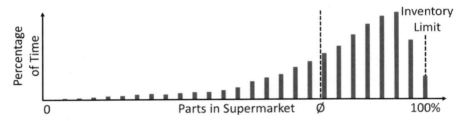

Figure 93: Supermarket inventory histogram for a system with a very fast replenishment time of approximately two cycle times (Image Roser)

Figure 94 shows the supermarket histogram of an example with a still good but slightly longer replenishment time. The replenishment time was approximately ten cycle times. On average, most of the inventory was still in the supermarket. The mean fill level was 68%. However, while it was sometimes close, the supermarket never contained 100% of the inventory limit.

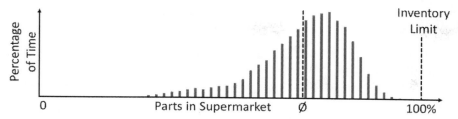

Figure 94: Supermarket inventory histogram for a system with a still speedy replenishment time of approximately ten cycle times (Image Roser)

Finally, Figure 95 shows a longer replenishment time of around 100 cycle times. Now, most of the inventory limit is waiting for production or is work in process. Usually less than half of the inventory level was in the supermarket. On average, only 28% of the inventory limit level was in the supermarket. The maximum supermarket inventory was never above 50% of the inventory limit. For the system shown in Figure 95 it would have been possible to make the supermarket smaller than the inventory limit, although I would be hesitant to cut it too close. Remember, every time your inventory exceeds your supermarket capacity, you need to do firefighting.

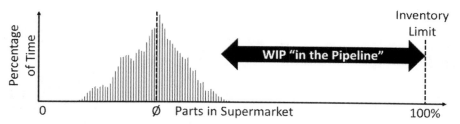

Figure 95: Supermarket inventory histogram for a system with a slow replenishment time of approximately 100 cycle times (Image Roser)

In reality, you easily can find systems that have even longer replenishment times of 1000 or more cycle times. Here, even less of your inventory limit will be in the supermarket.

Be aware, however, that the supermarket inventory is also influenced by the "chunkiness" of your material flow. The larger your lot sizes, the more your supermarket inventory will fluctuate between being (almost) empty and (almost) reaching the inventory limit. Leveling can also help to reduce the risk of all parts being in the supermarket at the same time.

I have seen such supermarkets that were **smaller than the inventory limit** but big enough most of the time. In the rare cases of a full supermarket, the material was stored in a general area as a sort of overflow storage. This storage elsewhere is of course a lot of additional effort, and should mostly be avoided. Hence, supermarkets that do not fit all kanbans are possible, but risky.

If you are unsure which case applies to you, make the supermarket big enough for all kanbans. If you have enough space for a supermarket, make the supermarket big enough for all kanbans. If you do not have enough space, see if you can reduce the replenishment time and hence reduce the number of kanbans to fit the available supermarket space. Only if all other options fail should you be forced to make the supermarket smaller than all kanbans.

Please prepare a "plan B" if you have more kanbans than space in the supermarket. In this case, your supermarket may overflow eventually. Your people will also need additional time and effort to handle this plan B.

5.7.4 Where Should the Supermarket Be Located?

Here we need to distinguish between kanban systems that reproduce and kanban systems that reorder. The supermarket is always managed by the processes that supply the supermarket. Hence, for **production kanban**, supermarkets are best located at the end of the production system. This will reduce the distance for both the material and the information flow. If you locate the supermarket for a production system at the location of the customer, it will be more cumbersome. Hence, **supermarkets for production systems should be close to the last process in the pull loop of the production system**.

On the other hand, the whole point for **transport kanban** systems that reorder is to bridge the distance between one location and another. Therefore, **for transport kanban, the supermarket should be close to the customer**. For example, a milk run using kanban collects material from a warehouse and feeds it into a supermarket right next to the production line. Hence, for kanban that reorder instead of reproduce, the supermarket should be close to the customer.

5.7.5 What If My Products Have a Short Shelf Life?

Some perishable products may have a short shelf life. This could be for example food products or medications. For larger replenishment times this may lead to products remaining in inventory for periods exceeding this usable shelf life. If your yogurt has a shelf life of seven days from the manufacturing date, you cannot hold ten days' worth of inventory. Even four days' worth of inventory may be too much if you include the rest of the value chain. This includes the customers desiring products that do not expire the day they bought them.

There are multiple angles on how you can address such a problem. You could try to **reduce the replenishment time**, including lot sizes, as well as reduce fluctuations to get the inventory limit down. You may also **reduce the inventory limit** anyway and **live with the higher risk of stock-outs**. If both are not possible, as for example with critical medication, you may have to **dispose of expired products.**

You could **change from make-to-stock to make-to-order**, and produce only if the customer orders, although a customer waiting time is then guaranteed. Similarly, you could **change from a pull system to a push** system, although you would lose all the benefits of pull with this. Finally, you could try to change the product in order to **increase the shelf life**. Depending on which measures you take, you may have to factor the additional expenses into the product cost.

5.7.6 Can I Have Only a Single Kanban?

Depending on your system parameters, your kanban calculation may end up with only a single kanban. Is this feasible? Usually not. It basically means that your demand is much slower than the replenishment time. This could work with a single kanban, but has an increased risk for stock-outs. Usually, at least two kanbans are highly recommended in most cases.

Let's take the simple case of **one kanban representing one part**. The customer takes one part. By the time the customer comes back, you have long since replenished the part. In this case, a single kanban would be sufficient. However, you would also have to consider fluctuations. If the customer is usually slower than your replenishment time, but on rare occasions faster, then your customer would have to wait on rare occasions.

Estimate how likely such an event would be, and if it is worth having a second kanban and hence a second part in inventory (almost) all the time. In most cases, however, the second kanban is recommended to reduce the risk of stock-outs.

It is different if **a kanban represents multiple parts**. The time to replenish one kanban is still much faster than the consumption of one kanban worth of parts by the customer. But now, however, the customer may consume in smaller quantities than one kanban. Assume a slow-paced assembly line, where a single kanban represents a box of 60 screws used at the assembly line. It takes 1 hour to replenish a box from the warehouse, but a box lasts for 5 hours at the line, so you should be fine, right?

WRONG! A box with 60 screws may last for 5 hours, but the assembly line takes a screw out of the box every 5 minutes! While an empty box will be replenished within an hour, the operator is looking for the next screw every 5 minutes. In the time it takes for the next box to arrive, the assembly line misses 12 cycles due to a lack of screws. In this case, definitely add a second kanban (i.e., a second box to cover this time). Alternatively, you could use smaller boxes that may have 20 screws instead of 60. This example is actually so common that it has its own name. Since it uses two bins, it is known as the two-bin kanban system, which I introduced in Chapter 5.2.2.

5.7.7 How Many Parts Should a Kanban Represent?

In *true north*, the perfect kanban represents one part. This would be the leanest possible system. However, for many kanban systems this is not feasible, and a kanban often represents multiple parts. Be aware that for one part type, **the number of parts per kanban should be identical for all kanbans of this part type**.

If your production system uses lot sizes, a kanban should never be more than one lot size. It makes no sense to have a kanban represent more than one lot size, as you could never produce just one lot. It makes sense, however, for a lot size to be an integer number of kanbans. Hence, **the number of parts per kanban should be an integer divisor of the lot size**. For example, if your lot size is 100, your kanban could represent 10 parts for 10 kanbans per lot; or 20 for 5 kanbans per lot; or 25 for 4; or 50 for 2; or 100 for 1 kanban per lot. 100 is evenly divisible by 1, 2, 4, 5, 10, 20, 25, 50, and 100. Hence, these are your best options for the number of parts per kanban. If your kanban represents 30 parts, then one lot size would be 3.33 kanban, which is very odd.

The number of parts per kanban is also influenced by the container size. **The kanban should not represent more parts than fit in a box**. If your box fits 10 parts, then do not make a kanban represent 11. It is possible to have a kanban represent fewer parts than which fit in the box. This is sometimes done with bulk items where the box is not filled completely. However, avoid using fewer if the package has slots for every part, which would cause one or more slots being empty by design. This is like opening a box of chocolates and finding one blister empty, which makes Figure 96 rather depressing.

Figure 96: Putting only 19 items in a blister made for 20 is more than just irritating! (Image Roser)

Finally, in the spirit of lean, **make the number of parts per kanban as small as feasible**. A smaller number of parts will make your information and material flow faster and reduce the inventory. In case of doubt, go for the lower number. And… keep in mind that both the lot size and the box size are values that you can influence!

5.7.8 Can I Use Kanban for Job Shops?

Kanbans are used for make-to-stock production (i.e., mass production of identical parts). This is usually well suited for flow shops. If you use a job shop for make-to-stock goods, consider rearranging production to a flow shop. A flow shop will be much, *much* easier to manage than a job shop.

However, there may be situations where every product type—even though it is produced in large quantities for stock—has a different path through your system. Or, you produce mainly make-to-order or general low-volume-high-mix, and you have only very few high-volume-low-mix make-to-stock parts which flow through the same job shops. In this case, a combination of kanban for make-to-stock parts and CONWIP for make-to-order parts may be best.

In any case, it is absolutely possible to manage the make-to-stock parts of a job shop using kanban. However, put in additional effort to control the material flow, i.e. the process sequence in which the parts are processed. For a flow shop, this would all be done almost automatically through a FIFO. The kanban system also does not take care of the workload within the system. Some processes may be overloaded, others idle.

Yet, this is the general problem of any job shop, and so far, there is no good solution yet to master the frequent chaos in a job shop. If you want to use kanban to produce make-to-stock in a job shop, go ahead. It is possible, although with all the usual problems of controlling flow, utilization, and scheduling within the job shop, the preferred approach is of course first to turn your job shop into a flow shop before implementing pull.

5.7.9 Can I Just Use an Excel File for Calculation?

Yes, you surely can. Lots of companies do. However, in my experience, mistakes often happen due to a mix-up in the units, or a misunderstanding of what should be added. If your Excel file expects a lot size as a number of kanbans, but your people enter it as a number of parts, the results will be wrong. Make sure you provide adequate training. Also, make it crystal clear what the definition and unit for each entry in the Excel sheet is. A mathematically sound kanban tool is easily defeated by people entering the wrong numbers.

5.7.10 When and How Should I Use Extra Kanbans?

The number of kanbans is determined by calculation or estimation. This number of kanbans should be adjusted occasionally to adapt the kanban system to the changing environment. The everyday normal fluctuations are decoupled by inventory buffers and sometimes capacity adjustments.

However, sometimes you have rarer and larger fluctuations. These could be **unexpected**. For example, a process suddenly breaks down and it will take days to get the spare parts. These could also be **expected**, in which case they can be planned for. For example, you know your ski boots sell a lot in fall but very little in spring due to seasonal behavior. Or you have a planned annual maintenance that shuts down a process for a week.

In any case, if you have rare and large fluctuations, you can sometimes mitigate the problem using extra kanbans. It would make no sense to set up the pull system to cover these few and far-between but extraordinary fluctuations, just to have tons of material sitting around for the rest of the time.

The idea of extra kanbans is simple. You keep a stack of extra kanbans to insert into the system temporarily and then remove these cards again once the fluctuation has passed. You build up temporary inventory for the duration of the extraordinary event and remove kanbans again after the disruption has passed.

However, these extra kanbans can help you only sometimes, not always. The goal of these extra kanbans is to decouple these fluctuations with extra material. However, this is not always possible.

- It depends on whether the fluctuations temporarily **reduce capacity or demand** (e.g., breakdowns, maintenance) or if they **increase capacity or demand** (e.g., seasonality).
- It also depends on the **location of the bottleneck**. It makes no sense to increase inventory if the bottleneck can never catch up anyway.
- Finally, it depends on whether you **know the disruption beforehand** and can react before it happens (e.g., seasonality, planned maintenance) or if you **know it only after it hits you** (e.g., breakdowns).

Overall, extra kanbans can only help if the buildup of an extra inventory buffer (i.e., the extra kanbans) are helpful. Let me give you a few examples. The example in Figure 97 shows three pull loops in sequence. The process in the last loop has a breakdown that will take longer to fix. The bottleneck is somewhere before this disrupted process. In this case, it is viable to temporarily increase the number of kanbans in the pull loop before the disruption. The bottleneck can keep on working and build up inventory. After the disruption ends, the subsequent processes can catch up with the previous processes and reduce the inventory again. This reduces the overall loss of capacity due to the disruption.

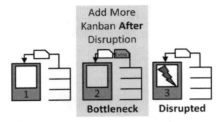

Figure 97: It is possible to add temporary kanbans at the bottleneck after a disruption if the disruption is downstream of the bottleneck. (Image Roser)

It is different, however, if the disruption happens in a process in front of the bottleneck, as shown in Figure 98. Here we would need to know the disruption beforehand to build up inventory in the disrupted loop before the disruption. During the disruption, the bottleneck keeps on working using the inventory built up in preparation for the disruption. Naturally, this works only for disruptions that are known beforehand, like planned maintenance.

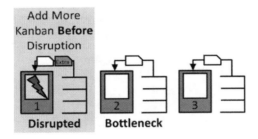

Figure 98: It is possible to add temporary kanbans at a disrupted process before disruption if the disruption is upstream of the bottleneck. (Image Roser)

It is also possible that a disruption does not decrease capacity but increases capacity or demand. The most common example is seasonality, where the customer temporarily orders more parts than the pull system is set up for. Usually this is resolved through a seasonal adjustment of the pull systems and the provided production capacity. It is also possible to build up an inventory beforehand using extra kanbans if the capacity is not enough to satisfy peak demand, as shown in Figure 99. Here, too, we would need to know this beforehand to prepare.

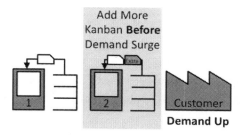

Figure 99: It is possible to add temporary kanbans upstream of the process or customer with an increase in demand before a demand surge. (Image Roser)

In some cases, however, disruptions cannot be remedied with extra kanbans. This could be a disruption before the bottleneck, as shown in Figure 98, where we do not know the disruption beforehand. In this case, we cannot make additional parts for the bottleneck after the fact.

Figure 100 is an example, where the disruption happens at the bottleneck. Having more parts before the bottleneck won't help, since the bottleneck can't use more parts than provided by the preceding process anyway. At best we can stock up on finished goods to keep on supplying the customer, but only if we know the disruption beforehand.

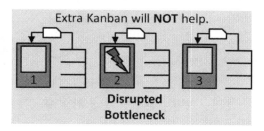

Figure 100: Example with a disruption at the bottleneck where extra kanbans will not help (Image Roser)

Overall, think it through for your system to see if additional kanbans can help or not. In the worst case, you create additional inventory with no benefit for the production system.

It helps to have these **extra kanbans clearly marked as temporary**. Besides some additional label, they could also be of a different color for easier identification. This way it is easier to remove the kanbans when they are no longer needed.

You should also consider how many extra kanbans you should add. It could be enough to cover the disruption, but you may be constrained by the available storage space. Often it can make sense to cover only part of the disruption to avoid excess storage and handling fees. The additional kanbans are added in the list of kanbans that have to be produced. Ideally, they are not a big block of the same part type, but **mixed in suitable lot sizes**.

When you want to remove these extra kanbans, you **take away only cards that are not attached to an item**. If such a card is attached to an item in the supermarket, then you have to wait until the item is taken out of the supermarket. For low runners you may also swap an extra kanban with a normal one taken out of the production queue before production.

Please note that **this is not a fancy new method for pull, but a quick fix of the symptoms of another problem**. Much better would be, of course, to prevent the disruption in the first place. Better than having extra kanbans is to have no large fluctuations, albeit that is easier said than done. Hence, **using extra kanbans is usually a sign of other problems rather than excellence**.

5.7.11 How Do I Use Kanban for a Milk Run?

A milk run is a cyclic delivery of consumed parts. This is common on the shop floor, but is also used across multiple plants or warehouses. The milk run transports the items to a supermarket closer to the destination. On the shop floor, it also commonly returns the physical kanbans, often as a labeled box that is refilled. The milk run within the plant is often a small vehicle pulling a train of trailers with materials. Across different plants or warehouses, it is commonly a truck. In the latter case, a digital system is often used to return the kanbans to improve speed.

A milk run is very well suited for transport kanban. It is a cyclic delivery, which makes the calculation easier. Assume a simple example, where the milk run drives every hour, and the kanbans are represented by boxes. In the best case, the replenishment time takes one cycle (one hour). The milk run picked up the box just when it got empty and replaces it with a full box during the next cycle (one hour later). However, in the worst case, the milk run just missed the empty box. One cycle later, it picks up the empty box, and replaces it with a full box one cycle later. Hence, in the worst case a milk run delivery will require two cycles to replenish the parts (two hours in our example). Therefore, **the replenishment time for a milk run in a plant is two cycles plus additional fluctuations.**[45]

It is a bit less for long-distance milk runs where the kanban is returned digitally. Without going into too much detail, **the replenishment time for a milk run with a digital kanban is the time to return the digital kanban, plus one milk run cycle, plus the outbound leg of the journey, plus additional fluctuations.**[46]

The material at the destination should be enough to cover the worst-case demand during the replenishment time, similar to any other transport kanban.

5.7.12 What If My Parts Have Very Different Cycle Times?

You may have different part types within your pull loop. Ideally, with kanban these part types have similar cycle times at the processes. However, sometimes you may have part types that have large differences in cycle time, while still being make-to-stock parts. This is a fluctuation and can create a headache for you.

Let's make an example. Your system with four processes has two different part types. Part type A takes 6 minutes at every process. Part type B takes 60 minutes at every process, a tenfold increase. The product mix will have a significant influence on the lead time. All other things being equal, the lead time will increase tenfold if you produce only part type B. This needs to be considered for the replenishment time in the kanban calculation.

---

[45] Christoph Roser, *Calculating the Material for Your Milk Run*, in *Collected Blog Posts of AllAboutLean.Com 2018*, Collected Blog Posts of AllAboutLean.Com 6 Offenbach, Germany: AllAboutLean Publishing, 2020, 268–72, ISBN 978-3-96382-022-9.

[46] Christoph Roser, *External Milk Runs*, in *Collected Blog Posts of AllAboutLean.Com 2018*, Collected Blog Posts of AllAboutLean.Com 6 Offenbach, Germany: AllAboutLean Publishing, 2020, 286–93, ISBN 978-3-96382-022-9.

With small lot sizes, you would need large buffers between the processes to keep utilization reasonably high, increasing the lead time even more. An alternative could be to have larger batches. The first shift makes only parts A, and the second shift makes only parts B. In this case **you can calculate this as two separate systems**, one for part A with a short lead time, and one for part B with a long lead time.

Depending on how much effort you want to put into this, you can also look at the buffers between the processes. The inventory or space buffer between processes is needed to decouple fluctuations in the processing times. If the cycle times for part B are longer than for part A, the fluctuations will also be larger. However, often the increase in fluctuations is less than the increase in the processing times. If part B takes ten times longer, then the fluctuations may be only eight times larger. The details depend heavily on your production system.

Hence, you could get away with less buffer inventory for the part with a longer cycle time. You could reduce the buffer size somewhat for the production run with the larger cycle time. On the other hand, this may be cumbersome to change between different product types. I have also heard of functioning production systems where a second CONWIP pull loop overlaps the kanban pull loop. The CONWIP pull loop measures the workload in the system. A kanban can only enter the queue for production if enough workload is available. This is visualized in Figure 101. It depends on your system if the benefit is worth the effort.

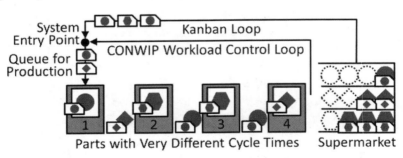

Figure 101: Overlapping CONWIP and kanban loop example for make-to-stock parts with very different cycle times (Image Roser)

5.7.13 What Are Toyota's Six Rules for Kanban?

As part of their guidelines for kanban, Toyota has established "six rules for kanban". They can be found, for example, in the 1973 Toyota Production System Handbook. The Toyota handbook lists six rules as prerequisites for a kanban system. Please note that often, anything from Toyota is seen as an ironclad rule that must not be violated. These six rules do indeed make sense to me.

However, I feel that Toyota mixes up prerequisites with other factors like performance and maintenance of the system. Similarly, there also seem to be some gaps in their rules. An important rule I am missing is, for example, that "any material in the system must have a kanban attached".

Lots of other information would be helpful to create a kanban system. What has to go onto a kanban? How should a supermarket look? How do I determine the number of kanbans? The famous "six rules for kanban" by Toyota omit many such important details. Hence, these rules are here more for inspiration, and less as a step-by-step guide to establish a kanban system. Anyway, here are these rules and their explanation.

5.7.13.1 No Defective Products to the Next Process

The first rule is pretty much a no-brainer. Defects are one of the seven types of waste. Effort goes into production that brings no benefit. The later you find a defect, the more expensive it is. Hence, the goal is to catch defects early. Only good products can be added to the supermarket. This avoids costly subsequent mistakes and also allows earlier detection of systematic errors. Ideally, every process at every step should be able to detect defects. In Japanese this is called *jidoka*.

5.7.13.2 Next Process Comes to Pick up the Parts

The kanban system needs to know how many parts it has in the system to replenish more items. Therefore, the supermarket with completed goods is the responsibility of the supplying kanban process. The subsequent process knows best when it needs more material. Hence, it makes sense for the subsequent process to come and pick up the items as needed, so that they can be replenished by the kanban system. If the supermarket would be the responsibility of the subsequent process, then there would be a risk of delays, gaps, and mistakes in the information flow. Information for replenishment may come too late or not at all.

5.7.13.3 Only Replenish Quantity Picked Up by Next Process

This rule is one of the key elements of the kanban system. The idea is only to reproduce or reorder what was consumed. If the next process takes four parts, you produce four more of these parts—not more, not less. This allows you to maintain an upper limit on inventory. It also requires a method to start replenishment if a part leaves the system. Together they are the definition of pull production.

5.7.13.4 Reduce Fluctuations

This step is an important part of lean. It is often underestimated in the Western world. The kanban system should be able to replenish parts reliably within the replenishment time. The kanban system also assumes that there is always material in the supermarket for the subsequent process. Large fluctuations either mean occasional lack of material in the supermarket or require much larger inventory levels to cover these fluctuations. Both are not good. The first causes stoppages and subsequent lack of material downstream. The second increases the negative effects of inventory. Hence, reduced fluctuation, including some form of leveling, allows for cheaper and more efficient production. Be warned, however, that reducing fluctuations is a hard and Sisyphean task.

5.7.13.5 Kanban Is a Means of Fine-Tuning

Over time, the demands on your system will change, as will the system itself. Therefore, adapt the system. Adjusting the number of kanbans is an approach to fine-tune your production. If your demand or your replenishment time increases, you need more kanbans to cover for this demand (assuming that you can satisfy this increased demand). If your demand or your replenishment time decreases, you may get away with less kanbans. This can be easily tracked by monitoring the inventory in the supermarket. If you are often out of stock, you may need more kanbans. If you are never out of stock, you may get away with less kanbans.

5.7.13.6 Stabilize and Rationalize the Production Process

The last rule aims to stabilize the system. When you establish your kanban loop, you must put in a lot of effort to debug the newly implemented kanban system, create the standards for the new system, make sure the new standards are actually good, and find problems and resolve them. This is actually the Check and Act of the PDCA circle. See if the kanban system actually works well; fix it if it doesn't. The success of a kanban system depends on such good standards. As with all lean projects, **failure to verify and improve the system will end up with a broken system and frustrated employees.**

Chapter 6
CONWIP

CONWIP stands for "constant work in process" and was developed by Mark Spearman and Wallace Hopp in 1990.[47] It is almost identical to kanban, but with one major difference. A kanban is permanently assigned to one part type. **CONWIP cards, however, switch part type with every iteration in the pull loop.** This makes CONWIP well suited for make-to-order production. CONWIP is the make-to-order equivalent to the make-to-stock kanban.

This concept of CONWIP is used frequently in manufacturing, sometimes even without realizing that this is a pull system. A common example is a make-to-order production line with a limited inventory within the line. Whenever an unused space at the beginning of the line opens up, the highest-priority job available is assigned. This is a simple CONWIP-type pull system.

---

[47] Mark L. Spearman, David L. Woodruff, and Wallace J. Hopp, *CONWIP: A Pull Alternative to Kanban, International Journal of Production Research* 28, no. 5 May 1, 1990: 879–94.

However, **naming this chapter was for me a bit of a conundrum**. This fundamental approach to establish pull systems for make-to-order production is quite relevant, but it lacks a well-known and catchy name. The term CONWIP is not yet widely used in industry. Some authors (like me) refer to this as CONWIP. Others call it kanban, but I believe this to be confusing. At Toyota, they call this a type B pull system, which is for make-to-order. Type A would be for make-to-stock using kanban. Type C would be a mixed system for both make-to-stock and make-to-order production. However, this type A, B, and C nomenclature is not really used outside of Toyota.

To be even more confusing—and to show that the nomenclature in lean is anything but standardized—you can even call kanban CONWIP by defining the CONWIP card to be part specific. This is known as *S-Closed CONWIP*[48] or sometimes *m-CONWIP*. The confusion doesn't stop there. Some authors call any pull system in flow shops kanban, and any pull system in job shops CONWIP.

Overall, it is a bit of a mess. For the lack of a better name, within this book I will refer to this approach where cards change their part association every loop as CONWIP. But please, don't let the confusion on the nomenclature distract you from the benefits of this method. If you do not like the name CONWIP, feel free to use another name. **I don't care what you call it as long as it works!**

6.1 Fundamentals

The CONWIP system is very similar to a kanban system, except that the CONWIP card is not associated with a certain part type, but is a generic card for any kind of job. This makes **CONWIP excellently suited for make-to-order production.** It could be also used for ship-to-order, but since it is usually unnecessary to limit the total number of orders across all products, this has no benefit and is rarely done.

Figure 102 shows the basic information and material flow in CONWIP. Every part or job in your value stream has a CONWIP card attached. If the

---

[48] Izak Duenyas, *A Simple Release Policy for Networks of Queues with Controllable Inputs, Operations Research* 42, no. 6 December 1, 1994: 1162–71.

part or job leaves the system (e.g., it is sold, used downstream, etc.), the information on the card is removed. Next, the blanked CONWIP card returns to the system entry point at the beginning of the loop. Remember, the card is no longer associated with a part type or job. On its way to the beginning of the loop, it meets the backlog of open jobs at the system entry point.

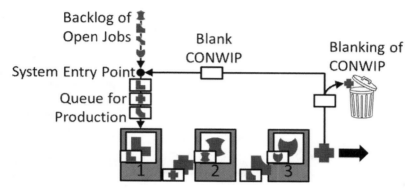

Figure 102: Schematic example of a CONWIP system (Image Roser)

The backlog is a list of jobs that need to be produced. It is sorted by priority. The first part in the backlog is the most urgent one. If a blank CONWIP card comes back from the finished-goods inventory, the next job in line is assigned to the returning card at the system entry point. This is sometimes also called *matchmaking*.

The card is hence a signal that capacity is available, and the backlog defines what to do with the capacity. CONWIP cards that had a job attached at the system entry point wait in the queue for production until the system can start the job. The job then gets produced and eventually makes its way back to the finished goods at the end of the loop. When the part leaves the system, the cycle repeats and the blank CONWIP card goes back to the system's entry point. Hence, **a CONWIP card is like a kanban, except the part type or job gets assigned again at the system entry point** when it meets the most urgent demand in the backlog.

Such a CONWIP system works both for flow shops and for job shops, and even for project shops as we will see below. Similar to kanban, the material flow in a flow shop is almost automatic using FIFO. However, for job shops you need to invest additional work for the routing of the job, the assignment of the operators, the process utilization, and the tracking of the deadlines in a job shop. This is the same just as in every other job shop.

6.2 Variants

There are quite a few variants for CONWIP. Some are related to the organization of the inventory limit. Others are mixed systems, usually combined with kanban. There is also the option to limit the workload instead of the inventory.

6.2.1 CONWIP for Limited Space Production Lines

Probably the easiest and most common way to implement a CONWIP system is a make-to-order production line that has limited space to store parts. This could be a long FIFO, as shown in Figure 103. For this type of system, you don't even need CONWIP cards, which makes it a lot simpler. This approach also has no specific name, even though the principle behind it is CONWIP.

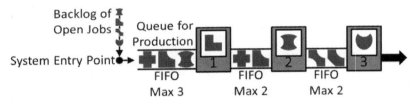

Figure 103: Example of a CONWIP system in a production line with limited space (Image Roser)

The production line example in Figure 103 has three processes and seven FIFO spaces for a total of ten slots for products. This is the equivalent of ten CONWIP cards. Whenever a free slot opens up at the queue for production, the next open job from the backlog of open jobs is added to the system. There can never be more jobs in the system than these ten slots in the production line.

This is probably the most common type of production system that follows the CONWIP principle, even though it is rarely known as CONWIP. It is also **one of the easiest ways to set up a CONWIP system**. You don't even need to worry about CONWIP cards. You only need to ensure there is a limit on the inventory, and to organize the prioritization in the backlog of open jobs.

This is one of the reasons why it is so beneficial to arrange your production as a flow shop rather than a job shop. Common examples are the automotive industry final assembly line, where often every car is different. An example is shown in Figure 104. Other examples are aircraft manufacturing at Boeing or Airbus. Even large commercial airliners are often assembled in such a production line. Even more examples are Trumpf machine tools or MAN container ship diesel engines, which are also heavily customized make-to-order products.

Figure 104: An automotive assembly line is a typical example of a line with limited space. There can never be more cars in the system than there are slots. (Image Siyuwj under the CC-BY-SA 3.0 license)

6.2.2 CONWIP for Project Shops

An (almost) automatic way to establish CONWIP can be done for project shops. In a flow shop or a job shop, the products move through the system. In a project shop the product itself does not move, and all the material, labor, and machines come to the production location. A common example is shipbuilding. The ship in the dry dock does not move at all. The material, machines, and the workforce come to the ship. In this case, you cannot have more ships in production than what fits in your dry dock space.

Hence, the work content is limited by the number of available dry docks. Whenever a ship is completed, a dry dock becomes available. The most urgent job from the backlog of open orders is then assigned to this dry dock. Therefore, the dry dock is in effect a CONWIP card.

6.2.3 Joint Production Queue Kanban-CONWIP System

The loop of the kanban and the loop of the CONWIP cards are very similar. Therefore, it is easy to create a mixed system. Usually, **kanbans are assigned to the make-to-stock part types that have a buffer stock in the supermarket and CONWIP to the more exotic make-to-order parts that have no buffer of completed products and go directly to the customer**. Whenever a kanban comes along, the corresponding parts are produced. Whenever an empty CONWIP card comes along, the most urgent part from the backlog of low-volume-high-mix exotic parts is produced.

Both kanban and CONWIP cards can wait in a joint queue for production, as shown in Figure 105. The priority within the queue for production is simply first-come-first-serve, or FIFO. The only difference is that returning blank CONWIP cards are assigned a production job from the backlog before being added to the production queue.

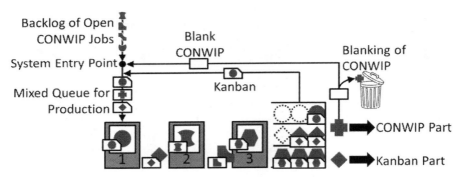

Figure 105: Example of a mixed kanban-CONWIP system with a single queue (Image Roser)

When determining the number of kanbans for such a joint system, you may have to include the additional waiting time due to CONWIP cards in the queue for production. If you have only a small CONWIP workload compared to the kanban workload, this may be negligible. However, if you have a lot of CONWIP cards compared to the kanbans, the effect on the replenishment time and hence the inventory limit may be significant.

6.2.4 Separate Production Queues Kanban-CONWIP System

It is also possible to create a mixed kanban-CONWIP system with separate queues for production. There is one queue for kanban and a separate queue for CONWIP, as shown in Figure 106. Since you now have two queues with work waiting for the first process in the loop, you must add a **clear priority rule for the operators when to use which queue**. Should they prioritize kanban? Should they prioritize CONWIP? Should they alternate between kanban and CONWIP? Or is random picking okay?

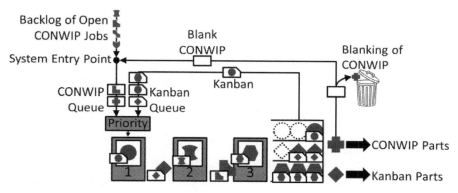

Figure 106: Example of a mixed kanban-CONWIP system with separate queues (Image Roser)

Different approaches are imaginable. **If CONWIP makes up no more than 20% to 30% of your workload, the operator should always prioritize the CONWIP queue**. Prioritizing CONWIP cards over kanbans allows faster lead times to the customer for make-to-order items. The additional delay of the make-to-stock kanbans can easily be compensated with extra kanbans to create a bit more buffer inventory. This separate queue is recommended if CONWIP make up no more than 30% of your work, as it will significantly speed up the lead time of CONWIP while requiring only a small increase in kanban inventory.

If CONWIP makes up over 40% of the workload, this prioritization is risky. If over 40% of the workload has priority over other jobs, the other jobs may have to wait for a long time before being processed. You may need more and more kanban inventory to cover for the long delay of the kanbans. In this case, I recommend using only a single queue without prioritization having both kanban and CONWIP in a simple FIFO order. See Chapter 5.4.2.1.5 and especially Figure 78 for details.

6.2.5 Kanban and CONWIP Cards at the Same Part

There is also another type of hybrid CONWIP-kanban system in academic literature, where both a CONWIP *and* a kanban are attached to the same part. In this system, CONWIP has one big loop and kanban has smaller loops within the CONWIP system. However, this would mean that you now have *two* cards attached to each part, a CONWIP and a kanban. This is twice the work, and two times the opportunity for mix-ups with little benefit. Matching CONWIP cards with kanban will be quite a challenge. **Stay away from this type of hybrid system**, since it requires extra work, has more possibilities for mistakes, and does not really have any big advantage.

6.2.6 CONWIP System Using Workload Limit

In a normal CONWIP system, a blank CONWIP card permits the release of one job from the backlog at the system entry point. It does not matter if this job is big or small; exactly one job is released per arriving CONWIP card.

However, instead of an inventory limit represented by a number of products, it is possible to use a limit on the workload, or generally a limit on a continuous quantity.[49] When a completed job leaves the system, it is not a blank CONWIP card returning, but the information on the quantity of work that just departed the system.

This workload is again available for the next job. The workload is pooled before the system entry point. **Whenever the available workload exceeds the work content of the next job in the backlog, this job is released.** In this case, the required workload is taken from the pool and assigned to the job released into the queue for production. This is visualized in Figure 107.

---

[49] Matthias Thürer et al., *On the Meaning of ConWIP Cards: An Assessment by Simulation, Journal of Industrial and Production Engineering* 36, no. 1 January 2, 2019: 49–58.

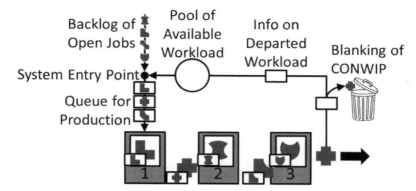

Figure 107: CONWIP system using a workload limit instead of an inventory limit (Image Roser)

This allows a finer control of the workload in the system, which can be useful if the open jobs vary significantly in work content. It requires, however, a more complex system and is usually best done digitally — although the software implementation will also be a lot of work. I would still recommend sticking with the conventional CONWIP cards where one card represents one job of whatever size. If you already have such a system, you may consider upgrading, but start with small steps.

Furthermore, while it feels much more accurate to have the workload included in the CONWIP loop, it quickly becomes fuzzy as to which workload to use. First, **the workload is not the sum of all cycle times! It is also not the lead time!** This would mash together the workload for non-critical processes that have plenty of available capacity with the bottlenecks that have little free time.

I have to go a bit deeper into the theory here. A production system has a system takt (i.e., the average time between the departures of products from the system). This includes losses like breakdowns or lack of materials. The workload we want is the "takt" for this single product. This is easy in theory, but how do you measure it in reality? It relates to the bottleneck, but this helps us only a bit. Let me show you some options.

Using a workload limit is much easier if your CONWIP loop contains only one process. In this case, this process is automatically the bottleneck, and **the workload is the expected time that this job will occupy this process in the one-process loop, including losses**. This is visualized in Figure 108.

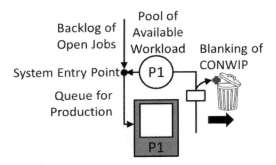

Figure 108: A workload-based CONWIP system with a single process needs to track only this process (Image Roser)

If you have multiple processes in the loop, it becomes a bit trickier. You track the **time that this job occupies the bottleneck process**. This is visualized in Figure 109. This approach has the advantage of a simple calculation similar to Figure 108. On the downside, it requires you to have one single bottleneck process. However, in reality the bottlenecks often shift, making this approach less precise—assuming that you even know your bottleneck process.

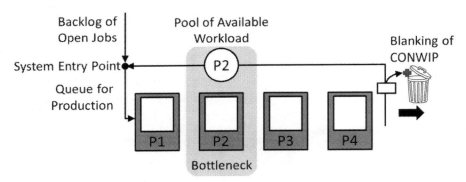

Figure 109: A workload-based CONWIP system can also track only the bottleneck if it is known and not shifting (Image Roser)

A much more precise but also more cumbersome approach is to **track the workload for all processes in the loop separately**. This is visualized in Figure 110. This is probably the most precise approach. The upper workload limit is applied separately to all processes. Please note that the upper workload limit is not distributed among the processes, but each process has the same upper workload limit.

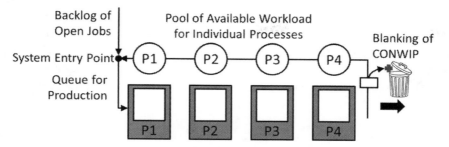

Figure 110: A workload-based CONWIP system can also track all processes separately (Image Roser)

A job can only enter if all required workload pools have enough available capacity for this job. Thus, whichever process is currently the bottleneck will limit the release of new jobs at the system entry point. **Make sure that you still stick with the sequence in the backlog!** A job should not overtake another job just because this job fits in the available workload.

Finally, you could pick only the processes that are possible bottlenecks (i.e., where the capacity may be tight sometimes). In this case, you **track only the workload of these critical processes**. This is a compromise between tracking only the bottleneck, which may shift, and tracking all processes, which may be a lot of work. This is visualized in Figure 111.

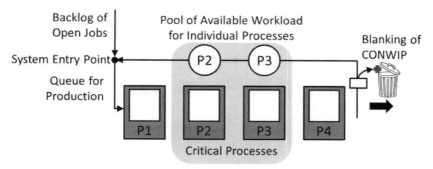

Figure 111: A workload-based CONWIP system could also track only the processes where the capacity is critical (Image Roser)

Many other definitions of workload are imaginable. For example, you could use the average time across all processes. However, all of these methods are much more cumbersome than simply counting the number of jobs or parts. In my opinion, **the benefit of a workload control pull system is rarely worth the effort, even if the jobs have quite different workloads.** Hence, I recommend simply having an inventory limit instead of a workload limit.

Instead of a workload limit, it is also possible to use continuous quantities like liters or kilograms. This usually makes less sense for CONWIP cards. The work-related information on a CONWIP card is blanked after the card is removed from the material. You would keep only the information on the released workload. Using the workload is very generic, and the workload can be applied to any kind of subsequent job. However, for continuous quantities it is not common for departing material of one type to release production of another type. Hence, while a workload limit is common for CONWIP, continuous production quantities are more likely to be found using kanban.

Besides CONWIP, there are other pull methods to handle this problem. The pull method specialized for job shops, POLCA, avoids this problem by having a separate loop for every process by default. See Chapter 7 for details. The hypothetical method COBACABANA described in the appendix does indeed track the workload separately for every process in the system. As COBACABANA is purely paper based, this is actually a lot of work if you have more than a few processes. See Appendix C for details. There is actually a large body of scientific literature on workload control, many of it in German.[50, 51, 52, 53, 54] Feel free to go down that rabbit hole if you are interested.

---

[50] Jan-Wilhelm Breithaupt, Martin Land, and Peter Nyhuis, *The Workload Control Concept: Theory and Practical Extensions of Load Oriented Order Release*, Production Planning & Control 13, no. 7 October 1, 2002: 625–38.

[51] Bas Oosterman, Martin Land, and Gerard Gaalman, *The Influence of Shop Characteristics on Workload Control*, International Journal of Production Economics 68, no. 1 October 30, 2000: 107–19.

[52] Lawrence D. Fredendall, Divesh Ojha, and J. Wayne Patterson, *Concerning the Theory of Workload Control*, European Journal of Operational Research 201, no. 1 February 16, 2010: 99–111.

[53] Hans-Peter Wiendahl, *Die belastungsorientierte Fertigungssteuerung*, in *Fertigungssteuerung: Grundlagen und Systeme*, ed. Dietrich Adam, Schriften zur Unternehmensführung Wiesbaden: Gabler Verlag, 1992, 207–43, ISBN 978-3-322-89141-9.

[54] Peter Nyhuis and Hans-Peter Wiendahl, *Logistische Kennlinien: Grundlagen, Werkzeuge und Anwendungen*, 3. Aufl. 2012 Edition Berlin Heidelberg Dordrecht London New York: Springer, 2012, ISBN 978-3-540-92838-6.

6.3 Elements

CONWIP-based pull systems are very similar to kanban-based pull systems. The fundamental difference is that the content of the CONWIP card changes every time it gets a new job. Hence, the differentiation is mainly in the **card design**, the **blanking of the CONWIP card**, the **backlog**, and the **system entry point** where the backlog is merged with the card. Figure 112 gives you an overview of the elements.

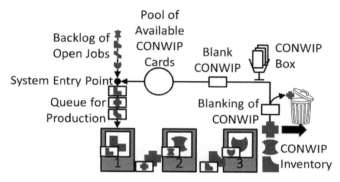

Figure 112: Elements of a CONWIP system (Image Roser)

6.3.1 CONWIP Card

A CONWIP card differs from a kanban, as it has two possible states. The CONWIP card can be blank (i.e., there is no information about any part or job attached). However, the CONWIP card can also be connected to a part or job that is to be produced. In this case, details about this job can be found within the CONWIP card.

Frequently, the basic CONWIP card is an empty folder, in which a job may be inserted at the system entry point. These are usually plastic folders, as shown in Figure 113, but you could also use an empty box or pallet that contains the finished goods. The part information is attached to the box at the system entry point. You could also use a digital version of a CONWIP card. These plastic folders often have at least one transparent side so that the information can be seen easily without removing the paper. It is possible to make both sides transparent, but a colored backing may also give visual clues. For simplicity, and because it is done so on other literature, I will also call this a CONWIP card and not a CONWIP folder.

Figure 113: Selection of folders suitable for CONWIP. Some have wire frames for hanging, others have a magnetic back, and others are just plastic folders. Pen for scale. (Image Roser, sample folders from ORGATEX)

Since the information changes frequently, it is important that the content of the CONWIP card can easily be exchanged. Such plastic folders can be of varying size, ranging from a full page (A4 or letter) to the size of a postcard. For smaller cases, the paper can be folded or cut to match size. Similar to kanban, these CONWIP folders can come with holes or hooks for hanging it up, or a magnetic back for easy attachment to the part or the metal work-piece carrier.

Even a blank CONWIP card should contain the **information on where the card belongs**. You could add a sticker with information on the CONWIP card (i.e., which pull loop the card belongs to) and an index number of the card. It may also contain a barcode.

More information is added at the system entry point. This added content of the CONWIP card is basically a work order, containing all the necessary details on **what to produce, how much to produce**, and possibly **how to produce** and **what raw materials** it requires. It may also include elements like information on the end customer, the **start date, deadlines, milestones**, or even **work instructions**. If the card is folded, make sure that the most relevant information is shown on the front, visible through the transparent window.

6.3.2 Blanking of CONWIP Cards

When a part leaves the system, the CONWIP card is removed from the part. At this point, the card or folder still contains the information on the part or the job that was just removed. It is now necessary to blank the CONWIP card (i.e., to remove the information of the previous job).

In Figure 112 this is simplified by throwing the information on the job in the trash. In reality, however, this information is often used at other locations (i.e., to track the completion of jobs, forwarded to the backlog of the next loop, or in general to document the work). Regardless of what you do with the information, the CONWIP card has to be blanked and must no longer be associated with a job. The exception here are workload CONWIP systems, where the card should keep the information on the workload so it can be added again to the pool of available workload.

6.3.3 CONWIP Box

The CONWIP box is very similar to the kanban box in Chapter 5.3.3. If it is feasible, you may bring every blanked CONWIP card to the system entry point immediately. However, it may be impractical to do this transport right away. In this case, similar to a kanban box, blank CONWIP cards are collected and brought to the system entry point periodically. For digital CONWIP cards the cards may be scanned, and it may or may not be easier to wait until multiple cards are together before they are scanned.

6.3.4 Pool of Available CONWIP Cards

In the ideal case, any empty CONWIP card that arrives at the system entry point is used immediately for the next available job. However, if there is not enough work, it may be that the backlog of open jobs is empty. In this case, the empty CONWIP card has to wait in front of the system entry point until the next job becomes available through the backlog of open jobs. Ideally, this pool of available CONWIP cards should be mostly empty.

If you use the **CONWIP variant that has a workload limit** instead of an inventory limit, the blank CONWIP card comes with a quantity of workload that just became available again. This workload is added to the pool of available workload. Please note this pool may consist of separate pools for multiple processes, as shown in Figure 110. The next job in the backlog of open jobs is started if the available workload in the pool is sufficient. In this case, the required workload is removed from the pool and added to the CONWIP card attached to this job.

If there is insufficient workload for the next job, **you must not skip to another job in the backlog of open jobs**, even if this lower-priority job would be possible with the available workload. Doing this would dramatically increase the waiting time and hence also the lead time of larger jobs.

6.3.5 Backlog of Open Jobs

The backlog is a list of open jobs or open work orders that are not yet associated with a CONWIP card. Usually these are a number of printed work orders. Since they go into the CONWIP card at the system entry point, these prints should fit into the CONWIP card, although often they are also folded in half. It helps if the important information is visible through the clear window of the CONWIP card. Nowadays the backlog is also often managed digitally, as is the CONWIP card, but a printout of the job is still common.

This backlog queue is **sorted according to overall priority**. The most urgent products are produced first as soon as a CONWIP card becomes available — if the required material is available. Please note that **any job in the backlog should have the required materials available** or the materials should be expected to be delivered on time. There is no point in starting production if you cannot get the material in time.

Someone has to determine the backlog sequence. Someone has to decide which part type is more urgent than the other one. Spearman et al. suggest the production and inventory control staff for this task. I would phrase it more generally as the people who know the urgency best. It could be, for example, a clerk in the production planning or production control department, or a supervisor within manufacturing for internal supply lines. In modern manufacturing, the sequence will probably be primarily based on the available ERP data, combined with additional information through telephone or email.

The deciding element for the sequence is usually the **due date of the job**, with earlier due dates having a higher priority over later due dates. This can also be modified to include the work content, and an earlier due date job with little work could be less urgent than a later due date with a lot of work content.[55]

When implementing CONWIP, you can probably use the same sequencing rules you may have used before implementing a CONWIP system. People with good knowledge of the priorities can help with the sequence, but people who merely think that they have a good knowledge can also seriously mess it up.

Furthermore, note that **it is not necessary to create a sequence for all open orders**. If you or someone else is sequencing the backlog, you need to **sequence only the most urgent jobs to cover the time until the next sequencing**. Often, the sequencing is done at the beginning of the day, and enough jobs are sequenced to keep the system busy until the next day for the next sequencing.

There is no need to sequence all open orders in detail for the next three weeks, as this sequence is by no means fixed once it is created. In a usually highly volatile environment such as a manufacturing system, additional information comes up all the time. Customers may order more or cancel orders. Material availability may also change. However, if you update and change the sequence too often, you may increase the chaos. Also, make sure that the sequence is truly based on the needs of the customer. Prevent the operators from simply making the part in the backlog that they like best, or that gives them a better bonus.

If you use printed paper work orders within the backlog, make sure the sequence is clear. You could use, for example, specialized planning boards as illustrated in Figure 114. However, many other systems are imaginable, as for example magnetic CONWIP cards that are arranged on a labeled sheet metal board.

---

[55] Matthias Thürer et al., *On the Backlog-Sequencing Decision for Extending the Applicability of ConWIP to High-Variety Contexts: An Assessment by Simulation,* International Journal of Production Research 55, no. 16 August 18, 2017: 4695–4711.

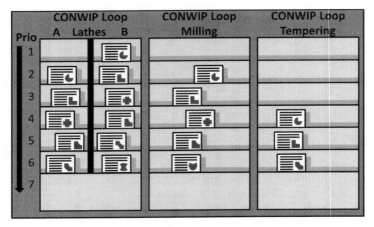

Figure 114: The sequence in a CONWIP backlog should be easy to understand (Image Roser)

6.3.6 System Entry Point

The system entry point is the point where the blank CONWIP card meets the backlog. Whenever a blank CONWIP card arrives, the next entry in the backlog is attached to the CONWIP card and released in the queue for production. This is sometimes also called *matchmaking*.

In practice, this usually means putting the printed work order into the blank CONWIP folder. **If there are no available blank CONWIP cards, the jobs have to wait until a CONWIP card is available. If there are no available jobs, the CONWIP card has to wait until a job is available.** Often, the person bringing the blank CONWIP cards to the system entry point also adds the next jobs from the backlog to the CONWIP cards.

If you use the **CONWIP variant that has a workload limit** instead of an inventory limit, then you need enough available workload for the first job in the backlog before releasing this job. Remember, you could have separate workload pools for multiple processes. **The available workload in these pools must be enough to cover the needed workload for the job at the respective processes**.

If there is insufficient workload available, both the CONWIP cards and the jobs in the backlog have to wait until there is enough workload available. As mentioned already in Chapter 6.3.4, you should **follow the sequence in the backlog**. If the available workload is insufficient for the first job, do not skip to a subsequent job that has a smaller workload. This would drastically increase the lead time for larger jobs.

6.3.7 Queue for Production

The queue for production should use a FIFO system, where the first part that goes in the manufacturing system is also the first part that goes out. Spearman et al. more generally speak of a "First in System, First Served" approach. The card with the oldest time of entry into the system gets produced first.

Spearman et al. also suggest that this rule must be followed, except for rework. The assumption is that rework is long past overdue and therefore has to rush through the system. In my view, this is one possibility to break FIFO. However, there may be others.

You can also establish a priority system. For example, it usually makes sense to always give make-to-order parts priority over make-to-stock parts. For make-to-order this can reduce the lead time, while it increases the make-to-stock inventory only slightly. **The lead time reduction for make-to-order exotic parts is probably much more beneficial than the slightly increased inventory for make-to-stock parts.** Nevertheless, a simple FIFO is often easier to manage.

In any case, you should make sure that no part is forgotten in the system. If it is entirely up to the operators, the more difficult, less pleasant, or worse-paid parts may be forgotten for the next shift indefinitely. If you are not sure which prioritization approach you should use for your system, stick to the simple FIFO.

If you want to have additional sequencing, for example due to a changeover optimization, you can do this in the queue for production. This may bind some CONWIP cards, and you may need a few more CONWIP cards to keep the system well utilized. It is also possible, however, **to do the sequencing already in the backlog**. Here you do not need to cover the sequencing delay with additional CONWIP cards. Often, the person creating the backlog or the person managing the system entry point may keep an eye on having a feasible sequence.

In any case, you can create and enforce sequencing rules, or leave it to the operators. In the latter case you run the risk that the operators make the part first that they like best, rather than the most urgent one.

It is possible to use a single FIFO also for mixed kanban-CONWIP systems. It is also possible to have separate queues for kanban and CONWIP cards. In the latter case there needs to be a clear rule for the operator which of these two FIFO has higher priority. See Chapters 6.2.3 and 6.2.4 for details.

6.3.8 CONWIP Inventory

A kanban system has a supermarket at the end of the loop. A CONWIP system has inventory at the end too. However, since this is for make-to-order production, the customer is usually more than happy to take the completed job right away, and you have very little inventory.

A supermarket ideally has a line for each product type, similar to many parallel FIFO, one for each type. This is not necessary for CONWIP, as there is rarely more than one part of the same type in the finished-goods inventory.

If there are multiple parts of a certain part type in the finished-goods inventory, the one with the oldest CONWIP card attached to the part should be sent out first. In any case, similar to kanban, the CONWIP cards return to the beginning if the attached parts leave the system.

6.4 Calculation

The calculation for the number of CONWIP cards is related to the kanban calculation, but with some major differences. I will first talk about the fundamental differences, before I will show the calculation of the number of CONWIP cards for flow shops in detail. Thereafter I also discuss the calculation for job shops.

I will also explain how to calculate this for CONWIP systems that do not have a discrete inventory limit. These have instead, for example, a target limit on the workload or a target limit on a continuous quantity like volumes or masses. Since CONWIP calculations are very messy and imprecise, however, similar to kanban, I recommend using an estimation approach.

6.4.1 CONWIP Calculation Fundamentals

CONWIP in particular or make-to-order in general has quite different goals from kanban or make-to-stock. With kanban, or generally make-to-stock, the goal is a high material availability for the customer while avoiding excess inventory. With CONWIP, or generally make-to-order, the customer always has to wait, and **the goal is a trade-off between a good system utilization and shorter lead times**. There is no inventory that is kept in case a customer shows up. Instead, it is all made-to-order. Furthermore, most inventory will leave the CONWIP system right after completion since the customer is already waiting for the goods.

Hence, the goal is not to have a good material availability, but to have a good trade-off between keeping the system busy and well utilized while still keeping a competitive lead time. Both of these are influenced by the inventory limit in the system, and hence the number of CONWIP cards. Starting too many jobs in a CONWIP system will increase inventory and therefore the lead time, whereas too few jobs will decrease utilization. Let me summarize this again since this is very important:

- A make-to-stock system has a trade-off between having completed goods in stock while not having too much costly and cumbersome inventory.
- A make-to-order system has a trade-off between keeping the system well utilized while having a competitive lead time.

Due to this fundamental difference, you usually need much fewer CONWIP cards than you would need kanbans for comparable systems. **With the kanban calculation, we often had to consider the worst case and make conservative assumptions. With CONWIP, it is perfectly fine to use averages, and maybe add a small bit of safety afterwards.** This will give a good trade-off between utilization and lead time.

However, many shop floor managers prefer to err on the utilization side. "The machines must run; inventory levels be damned". Please do not make this mistake. Try to have a good trade-off between utilization and inventory. **In case of doubt, go for fewer CONWIP cards and lower inventory as well as faster lead times.**

The differences between make-to-stock and make-to-order changes the underlying equation to calculate the number of CONWIP cards. First, for kanban we wanted to ensure a high material availability even under adverse circumstance's like large orders, breakdowns, and other fluctuations. For kanban, we used conservative and worst-case assumptions. For CONWIP, we do not need to assume the worst case, and hence can ignore fluctuations. Therefore, **for CONWIP use the average case, possibly with a small bit of safety**.

Second, we had to calculate the number of kanbans separately for every part type, using the part-specific takt time and the part-specific number of parts per kanban. CONWIP is not assigned to a specific part type, but is a generic card for *any* type of job. Besides, it is not common for many CONWIP systems to repeat an identical job, and usually every job is different. Hence, **for CONWIP you do not need to distinguish between the part types**.

Finally, while a kanban can represent multiple parts of the same type, a CONWIP card is usually generic and normally represents only one job. Hence, **for CONWIP you rarely need to consider a CONWIP equivalent to the number of parts per kanban**, as it is automatically one. However, if you have an unusual CONWIP system with multiple jobs for one card, you will need to include this again. Overall, Equation 15 from the kanban calculation simplifies into Equation 22 for CONWIP.

$$NC_{CONWIP} = \frac{RT_\emptyset}{TT_{All}} + S = RT_\emptyset \cdot DF_{All} + S$$

Equation 22: Generic formula to calculate the number of CONWIP cards

Where the variables in Equation 22 are as follows, under the assumption that one job equals one CONWIP card:

DF_{All} Demand frequency across all part types (jobs per time)
NC_{CONWIP} Number of CONWIP cards (card quantity)
$RT_\emptyset$ Average replenishment time (time)
S Safety factor (card quantity)
TT_{All} Customer takt across all job types (time per job)

If the target limit of your CONWIP system is measured in workload or a continuous quantity like liters, kilograms, or cubic meters, the equation will become a bit trickier again. More on this in Chapter 6.4.6.

6.4.2 Customer Takt for CONWIP Calculation

We also need to determine the customer takt. Please note that the customer takt in Equation 22 would now have to be measured in the average time between orders or jobs. The demand frequency would be measured in orders or jobs per time.

This is also usually similar to the line takt, which here would be the average time between the completions of a job in the CONWIP system. The inverse would be the throughput (i.e., the average number of jobs completed per time period). Since CONWIP cards do not distinguish between different jobs or part types, the customer takt, line takt, demand frequency, and throughput are all calculated across all part types, as shown in Equation 23 and Equation 24. This differs from kanban, where they are needed individually per part type.

$$TT_{All} = \frac{TW}{D_{All}} = \frac{1}{DF_{All}}$$

Equation 23: Customer takt across all part types

$$TL_{All} = \frac{TW}{Q_{All}} = \frac{1}{TP_{All}} \approx TT_{All}$$

Equation 24: Line takt across all part types

The variables for Equation 23 and Equation 24 are as follows:

D_{All}	Demand for all part types during a given time period (jobs)
DF_{All}	Demand frequency across all part types (jobs per time)
Q_{All}	Quantity across all part types (jobs)
TL_{All}	Line takt across all part types (time per job)
TP_{All}	Throughput across all part types (jobs per time)
TT_{All}	Customer takt across all part types (time per job)
TW	Working time period of a system (time)

6.4.3 Replenishment Time for CONWIP Calculation

The replenishment time for CONWIP differs from the replenishment time for kanban. It is the time a CONWIP card takes from the beginning of production until the empty CONWIP card arrives back at the system entry point. Technically, CONWIP does not "replenish" the same part type, but rather releases the next job in the backlog. However, for consistency we will still call this the replenishment time.

This replenishment time includes all the information transport times for the cards, the processing times in the different processes, and waiting between processes. It also includes the waiting with the finished goods, under the assumption that most parts leave the system shortly after completion. It usually does NOT include fluctuations. An overview of the replenishment time for CONWIP is shown in Figure 115. Please note the difference from Figure 75.

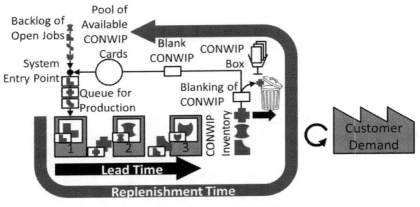

Figure 115: The replenishment time for CONWIP systems (Image Roser)

CONWIP in particular or make-to-order in general has quite different goals from kanban or make-to-stock. With kanban, or general make-to-stock, the goal is a high material availability for the customer. Hence, for the kanban replenishment time we did not include the waiting time of kanban in the supermarket, as these cards are already "ready" for the customer.

With CONWIP, or generally make-to-order, the customer always has to wait. The goal is more a combination of good system utilization with low lead times. Hence, in CONWIP systems, blank CONWIP cards or CONWIP cards waiting in the queue for production are similarly "ready" for the system and therefore are not included in the replenishment time. As the supermarket inventory was the buffer against fluctuations for kanban, so are the CONWIP cards in the pool or the queue for production the buffer against fluctuation for the CONWIP system.

Or, in other words, **the goal of a make-to-stock system is to provide a steady flow of parts to the customer, and hence the replenishment time** ignores the completed inventory. The goal of a make-to-order system is to provide a steady flow of work to the system, and hence the replenishment time ignores the not-yet-started work.

6.4.4 CONWIP Calculation for Flow Shops

Determining the number of CONWIP cards for flow shops is a lot easier than for job shops. You just need enough cards to keep the line busy. Hence, here we look separately at flow shops and job shops.

The relevant entries for the replenishment time for CONWIP are different from kanban. Figure 116 gives you an overview of the possible elements that could go into the calculation of the number of CONWIP cards. This figure also shows all the elements that do NOT go into the calculation of the CONWIP cards.

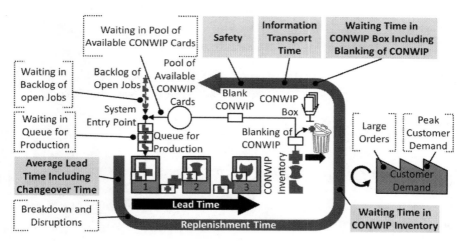

Figure 116: The relevant and (in dotted brackets) irrelevant elements of the replenishment time for CONWIP systems (Image Roser)

6.4.4.1 Elements NOT Relevant for CONWIP

Let's first look at the elements in Figure 116 that are not relevant. All fluctuations can be ignored. On the customer side, while the average customer takt or demand frequency is still relevant, the effect of **peak demand** does not influence the number of CONWIP cards. Similarly, **large orders**—effectively ordering multiple jobs at once—also do not affect the number of CONWIP cards. On the production side, **breakdowns and**

disruptions are only included as averages in the lead time, but the fluctuations do not need to be covered.

As the goals of CONWIP differ from kanban, the replenishment time starts and ends at locations different from kanban, as shown in Figure 116. CONWIP systems buffer work for the system rather than parts for the customer, and hence the work waiting for production is not included in the replenishment time. This includes the **waiting time in the pool of available CONWIP** cards and the **waiting time in the queue for production**.[56] Albeit, if you have a very rare mixed kanban and CONWIP system that also prioritizes kanban over CONWIP, you may have to include the waiting time caused by prioritizing kanban.

Finally, the **backlog of open jobs** would not be part of the replenishment time, regardless of how the replenishment time is defined, as it is completely outside of the CONWIP loop. Therefore, it is not included in the CONWIP calculation.

6.4.4.2 Elements of the CONWIP Calculation

Here are the details on the elements relevant to the calculation of the replenishment time for CONWIP cards. See Figure 116 for an illustration.

6.4.4.2.1 Average Lead Time Including Changeover

The lead time is the time for an average job to pass through the production system. Please note that the average here means the mean, not the median. A few outliers of jobs that take a long time will not change your median, but will definitely change the mean. Furthermore, this average also includes changeovers, breakdowns, and any other losses that may happen.

This is based on the number of jobs in the system. This number of jobs could be the current number of jobs in the system, which hopefully is a representation of the average number of jobs in the system. It could also be a long-term average or an estimate. Probably best is to use the average number of jobs you **want** to have in the system. Dividing the number of jobs

---

[56] Truth to be told, I was pondering for a long time if I should include the time in the queue for production or not. I eventually decided not to include this time in the replenishment time for make-to-order systems, but this is up for discussion.

you have or want to have in your system by the customer takt gives you the lead time, as shown in Equation 8.

6.4.4.2.2 Waiting Time in CONWIP Inventory

The replenishment time for the CONWIP calculation can also include the time for completed parts waiting in the inventory before being delivered to the customer. However, this is often only a short time. It should only include the waiting time while the CONWIP card is still attached to the product. As we will see later, in Chapter 6.7.1, there are different options when to return the CONWIP card. If you return the card as soon as the product is completed, regardless of whether the parts wait, then the waiting time would not be included. **We are interested in the waiting time of the CONWIP cards, not the waiting time of the parts.** Hence only the waiting time of parts with cards are included.

However, even if you keep your cards attached to the parts until they are sent to the customer, the waiting time is usually quite short. The customer is in all likelihood already eagerly waiting for the goods and does not want the purchases to be sitting around in your warehouse. Therefore, **most times this waiting time in the CONWIP inventory can be ignored**. Only if you frequently have a significant number of completed jobs waiting for longer times while still being attached to the CONWIP card should you include this time. This often happens with larger machinery or equipment, where delays on the customer side postpone the installation.

6.4.4.2.3 Waiting Time in CONWIP Box

The waiting time in the CONWIP box is similar to the waiting time in the kanban box. It mostly depends on how often a person comes and brings the CONWIP cards to the pool of available CONWIP cards or to the system entry point. For digital cards, this would depend on how often the waiting cards are scanned. If a person comes by every hour to transport or scan the cards, then the waiting time would be at most one hour. Please note that here, too, we use the average instead of the worst case. Hence, for a pickup every hour, the average waiting time in the CONWIP box would be thirty minutes.

A kanban only has to be detached from the part. A CONWIP card also has to be blanked, and the information of the previous job has to be removed. This time would be included in the waiting time in the CONWIP box. However, the time needed to blank the cards is usually much, much smaller than the overall replenishment time. It probably won't make much difference if you ignore the time for blanking of the CONWIP cards.

6.4.4.2.4 Information Transport Time

Similar to kanban, the CONWIP card has to be transported from the CONWIP box back to the system entry point. For digital systems, this information transport time is a magnitude of milliseconds, and even for physical cards, it is rarely more than a few minutes. Hence, like kanban, **this information transport time can often safely be ignored**.

6.4.4.2.5 Safety

We could add some safety factor to the CONWIP calculation. Similar to kanban, this is also a comfort factor for your people to reduce their worries. However, since the rest of the CONWIP calculation uses averages rather than worst-case scenarios, you don't have to add safety. Merely rounding up to the next number is often sufficient. In most cases, you will have to adjust the number of CONWIP cards later anyway when the system is running. The safety here is merely a feel-good factor for your people, and otherwise unnecessary. But **avoid too much safety, as this will increase the lead time and inventory**.

6.4.4.2.6 Other Elements

Similar to kanban, your system may have unusual additional elements that would go into the replenishment time for CONWIP cards. This could be, for example, the waiting time in mixed kanban and CONWIP systems where the kanban has priority — although usually it is the other way around. In this case, the additional waiting time for the CONWIP cards caused by the kanban should be included. The elements detailed above, however, should suffice for most cases. Also, keep in mind that you are not interested in unusual fluctuations, but only the average effect on the system.

6.4.4.3 Calculating the Number of CONWIP Cards

The elements shown here cover most cases, but if your CONWIP system has additional delays or fluctuations, please do include them in the calculation. Table 14 gives you an overview of these elements.

Group	Element	Unit	Usually Relevant?	Variable
Replenishment Time	Lead Time	Time	Yes	LT
Replenishment Time	Waiting Time in CONWIP Inventory	Time	No	WI
Replenishment Time	Waiting Time in CONWIP Box	Time	Yes	WB
Replenishment Time	Information Transport Time	Time	No	TI
Other	Safety Factor	Cards	No	S
Other	Other Elements	???	No	n/a

Table 14: Overview of variables contributing to the number of CONWIP cards

Similar to kanban, the elements shown above have to be converted to represent a number of cards. Since all elements but the safety factor are measured as a time, you would convert these into a number of CONWIP cards similar to Equation 9, where one CONWIP card represents one job. The safety factor can be added afterwards, and may also round to the next largest integer number of CONWIP cards. Remember, you do not need much safety for make-to-order production, if any at all. The complete formula for calculating the number of CONWIP cards is shown in Equation 25.

$$NC_{CONWIP} = \frac{LT + WI + WB + TI}{TT_{All}} + S$$

Equation 25: The formula for calculating the number of CONWIP cards

The variables for Equation 25 are as follows, under the assumption that one job equals one CONWIP card:

LT   Lead time (time)
NC_{CONWIP} Number of CONWIP cards (card quantity)
S   Safety factor (card quantity)
TI   Time for the transport of information (time)
TT_{All} Customer takt across all part types (time per quantity or job)
WB   Waiting time at CONWIP box (time)
WI   Waiting time in inventory (time)

This is also only a very rough estimate, useful as a starting number for a new CONWIP system. Similar to kanban, this is also very robust. Hence, don't worry too much about the precision of your numbers, or if you have a CONWIP card more or less. In any case, the number of CONWIP cards is adjusted as the system evolves over time.

6.4.4.4 Example CONWIP Flow Shop Calculation

Let's do an example calculation. I will again first give you all the parameters and information on the system. Thereafter I will calculate the number of CONWIP cards step by step. For optimal learning, you may first try to calculate this yourself, and then compare your calculations with the example given here. As there will be quite a few assumptions, your result may differ somewhat from mine depending on these assumptions. Try to understand these differences, and see if these are based on different assumptions or an actual error somewhere.

6.4.4.4.1 Production System Data

Similar to the kanban example calculation, we will also produce wooden toy cars, but now these cars are all custom made. Examples of such cars are shown in Figure 117.

Figure 117: The example system produces custom-made toy cars. (Image Roser)

There is an expected demand of 2000 cars per month. The production line works 20 days per month with 7 hours per day. Scrap and rework are negligible. The CONWIP production line for custom-made cars is similar to the kanban production line and shown in Figure 118. The difference is that all steps are more complicated and time consuming due to the high level of customization. The buffers are on average half full, although with a lot of fluctuation. Furthermore, management wants to reduce the lead time by 30%.

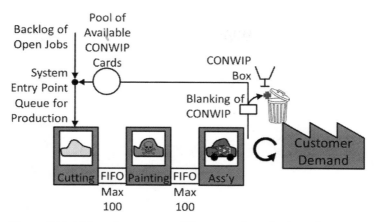

Figure 118: Value stream map of the example make-to-order system (Image Roser)

All completed goods are shipped to the customer right away. The CONWIP cards are transported back to the system entry point once every two hours, which is a 2-minute walk for the supervisor.

6.4.4.4.2 Calculation of the Elements

Similar to the kanban, we have to start with the customer takt. The demand was 2000 pieces per month, and a month had 20 work days with 7 hours per day and 3600 seconds per hour. Using Equation 23, we get the customer takt, as shown in Equation 26 of 252 seconds per part.

$$\text{TT}_{\text{All}} = \frac{\text{TW}}{\text{D}_{\text{All}}} = \frac{20\text{d} \cdot 7\frac{\text{h}}{\text{d}} \cdot 3600\frac{\text{s}}{\text{h}}}{2000\text{ cars}} = \frac{504\,000\text{s}}{2000\text{ cars}} = 252\frac{\text{s}}{\text{car}}$$

Equation 26: Customer takt for CONWIP example

The **lead time** is now no longer based on the worst-case scenario. Hence, we no longer assume that all buffers are full. Since they are on average only half full, we have on average 103 jobs under production, 50 for each FIFO and 1 in each process. This would give an average lead time of 103 jobs multiplied by 252 seconds per job, or 25 956 seconds, or 7 hours 13 minutes. However, management wants to cut the lead time by 30%. Instead of 103 jobs in the system, the target is now to have only 72 jobs in the system. This gives a target lead time of 18 169 seconds, or 5 hours and 3 minutes. This may reduce our utilization slightly, but this is worth the improved lead time. We will now use the target lead time for the subsequent calculations.

Since all goods are shipped right away, we can ignore the **waiting time in the CONWIP inventory**. The **waiting time in the CONWIP box** is based on the frequency of the transport of the CONWIP cards. Since the cards are transported every two hours, the worst case would be a two-hour wait. However, for CONWIP we do not need to use the worst-case waiting time, but only the average. With a transport time every two hours, the average cards wait one hour. This is significant enough to be included in the calculation. For easier subsequent calculations, we use 3600 seconds instead of one hour.

The **information transport time** is 2 minutes. Normally we could ignore this, but for didactic reasons I included this in the calculation. We will decide the **safety** later. We do not have any **other elements** that we want to include in the calculation of the number of CONWIP cards.

6.4.4.4.3 Example Calculation Results

Table 15 shows an overview of the elements for the number of CONWIP cards that we have determined so far.

Element	Unit	Value	Variable
Lead Time	Seconds	18 169	LT
Waiting Time in CONWIP Inventory	Time	0	WI
Waiting Time in CONWIP Box	Hours (Seconds)	1 (3600)	WB
Information Transport Time	Minutes (Seconds)	2 (120)	TI

Table 15: Elements for the number of CONWIP cards example, not yet including safety

Using these elements in Equation 25 gives us the result, as shown in Equation 27. This does not yet include the safety. We can see that the lead time has the largest influence on the number of CONWIP cards.

$$NC_{CONWIP} = \frac{LT + WI + WB + TI}{TT_{All}} + S =$$

$$= \frac{18\ 169s + 0 + 3600s + 120s}{252\frac{s}{car}} + S =$$

$$= 86.9\ cars + S = 86.9\ CONWIP\ cards + S$$

Equation 27: The number of CONWIP cards of the example excluding safety

We are very flexible regarding the safety factor, and may not need one at all. I would even be comfortable rounding down to 86 cards. However, the shop floor people may be more skeptical and would like to have a safety factor. After some discussion, the group agreed on a total of 90 CONWIP cards because "everybody likes round numbers". Please note that you probably won't hit the lead time target exactly. Adjust the number of CONWIP cards up or down to change the lead time—but also the utilization.

6.4.5 CONWIP Calculation for Job Shops

If the CONWIP calculation above was straightforward for a flow shop, it will be tougher for a job shop. Job shops by their nature are much more chaotic. While the CONWIP calculations for flow shops are still true also for job shops in principle, reality makes it more difficult. Since the jobs may have different sequences of different processes, a job occupying a lot of time at one process may not affect another job that does not use this process at all. Similarly, the lead times for jobs may fluctuate widely, since some jobs may overtake other jobs based on their process sequence or the production plan.

Overall, Equation 22 and Equation 25 still hold true, but the calculation of the replenishment time is much trickier. We now have to worry about fluctuations in the job shop due to the different process sequences. Ignoring these may lead to an undesired lower utilization. However, including fluctuations usually results in larger inventories in job shops, which leads to larger lead times. Hence, using this larger lead time for the CONWIP will handle these fluctuations. Alternatively, you could also increase the safety factor. In both cases, the additional CONWIP cards are needed to cover the increased fluctuations in job shops due to the different material flow. In any case, I strongly recommend updating the number of CONWIP cards based on the observations of the running system, especially for job shops.

6.4.6 CONWIP Calculation for Workload Limits

CONWIP can also be adjusted to an upper workload limit. Workload that becomes available through a returning CONWIP card goes into the pool with the available workload, as shown in Figure 107. Once the available workload is sufficient for the first job in the backlog of open jobs, the workload is assigned to the job and the job is released in to the queue for production.

In theory, this would also work for other continuous quantities like volumes or masses, although these are often product specific. However, such make-to-stock situations are better suited for kanban.

6.4.6.1 CONWIP Workload Limit Calculation

To determine the discrete limit on the number of parts or jobs, we used Equation 25. The same equation also works for workload limits with minor modifications, as shown in Equation 28. Instead of a number of CONWIP cards, we calculate the maximum workload in the system, which is a time unit.

$$WL_{Max} = LT + WI + WB + TI + S$$

Equation 28: The formula for calculating the CONWIP limit as a workload

The variables for Equation 28 are as follows:

LT   Lead time (time)
S   Safety factor (workload)
TI   Time for the transport of information (time)
WB   Waiting time at CONWIP box (time)
WI   Waiting time in inventory (time)
WL_{Max} Upper workload limit (workload)

The main difference to Equation 25 is the absence of the customer takt. The customer takt from Equation 25 was in time per item. For the new Equation 28 it would have been the time per workload quantity. It may be easier to understand this as its inverse, the throughput. Rather than items per work time, we measure a workload per work time. However, the system works exactly one hour per working hour, and hence the workload throughput is one. Hence, if calculated correctly, **this workload throughput always has a value of one with no units.** Its inverse, **the equivalent of the customer takt would also be one**, as we have one work hour for every hour of workload. Hence, all the replenishment times would be simply divided by one, and therefore we can skip this entirely in Equation 28.

The result is not a number of CONWIP cards, but a target limit measured in workload hours. When a CONWIP card merges with a job at the system entry point, the workload of the job is assigned to the CONWIP card. When this card eventually returns, the workload is added to the pool of available workload. Hence, a CONWIP card no longer stands for a fixed quantity, but is customized to represent exactly the workload of the current job it is assigned to.

6.4.6.2 Workload for Individual Jobs

The challenge is now to determine the workload needed for a job in the backlog of open jobs. The workload of a job is NOT its lead time! Nor is it the sum of all cycle times. Instead, it is the **expected average time that a job will take at a process**. This must include the average delays and losses, but should not include any worst-case delays. If you use worst-case scenarios, you will have fewer jobs in the system, and your utilization may suffer.

If you have only a single process in the loop, track only the workload at this process. If you have multiple processes in the loop, you can track either only the bottleneck—assuming you actually know the bottleneck and it is not moving over time—or you can track all processes separately. If you do not know exactly where your bottlenecks are and you don't want to track all processes separately, you can track only the processes where you think the capacity is critical. See Chapter 6.2.6 for details.

Sometimes you have this information based on historic data. In other cases, you may have calculated working times, for example, based on *methods-time measurements* (MTM). Make sure that this includes the average expected delay and other losses. If you have neither, then a person familiar with the processes at the shop floor would have to make an estimate. Do not worry too much about the accuracy, as pull systems are generally robust against some deviations.

6.4.6.3 Example Workload Calculation

For the example calculation of the upper workload limit for a CONWIP system, we use the same example as in Chapter 6.4.4.4.

6.4.6.3.1 Target Workload Limit

The target **lead time** was 18 169 seconds, and the **waiting time in the CONWIP box** was 3600 seconds. We ignored the **waiting time in the CONWIP inventory**. The **information transport time was 120 seconds** and could also be ignored, but we include it for didactic purposes. An overview of the data is given in Table 16. Hence, the total replenishment time is 21 769.2 seconds, as shown in Equation 29. This is also our target workload in the system without safety.

Element	Unit	Value	Variable
Lead Time	Seconds	18 169	LT
Waiting Time in CONWIP Inventory	Time	0	WI
Waiting Time in CONWIP Box	Seconds	3600	WB
Information Transport Time	Seconds	120	TI

Table 16: Elements for the CONWIP workload example, not yet including safety

$$WL_{Max} = LT + WI + WB + TI + S =$$

$$= 18\ 169s + 0 + 3600s + 120s + S = 21\ 889s + S$$

Equation 29: The formula for calculating the number of CONWIP cards example as a workload

The final workload limit including the safety factor could be simply rounded up to 22 000 seconds. However, with the same logic we could also have rounded down the value to 21 600 seconds, which is exactly 6 hours. Remember, we do not need any safety when calculating pull systems for make-to-order productions. Whichever way fits your system best. For the subsequent calculations, we use the 22 000 seconds workload limit.

6.4.6.3.2 System Entry Tracking Bottleneck

The more challenging part is to decide which car has how much workload. We would need to determine the workload of each car at each process. This is the expected time that the car will occupy this process, including the average (but not worst-case) delay.

Table 17 shows a sequence of cars including the workload on the individual processes. The average of these workloads is also shown in the last row. Some customers want to have an unpainted toy car, in which case the time for painting is zero.

	Car Number	Cutting (s)	Painting (s)	Assembly (s)
Soon to Be Completed	224	180	440	300
	225	320	0	200
	226	200	350	210
	...	...	...	...
Waiting in Backlog	308	300	310	200
	309	245	0	280
	310	200	370	120
	311	180	440	300
Average		240	250	210

Table 17: Cycle times and hence workload for different cars in workload calculation example

Some cars are already worked on. The next car to be completed is car #224. Other cars are still waiting in the backlog for available capacity before they can enter the system. The next car to enter if capacity becomes available is car #308. This is also visualized in Figure 119.

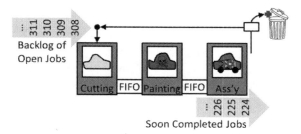

Figure 119: List of cars waiting in the backlog or nearing completion for the example CONWIP system using a workload limit (Image Roser)

To show the calculation, we assume that the painting process is the bottleneck and calculate only the workload for the bottleneck. This is easier than calculating the workload for all processes, which I will show you afterwards.

Let's assume the current painting workload already in the system is 21 660 seconds, and we have an available workload of 340 seconds at the bottleneck process of painting. We can start car #308, which requires 310 seconds of workload and increases the workload to 21 970 seconds. We can start car #309, since this does not require any painting time. However, we cannot start car #310 yet since we only have 30 seconds of workload left, but need 370 seconds to start.

Only after the completion of car #224 is another 440 seconds of workload released, and we can start car #310. Afterwards we have a workload of 21 900 seconds. The available workload of 100 seconds is not enough to start car #311. The departure of car #225 does not change this, as this car had no painting workload. Only after the departure of car #226 do we again have enough available workload for car #311. This is also shown in Figure 120.

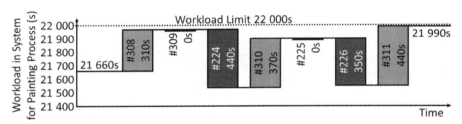

Figure 120: Workload over time while adding and removing cars for the painting process (Image Roser)

6.4.6.3.3 System Entry Tracking All Processes

The same can be done for all processes. We also assumed that besides the current workload already in the system for painting of 21 660 seconds, we have 21 680 seconds of workload for cutting and 17 680 seconds of workload for the assembly process. The assembly process has much less workload, since it is not the bottleneck. The resulting sequence is shown in Figure 121.

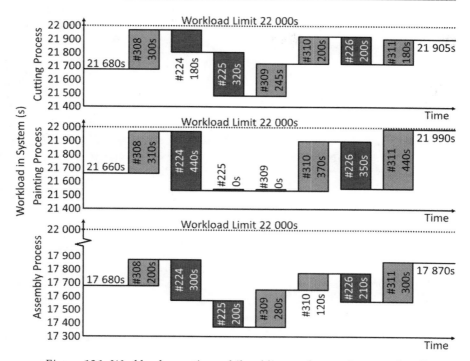

Figure 121: Workload over time while adding and removing cars for all processes (Image Roser)

Please note the slight difference in sequence. If you would look only at the bottleneck, as in Figure 120, car #309 could be started right after car #308. However, if we look at all processes, the cutting process will not have enough available workload to start car #309 right after car #308. The previous cars #224 and #225 have to be completed first before there is enough available workload for the cutting process to start car #309.

Also, note in Figure 121 that the assembly process never even comes close to the workload limit. Hence, you could choose not to track the workload of the assembly process to simplify the management overhead. Of course, if you use an ERP system, the additional tracking effort is negligible.

6.4.7 The Alternative: CONWIP Estimation

Similar to the kanban calculation, I would recommend to use an estimation to determine the number of CONWIP cards. Simply use enough CONWIP cards to make sure it runs smoothly. Then reduce them as needed. If you feel uncertain about the estimate, use the CONWIP formula as a guidance and estimate the different values.

If you encounter repeated problems with low utilization due to insufficient cards, increase the number slightly. If your lead time is too long, remove CONWIP cards or add production capacity. Repeat until you have found the sweet spot in your system. Do not forget to adjust every now and then, especially if your system changes (e.g., due to seasonality, new machines, new products, or other changes). This method works both for flow shops and job shops.

6.5 Advantages

There is one major advantage of CONWIP, and that is its use for make-to-order production. Another advantage on the inventory is claimed, but I am doubtful.

6.5.1 The Big Difference: Number of Variants

Kanban works well with make-to-stock parts. Since every card has a part number permanently associated with the card, the cards always replenish this part number. Of course, this works only if there is a continuous demand for this particular part number.

On the other hand, if you produce make-to-order, a kanban simply will not work. If every product you make is unique, then you would need a unique kanban for this product. But since kanbans are always assigned a part number, this will be difficult.

CONWIP, on the other hand, by default has no part number assigned to the CONWIP card. Hence, any part number can be assigned (temporarily) to the CONWIP card, even if the part is produced only once. Therefore, **CONWIP is well suited for made-to-order production**. You may also force make-to-stock production on CONWIP by managing the backlog accordingly, but this would be inferior to the kanban system. But for make-to-order production, CONWIP is the way to go.

6.5.2 Less Inventory Than Kanban

Mark Spearman claimed that a CONWIP system will have less inventory than a kanban system, since "in a kanban system, there will be generally WIP [...] upstream from the bottleneck [...]. In a CONWIP system, WIP will tend to collect at the bottleneck". I respect Hopp and Spearman very much (e.g. for their excellent book *Factory Physics*[57] and its update, *Factory Physics for Managers: How Leaders Improve Performance in a Post-Lean Six Sigma World*[58]), but here I cannot follow their logic, and bottlenecks are actually one of my key research topics. Hence, I disagree with this statement.

If I understood it correctly, this inventory reduction is due to CONWIP having one big loop compared to kanban often having multiple loops in sequence. One of my master students, Denis Wiesse, analyzed this in detail. He found that indeed having one big loop requires slightly less inventory for the same delivery performance.[59, 60] However, I believe this is only a minor advantage, and other reasons for breaking loops may be more significant. CONWIP could also benefit from multiple smaller loops depending on the circumstance. More on this in Chapter 11.

There is, however, less inventory due to CONWIP ignoring most fluctuations. Yet, this is a general difference between make-to-stock (which aims for a high availability) and make-to-order (which aims for a good trade-off between utilization and lead time).

---

[57] Wallace J. Hopp and Mark L. Spearman, *Factory Physics*, 3rd Edition New York, NY: Waveland, 2011, ISBN 978-1-57766-739-1.

[58] Edward S. Pound, Jeffrey H. Bell, and Mark L. Spearman, *Factory Physics for Managers: How Leaders Improve Performance in a Post-Lean Six Sigma World* New York: McGraw-Hill Education Ltd., 2014, ISBN 978-0-07-182250-3.

[59] Denis Wiesse, *Analyse des Umlaufbestandes von Verbrauchssteuerungen in Abhängigkeit von der Nutzung von Supermärkten und FiFo-Strecken* Master Thesis, Karlsruhe, Germany, Karlsruhe University of Applied Sciences, 2015.

[60] Christoph Roser, *Supermarket vs. FiFo – What Requires Less Inventory?*, in *Collected Blog Posts of AllAboutLean.Com 2016*, Collected Blog Posts of AllAboutLean.Com 4 Offenbach, Germany: AllAboutLean Publishing, 2020, 82–88, ISBN 978-3-96382-016-8.

6.6 Disadvantages

CONWIP also has a few disadvantages, but I believe they can all be managed, and CONWIP is still very well suited for make-to-order production. There is no major disadvantage against CONWIP.

6.6.1 Does Not Manage the Production Sequence Automatically

Kanban automatically manages your production sequence. If you have enough kanbans of each part type, then the kanban system automatically replenishes what is needed. The sequence could be a simple FIFO, or a more complicated sequencing.

CONWIP, on the other hand, needs human input for sequencing. This usually works if the people organizing the backlog know what they are doing. However, this is not always the case. **Bad sequencing can mess up both your process utilization and your lead time and hence your customer satisfaction.** Yet overall, I think the risk is reasonable and can be managed.

The sequencing usually depends on the due dates, often with consideration of the remaining workload. Multiple different methods are used in industry. **If your current sequencing approach seems to work, keep it for the CONWIP system.** Keep an eye out for disruptions and delays in your systems. Also, be aware of the risk of human decisions messing things up.

6.6.2 Uses Quantity Instead of Time to Keep Workload Constant

CONWIP—and for that matter, kanban—both normally use the quantity of parts or jobs to define the inventory limit. This works well if all parts have similar production workload. However, if the parts have very different production workloads, then 500 *quick-and-easy* parts will have a totally different workload for the production system than 500 *hard-as-nuts* parts. Again, this problem is shared by both kanban and CONWIP in its usual form (although there are some workarounds). However, it is possible to modify CONWIP to use workload instead of the number of jobs. You replace the inventory limit with a workload limit. But do not underestimate the additional effort! Ask yourself if the benefit here is worth the effort.

6.6.3 A (Bit) More Work

The CONWIP approach includes a separate sorting of the backlog and matching the backlog with the CONWIP cards. This, of course, is extra work that the kanban system does not have. Additionally, these may be more sources of errors. On the other hand, if you have lots of made-to-order or exotic parts, you cannot use kanban. In this case, a CONWIP despite its larger organizational overhead is quite usable.

6.7 Frequently Asked Questions

6.7.1 When to Return the CONWIP Card?

When exactly should you return the CONWIP card? Good question. The literature does not quite agree on that. Two options seem to be used: Return the last card when the parts are removed for the next process or customer, or return the card as soon as the last process is completed. This is visualized in Figure 122.

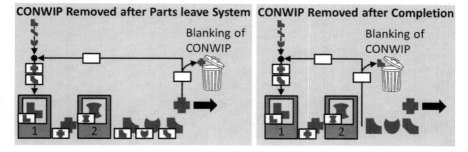

Figure 122: Two options on when to return a CONWIP card, when part leaves the system or when part is completed (Image Roser)

Spearman writes, "When the container is used at the end of the line, the card is removed and sent back to the beginning". Others say to send the card back as soon as the last process is finished. Both are feasible approaches.

The goal of kanban is to always have enough inventory in the supermarket. The kanban is sent back only after the part leaves the supermarket. This prevents overproduction. The goal of CONWIP is different. The goal of

CONWIP is to have a good trade-off between process utilization and lead time. The limit on the number of CONWIP cards is less to reduce finished-goods inventory, and more to avoid overcrowding of the production system. Since the production is make-to-order, the customer is probably already waiting for the product, and there is usually little finished-goods inventory. Hence, it makes sense to **send the CONWIP card back as soon as the item is completed**. Otherwise, accumulated finished goods may bind CONWIP cards, and the production system may not have enough jobs released due to a lack of CONWIP cards returning to the system entry point.

However, **it is also possible to keep the CONWIP card with the item until it actually leaves the system**. In most cases, the completed product will leave the system shortly after completion anyway, since the customer is probably eagerly waiting for the goods. In the event of an accumulation of finished goods, the problem can be mitigated by having a few extra CONWIP cards in the system.

The advantage of this approach is that it is **the same rule as for kanban**. Remove the card before the part leaves the system. Operators are less likely to mix up the rules if the rules for kanban and CONWIP are the same. This is especially true for a mixed system, but also for separate kanban and CONWIP systems on the same shop floor.

I have a **slight preference for releasing the CONWIP card as soon as the product is completed**, unless storage space is critical. In both cases, you have to keep an eye out for finished goods. If your finished-goods inventory increases despite being make-to-order CONWIP production, something is amiss with your customer. Check why your customer does not take your make-to-order products off your hands, then resolve this problem.

6.7.2 When Should the Line Run?

One question that is sometimes asked is when a CONWIP line should run. The answer is similar to other lines and does not depend on the control system (CONWIP, kanban, ERP, etc.). The production capacity of the line should match the customer demand as much as possible. If your customer demand is not so high, you may run the line less (fewer shifts, days, or hours). If your customer demand exceeds the line capacity, the line should run as much as possible (while still allowing time for maintenance and changeovers, etc.), even if you cannot fulfill the demand.

In any case, if there is no demand (i.e., if there are no customer orders), the line should stop. Particular to make-to-order is also the case if the first item in the backlog sequence is due only too far in the future. In this case, you also should stop the line. For example, if you have already produced all the parts for the next four weeks, do you really need to start with parts for five weeks ahead of time? Depending on your system, producing too far in advance may increase your finished-goods inventory and subsequently increase cost.

6.7.3 Does It Work for Job Shops?

Kanban works well for flow shops, where the material flow is clearly defined. Kanban may be more difficult for job shops, where the material flow is often irregular. As for CONWIP, Spearman et al. state that CONWIP does not work for job shops. I believe this to be incorrect, and **CONWIP will also work for job shops**, even though it is much easier for flow shops.

Regardless of whether in a flow shop or job shop, you would need to make sure all parts leaving the system will return their CONWIP card. Similarly, all open jobs have to wait in the backlog for a new CONWIP card.

Since the CONWIP cards may have a time of entry written on them, every process in the job shop knows which part waiting for the process is the oldest. **At every process, the next part to be produced should be the one with the oldest system entry time**, not the part that arrived at this particular process first. This improves the likelihood of meeting your deadlines. Hence, all products are much more likely to have similar throughput times through the entire system. After all, a balanced throughput time makes for overall smoother processing. It also increases the likelihood that the customer will get their goods on time.

There may have to be more CONWIP cards to ensure the job shop does not run out of work. Due to network effects, job shops may have neither their inventory nor their individual process workload distributed equally. Depending on the variable product mix, the busiest process (the bottleneck) will change. Additional CONWIP cards will buffer these changes and increase throughput, although at the cost of extra inventory and increased lead time. Find a trade-off between throughput and inventory, but in a job shop slightly more cards will probably make production smoother. Finally, just as with every other job shop, managing the process sequence and process utilization is a challenge. Nevertheless, CONWIP also works for job shops.

6.7.4 How Should I Handle Canceled Jobs?

In some very rare instances, it may happen that a job that is already released for production is canceled. Maybe the customer went bankrupt. Maybe the laws have changed and the product is no longer legal. Hopefully, it does not happen too often, but it can happen. In this case, the job is canceled, unused parts are returned to storage, and already completed components may be taken apart for their parts.

6.7.5 Can I Use CONWIP for Make-to-Stock Production?

In theory, it is possible to use CONWIP also for make-to-stock production. However, there are some problems that make this approach flawed.

In make-to-stock production using kanban or reorder points, the inventory for every part number is tracked separately. Every part has its own target limit. This is actually the big benefit of pull in make-to-stock production: You can treat every part type individually, and every part type has its own individual inventory limit in pull.

In make-to-order production like CONWIP and POLCA, however, every part is different. Hence, it is very cumbersome to treat them differently. In most cases, having an upper limit for all parts combined is much easier. Therefore, the inventory (or workload) is limited for all part numbers combined.

If you use **CONWIP with separate limits for every make-to-stock part number**, then CONWIP is identical to kanban, but with extra management effort for removing or adding the information. Hence, it is better to use kanban instead of CONWIP.

If you use **CONWIP with a combined limit for every make-to-stock part number**, then there is the risk of excess material for one part number on stock, limiting the available CONWIP cards for the other part numbers. You would have to prioritize the production queue very carefully to avoid excess inventory of some parts. In the worst case, you could end up with a warehouse full of obsolete parts taking up all the CONWIP cards, and all other parts are in short supply due to a lack of CONWIP cards going around the loop. This is not a theoretical example, but has happened. Hence, **do not use a combined upper inventory limit for different make-to-order parts!** Therefore, CONWIP is also not suitable for a combined limit for every make-to-stock part number.

Chapter 7
POLCA

POLCA stands for "paired-cell overlapping loops of cards with authorization" and was developed by Rajan Suri around 1990. It is designed for low-volume-high-mix production and intended for job shops. There is simply no good solution for job shops, but CONWIP and POLCA are often good enough. It depends very much on the specifics of your system if POLCA or CONWIP is better, and even that is difficult to determine beforehand. Hence, POLCA is a valid option to control job shops.

Please believe me, I have not come to this conclusion lightly, and changed my opinion a few times. However, now I believe that POLCA can work. If you go the POLCA route, I recommend the book by Rajan Suri from 2018 *The Practitioner's Guide to POLCA.* [61] It contains more information and

---

[61] Rajan Suri, *The Practitioner's Guide to POLCA: The Production Control System for High-Mix, Low-Volume and Custom Products* Productivity Press, 2018, ISBN 978-1-138-21064-6.

updates compared to his 1998 book.[62] It also contains details for designing and implementing a POLCA system. But first, let me explain to you how POLCA works.[63]

7.1 Fundamentals

POLCA is designed for make-to-order job shops, systems of work centers, or systems of cellular manufacturing of low-volume-high-mix or customized parts. Different jobs have different paths from one process to another process. Between each possible pair of processes or cells, POLCA establishes a loop similar to a CONWIP loop. Like CONWIP, the POLCA card is only temporarily assigned to a certain part or job and is blank on the return trip. As the word *overlapping* implies, these **loops are overlapping**. Different from CONWIP, **every possible pair of process sequences has their own POLCA loop**.

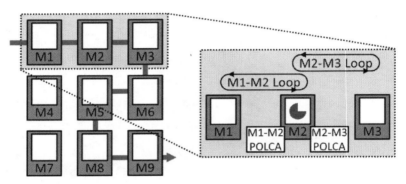

Figure 123: Illustration of the overlap of two POLCA loops spanning three processes within a job shop (Image Roser)

A simple example is shown in Figure 123. A product within a larger job shop moves from process M1 to M2. Afterwards, it will go to M3. There is one POLCA loop between the processes M1 and M2; and another loop between the processes M2 and M3. Coming from M1 to M2, the product had the M1–M2 POLCA card attached to it. However, process M2 can only

---

[62] Rajan Suri, *Quick Response Manufacturing: A Companywide Approach to Reducing Lead Times* Portland, Oregon, USA: Taylor & Francis Inc, 1998, ISBN 978-1-56327-201-1.

[63] Many thanks to Rajan Suri for his input to this book regarding POLCA.

start working if two conditions are met. Suri calls these conditions and the surrounding process "decision time", and they are explained in more detail in Chapter 7.3.4.

The current process needs a free POLCA card from a subsequent process before the start of the processing: Very similar to CONWIP, process M2 cannot start the work without a free POLCA card. This POLCA card must be from a subsequent process where the part would go next. In our example in Figure 123, the job would go to process M3 next, and hence would need a free M2–M3 POLCA at process M2. You could have more than one possible subsequent process. For example, the part could be processed on any of three identical processes next. In this case, process M2 needs one free POLCA card from any of these possible processes. Assigning a card to the part defines the corresponding next process.

The job release date for the product on the current process must have passed before the start of the processing: All jobs passing through the job shop have a job release date for each process. A part cannot be processed earlier than the job release date. The job release date is usually determined using ERP software. The goal is to ensure that the product is completed before the customer due date but does not sit around completed for weeks before the customer needs it. Determining the job release date typically involves a lot of uncertainty and significant time safety buffers.

Once the product at M2 is completed, the M1–M2 POLCA card goes back to M1 to permit the processing of the next product at M1. The M2–M3 card goes with the product to process M3. Each POLCA loop can have multiple POLCA cards.

You need a POLCA loop between every pair of processes and for every direction where material can flow. For example, if material can flow from a milling machine to a lathe, you would need a POLCA loop. If the part can also flow reverse from the lathe to milling, you would need a second POLCA loop for the other direction. It is necessary to provide all expected material flows between two processes with POLCA loops.

In the original literature [64] , POLCA supposedly works only with manufacturing cells. As described in more recent literature[65], it would work for any general job shop with multiple machines or processes. It would even work for a larger system where different processes are grouped together. It is feasible but far inferior to use POLCA for flow shops. POLCA is not really helpful for make-to-stock production.

POLCA is sometimes called a push-pull hybrid. While in my opinion the inventor uses an incorrect definition of pull in his book, POLCA is a pull system. The number of POLCA cards limit the inventory between two processes to a target limit. POLCA cards also signal the release of the next job. Since the system has both a limit on the inventory and a subsequent signal to release the next job, it is a pull system.

7.2 Variants

There are not any variants for POLCA that I know of. It is possible, however, to include small segments of linear production sequence similar to a flow shop within the POLCA loops. An example is visualized in Figure 124, where process M2 is actually a small flow shop with three sub-processes M2.1, M2.2, and M2.3 connected using FIFO. Similar examples can also be done with nonlinear groups of processes, although the routing of the part through this process group needs to be coordinated.

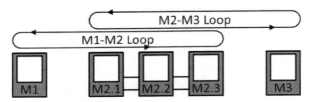

Figure 124: Overlapping POLCA loops including linear segments (Image Roser)

---

[64] Rajan Suri, *Quick Response Manufacturing: A Companywide Approach to Reducing Lead Times* Portland, Oregon, USA: Taylor & Francis Inc, 1998, ISBN 978-1-56327-201-1.

[65] Rajan Suri, *The Practitioner's Guide to POLCA: The Production Control System for High-Mix, Low-Volume and Custom Products* Productivity Press, 2018, ISBN 978-1-138-21064-6.

7.3 Elements

A system using POLCA needs three elements for control: POLCA cards, a backlog of open jobs, and an overview of the job release time.

7.3.1 POLCA Card

Similar to CONWIP, there are POLCA cards. There is little information needed on a POLCA card. Most important are the **source process** and the **destination process**. For management it is helpful to know the **index number of the card** in the loop and the **total number of cards** in the loop. A **barcode** can also help, as does color coding. An example is shown in Figure 125. It is possible to make the POLCA card as a folder or cover similar to CONWIP so it can contain information to the current job as for example the work order or technical drawings. Alternatively, it is possible to pin or clip the POLCA card to the work order, as long as it is clearly visible.

Figure 125: Example of a POLCA card (Image Roser)

Please note that this card represents one job, which is not necessarily only one part. A POLCA card can also be used for batches of material. If your batches get too large, however, you may use multiple POLCA cards for large batches.

For larger systems, it may be better to implement these cards virtually in an ERP or similar computer system, where a computer keeps track of the cards as well as the release dates. However, this also makes it less visual and more sensitive to computer problems.

7.3.2 Backlog of Open Jobs

At the beginning of each POLCA loop is a backlog of open jobs.[66] Each loop and hence each process has its own backlog. This backlog includes partially completed jobs from previous processes that have a POLCA card from the previous loop attached. It also includes jobs for which this process is the first process in the sequence. These do not have a POLCA card attached. Hence, you can find jobs both with and without POLCA cards in the backlog.

Except for some jobs having cards attached, this is similar to the backlog of open jobs in CONWIP. These open jobs should have the **material available,** or it should be expected that the material arrives in time during production. Similar to CONWIP, this list should be **prioritized**. Especially the jobs whose workload covers the time until the next prioritization should have a clear, prioritized sequence.

Different from CONWIP is that each job should have a sequence of **job release dates** for each process that the job has to pass through. Depending on the granularity of the system, these job release dates may also include a time. Often, the job release date is also the priority for the backlog of open jobs. An open job with an earlier job release date automatically takes priority over a later job release date. However, other sequencing priorities can also be used.[67]

7.3.3 Job Release Date

The job release date[68] is a date and possibly a time for each process of a job. The job cannot be started earlier than this job release date. Figure 126 shows an example of a job release date sequence. The first process can start on

---

[66] In the original literature, these are called list of open orders, but I have renamed them here for consistency with other pull system.

[67] Matthias Thürer, Nuno O. Fernandes, and Mark Stevenson, *Material Flow Control in High-Variety Make-to-Order Shops: Combining COBACABANA and POLCA, Production and Operations Management* 29, no. 9 2020: 2138–52.

[68] In the original literature, this is called order release date, but it is renamed here for consistency.

January 19 at the earliest. All six processes in the sequence have their own job release date.

Job Release Date Part 4711		
#	Process	Date
1	Cutting of Stock	19.01
2	Milling	20.01
3	Lathe	21.01
4	Tempering	23.01
5	Coating	26.01
6	Final Assembly	28.01
Customer Due Date 03.02		

Figure 126: Example of a POLCA job release date sequence (Image Roser)

The calculation of the job release date aims to have each item released so it is completed in time for the end customer deadline. At the same time, the release date should not be too early to avoid excess finished and work-in-process material clogging up the system. Such a calculation in a typical job shop has usually large uncertainties, and it is highly advisable to err on the side of caution for an earlier date. Hence, **the job release dates usually include time buffers**.

Please note that not every process needs a worst-case time buffer, since it is unlikely that every process encounters a worst-case scenario. However, please also note that the responsible people for every department often tend to give a worst-case duration if asked. It helps to clarify that these are not deadlines, but starting times. Furthermore, it is often sensible to have a larger time buffer at the end instead of many small time buffers in between.

Calculating the job release dates for a larger number of jobs with multiple processes can be time consuming. On a modern shop floor, this is often done through an overarching ERP system, although this includes the risk of undetected errors within the system.

7.3.4 Decision Time

The operator at the process has to make a few decisions to determine if and which part to process next. Suri calls this the "decision time". These rules are also shown in the flowchart in Figure 127 and explained below.

- At the beginning, the operator should **check if there are any available open jobs in the backlog of open jobs** for the operator's cell or machine where the job release time has passed. If there are no open jobs left that can be done, the operator should find work at another process or cell. This may involve a supervisor assigning the operator to a new task. The supervisor also decides when to move the operator back to the initial process. Other possible work may include training, improving the system (maintenance, cleaning, fixing smaller problems, changeover optimization...), or any other task that benefits the system.
- The operator **takes the highest-priority available job**.
- The operator **checks if there is the right POLCA card available from the subsequent process** that allows starting the job, or it is the last process for this job. If not, the operator repeats the process with the next open job. Please note that the last process in the process sequence has no subsequent process, and can be started with no subsequent POLCA card.
- The operator **checks if all the required material is available** to start the job. If material is missing, the operator repeats the process with the next open job attached.
- After the operator finds a feasible job, the operator **attaches the subsequent POLCA card to the job**. Again, the exception is if it is the last process in the sequence.
- Next, the operator **processes the job**.
- After completion of the job, the operator **returns the POLCA card of the previous loop** to the previous process to release more jobs. The exception here is the first process in the sequence, where the part has no preceding process and hence no preceding POLCA card.
- The operator then **moves the job with the subsequent POLCA card to the next station**.
- Having completed an entire POLCA cycle, the operator **repeats the cycle** by looking for open jobs. If there is no more work for this process, the operator moves to another process to continue working.

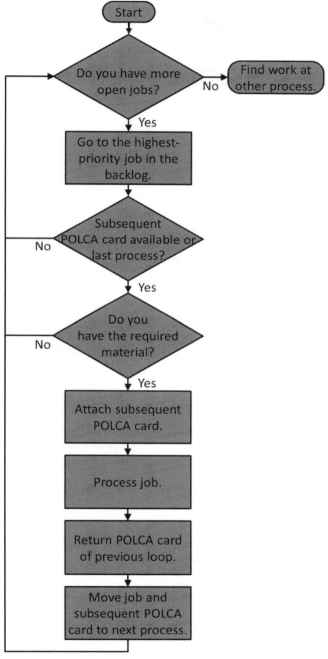

Figure 127: Sequence of the rules for POLCA "decision time" (Image Roser)

7.4 Calculation

Similar to CONWIP, **the calculation of the number of POLCA cards is a trade-off between the utilization and the lead time**. Also similar, you can estimate the number of cards. In any case, you should verify the number of cards afterward.

7.4.1 The POLCA Calculation

The equation used by Suri to calculate the number of POLCA cards has evolved over time. Similar to kanban and CONWIP, they also have a lot of assumptions and uncertainties. The underlying approach is also based on the replenishment time divided by the customer takt, with some additional safety similar to Equation 14.

The replenishment time is the sum of the lead time and the information transport time. In the original literature, the **lead time** is calculated as the sum of the processing time and waiting times at both the first and the second process in the POLCA loop, and the transport in between. The easiest way to calculate this is Little's law, which was presented already in Equation 8. The time at the first process is the number of jobs waiting or in processing at the first process multiplied by the average time per job at the first process (the takt time). Similarly, the time at the second process is the number of jobs waiting or in processing at the second process multiplied by the average time per part at the second process. Add an estimate of the transportation time, which is probably much less than the processing times, and you have the lead time.

The **information transport time** is the time it takes for the POLCA card to return to the first process after the part is completed at the second process, including organizational delays. Both the lead time and the information transport time are measured in time units.

The **safety factor** is added as a number of cards. Often, this is simply rounding up the value of the replenishment time divided by the customer takt. Keep in mind that unlike make-to-stock systems like kanban, you do not need much safety for make-to-order systems like POLCA or CONWIP. Similar to other calculations, there may be specific situations in your production system that cause additional delays to the replenishment time. In this case, you would have to include these **other elements** in the calculation. Keep in mind that since this is a make-to-order system, **we are interested in the averages rather than the worst case.** Furthermore, feel free to ignore anything that is insignificant compared to the other elements.

Table 18 summarizes the elements for the POLCA calculation. The formula for the POLCA calculation is shown in Equation 30. The number of POLCA cards equals the sum of the lead time and the information transport time divided by the takt time across all parts, plus some safety:

Group	Element	Unit	Usually Relevant?	Variable
Replenishment Time	Lead Time	Time	Yes	LT
	Information Transport Time	Time	Maybe	TI
Other	Safety Factor	Cards	No	S
	Other Elements	???	No	n/a

Table 18: Overview of variables contributing to the number of POLCA cards

$$NC_{POLCA} = \frac{LT + TI}{TT_{All}} + S$$

Equation 30: Calculating the number of POLCA cards

The variables for Equation 30 are as follows, under the assumption that one job represents one POLCA card:

LT   Lead time (time)
NC_{POLCA} Number of POLCA cards (card quantity)
S   Safety factor (card quantity)
TI   Time for the transport of information (time)
TT_{All} Customer takt across all part types (time per job)

7.4.2 How Important Is This Equation?

Maybe now you are thinking about how to calculate this for your case. Don't worry too much about it. While I think the equation is not wrong, I also believe that a good estimation will give a similar performance.

The equation is based on the current lead times. The underlying assumption is that the current system is—while maybe not as good as you want it—at least a functional system. Hence, **if you base your calculations on a** functional system, you probably get a functional number of POLCA cards. A trade-off between lead time and throughput happened probably somewhat automatically by your people trying to make the system work. Therefore, the POLCA calculation is probably not worse than what you have currently anyway. And Rajan Suri makes it very clear (and I agree) that this calculation is only an initial number that has to be refined by looking at how the system actually works. Nevertheless, I prefer to estimate the number of POLCA cards based on the information I have in the system.

7.4.3 Example POLCA Calculation

This example is loosely based on the example by Suri.[69] It looks at a single loop with two processes, P1 and P2, which are part of a bigger sequence of loops, as shown in Figure 128. The first process P1 has on average a lead time of 24 hours, and the second process of 8 hours, although there are significant fluctuations. Transport between process P1 and P2 takes on average 2 hours, again with some fluctuations. The free POLCA cards are transported back every 4 hours. The expected demand is 40 jobs per month with 20 workdays per month and 8 hours per day.

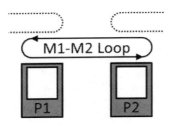

Figure 128: Example loop for the calculation of POLCA cards (Image Roser)

Based on this, we can calculate the **customer takt**. Twenty days per month with 8 hours per day gives 160 working hours per month. Since we will use hours as the basis of the subsequent calculation, we keep this unit also in hours. Dividing 160 hours by 40 jobs gives a customer takt of 4 hours per job. The **lead time** is simply the sum of the individual lead times of 24 hours for process A and 8 hours for process B, plus 2 hours for the material

[69]   Rajan Suri, *The Practitioner's Guide to POLCA: The Production Control System for High-Mix, Low-Volume and Custom Products* Productivity Press, 2018, ISBN 978-1-138-21064-6.

transport. This gives a total of 34 hours of lead time. The **information transport time** would be 4 hours in the worst case, but this will give an average information transport time of 2 hours. An overview of this data is given in Table 19.

Element	Unit	Value	Variable
Lead Time	Hours	34	LT
Information Transport Time	Hours	2	TI

Table 19: Elements for the POLCA calculation example, not yet including safety

Dividing the sum of these times of 36 hours by the customer takt gives us exactly nine POLCA cards plus safety, as shown in Equation 31. We could add a safety and round up to ten POLCA cards, but we may as well keep it at nine cards to maintain a better overall system lead time.

$$NC_{POLCA} = \frac{LT + TI}{TT_{All}} + S = \frac{34h + 2h}{4\frac{h}{job}} + S = 9 + S$$

Equation 31: Example calculation of the number of POLCA cards for one loop

7.4.4 POLCA Estimation

As explained above, the calculation above takes the inventory, converts it to a lead time, and converts it back to the number of POLCA cards (a representation of inventory), plus some optional safety and transport factors. An alternative and less mathematical approach is to simply look at the current inventory in the loop, and transform it into a number of POLCA cards. If one POLCA card represents one product, then you have one POLCA card per product.

Feel free to adjust the number if it makes you or someone familiar with the shop floor feel uncomfortable. **In case of doubt, go with the lower number,** as the instinct on the shop floor is to seek safety in large inventory, ignoring the damaging effect of this on the lead time. Lean manufacturing always tries to nudge you toward less inventory and faster lead times. In summary, don't worry too much about the exact number of POLCA cards. Rather, try it out and adjust based on what you observe in your system.

7.5 Advantages

POLCA does work in industry and has a few advantages for job shops. However, I still think CONWIP is a strong alternative too.

7.5.1 Limits the Inventory

POLCA is good at controlling the inventory. All processes (cells, machines, etc.) are connected using loops with a limited number of POLCA cards. Hence, they can prevent excessive inventory between two cells. If a process is blocked in one direction due to the lack of POLCA cards, it can use the available capacity to make products for another subsequent process that has free POLCA cards available. This allows for a better and also more timely use of the utilization of the different processes. The reduction in inventory also reduces the overall throughput time.

CONWIP systems could be set up across the entire job shop. In this case, it is still possible to accumulate inventory in some parts while others run dry. A POLCA system defines the inventory along every possible step in the value stream, and hence allows for a finer tuning of the inventory, although you could also set up multiple CONWIP loops for a similar effect.

7.5.2 Provides Capacity for All Upstream Processes

You could also limit the inventory at a process with a simple FIFO in front of the processes. However, in this case a single very busy upstream process may block other less busy upstream processes by filling up the FIFO and prohibiting other processes from getting their turn. With the individual loops for each two connected processes, every upstream process gets its shot. In other words, every upstream process has a chance to deliver its goods downstream, and the available capacity downstream is not hogged by a single upstream process.

7.5.3 Overlap Avoids Blocks and Helps Communication

Different from CONWIP, POLCA loops overlap, as shown in Figure 123. Whenever a part is processed in a process or cell, there should be two

POLCA cards attached to it, except for the first and last process in the sequence of processes for a job.

This has two main benefits, and a small disadvantage. First, this overlap helps with positive interactions between the operators of different processes. It avoids the "throw it over the wall" effect. It establishes a meaningful customer-supplier relationship between these processes. Operators will have a deeper understanding of the interaction between processes. They also can help each other out if a process starts to clog up with jobs, which also increases goodwill among the operators. This was actually not initially considered when POLCA was developed, but numerous operators gave feedback that this was very helpful and improved the cooperation.

Second, it avoids blocking, which otherwise is a permanent worry in job shops. Let's take a simple example of three processes, as shown in Figure 129, once without an overlap as it would be done with CONWIP, and once with an overlap in POLCA. There are two part types, circle segments, and crosses. Process M1 handles both processes. Afterwards the path splits, with the circle segments going to M2 and the crosses to M3.

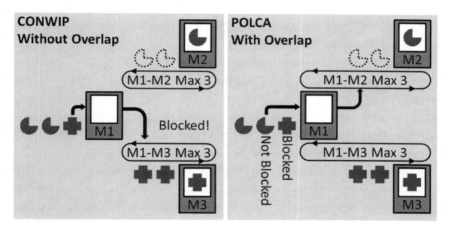

Figure 129: Comparison of CONWIP without overlap and POLCA with overlap (Image Roser)

Assume that there is a problem at M3. The entire CONWIP loop at M3 is full with crosses. Without the overlap, M1 would not know this, and would process the next part in line, which happens to be also a cross. However, afterwards it could not move the cross forward, and M1 would be blocked, as shown in Figure 129 on the left. In reality, this would often lead to chaotic shifting of jobs to get the processes moving again, requiring extra management effort.

POLCA avoids this through the overlap. Assume the same situation, but this time with an overlap, as shown on the right in Figure 129. Before starting the cross, M1 would have to check for an available subsequent POLCA card. Since no M1–M3 card is available at M1 for a cross, process M1 would check the next part. There is an M1–M2 card available for the circle segment, and hence this part is processed. Therefore, this overlap avoids the all-too-common blocking situations and resulting chaotic shifting around in job shops.

A minor worry of mine is that sometimes having two cards (during processing) and sometimes one card (whenever not processing) attached to the part may be a bit more confusing. However, overall the overlap is beneficial to the flow of material in job shops.

7.6 Disadvantages

There are a few issues with POLCA. None of them is a deal breaker, at least not for all production systems. And many of these issues are shared with other ways to manage job shops.

7.6.1 A Bit of Complexity

The method with its multiple overlapping loops of POLCA cards can be complex. The POLCA loops have to cover every possible path that a product can take. If it goes from one process to another, you need a loop. If it goes back, you need a second loop. In its extreme, it would need two loops between every possible process combination. Figure 130 shows an example with a maximum of thirty possible loops for six processes.

However, in actual application this seems to be manageable, and real-life systems have much fewer loops than the maximum possible. In any case, there are numerous reports from shop floors that POLCA works.

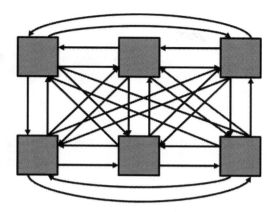

Figure 130: All thirty possible POLCA loops for six processes (Image Roser)

7.6.2 Accuracy of the Job Release Date

One requirement of POLCA is that every job has a job release date for every process it has to be processed on (and more, if it visits a process twice).

This will be very difficult to calculate. I have worked with job shops before, and it is quite difficult to determine the job release date for the first process, much less for every process along the line. Job shops are notoriously difficult to plan, and suffer from the butterfly effect, where a small random event can have a big impact. On the other hand, all control systems have similar problems in job shops, so this is also not a big handicap. It depends how much effort you need to determine these times and to get them to the people that need to know them. Regardless of the approach, it is common in industry to include a generous time buffer when promising delivery dates to the customer.

7.6.3 Possible Deadlocks

A POLCA system can in some rare cases cause a deadlock, where a combination of jobs and POLCA cards can cause processes to block each other. Figure 131 shows a simplified example, where M1 cannot continue without an M1–M2 POLCA card. All M1–M2 POLCA cards, however, are at M2, which cannot continue without an M2–M1 POLCA card. However, these cards are all at M1. A deadlock ensues, and neither process can continue.

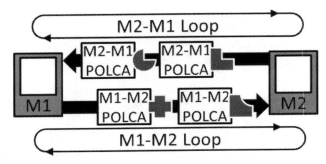

Figure 131: Unlikely but theoretically possible example of a block in POLCA (Image Roser)

It seems, however, that this happens very seldomly. It can happen only if the POLCA loops form a circle (i.e., following the loops you may eventually come back to the starting process, as in the image above from M1 to M2 and back to M1). According to Suri, this has happened only in simulations, but not yet in reality. Suri also developed a solution using a "cycle card". This is not a regular POLCA card that goes back and forth, but a card that always goes forward along the processes in the loop. Details are in Chapter 6: Preventing Gridlock When Loops Form Cycles in *The Practitioner's Guide to POLCA*.[70]

7.6.4 Overloading or Low Utilization

POLCA tries to balance the workload within the production system and tries to prevent overloading of a process—which is a worthy goal. However, it is easy to imagine situations where this breaks down. Take the example shown in Figure 132. Four processes (M1–M4) feed two other processes (M5 and M6). Hence, both M5 and M6 can receive work from multiple processes.

It is possible that there is temporarily a lot of work for M5 and none for M6. Hence, M5 would be overloaded, and M6 would be idle. The actual maximum inventory in each loop would be limited by the POLCA card, but multiple loops with a number of POLCA cards each can add up to a lot of material. In the example there are four loops arriving at M5, each with five POLCA cards, putting a whopping twenty products at M5 for production.

---

[70] Rajan Suri, *The Practitioner's Guide to POLCA: The Production Control System for High-Mix, Low-Volume and Custom Products* Productivity Press, 2018, ISBN 978-1-138-21064-6.

At the same time, M6 would starve for work. While planning aims to avoid such situations, short-term fluctuations can still cause such an effect.

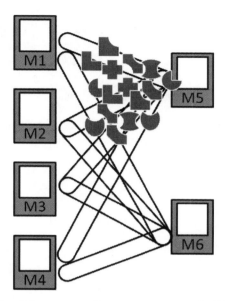

Figure 132: Possible overcrowding on one process in POLCA (Image Roser)

While this is an extreme example, similar situations can happen. But then, they can also happen with other job shop control systems. Again, any kind of planning in a job shop is difficult and failure-prone.

7.6.5 Reduced Flexibility

POLCA requires a job release date for every process the part has to go through. This usually means that the production sequence has to be fixed beforehand. This reduces flexibility.

In my experience, many job shops have alternative processes available. A part could be processed on process 1 *or* process 2. I also have experienced rerouting in job shops if one process is overloaded and another one is available. While not ideal, in a chaotic job shop it sometimes makes sense. For POLCA, however, it would require quite a bit of recalculation and rearrangement. Have a look at the overloading example from Figure 132 again. Do all parts have to go through M5? Or did a system quirk merely schedule all parts for M5 and none for M6?

7.7 Frequently Asked Questions

7.7.1 What About the First Process in Sequence?

A part in a process always has two POLCA cards attached, one from the loop from the preceding process, and one from the loop to the succeeding process. The only exceptions are the first and the last process. The first process in a process sequence needs a valid open job (i.e., a job that has the required material or expects it to arrive on time), and which job release date has passed. It also needs a POLCA card from the loop to the second process. Hence, the process can work on a part that has only one POLCA card attached from the subsequent process. This is shown in Figure 133.

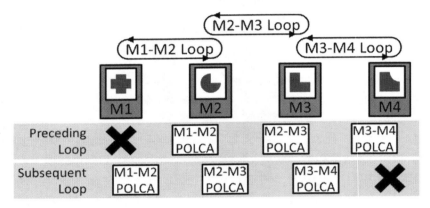

Figure 133: The first process and the last process in a POLCA workflow need only one POLCA card to work. (Image Roser)

7.7.2 What About the Last Process in Sequence?

Similar to the first process, the last process in the sequence does not feed into another loop. Hence, the part has only a POLCA card from the preceding loop attached.

Since the system is a job shop, the first and the last process may be different for every product produced. It is usually not the same process for the entry and exit of the part into the system. Hence, while processes usually have two POLCA cards for each part under processing, they occasionally have only one POLCA card if it is the first or last process in the sequence for this job. This is also shown in Figure 133.

Chapter 8
Reorder Point

Yet another way to establish a pull system is to use a reorder point. Okay, now you may be surprised. You may have heard about reorder point before, but maybe never in relation to lean manufacturing. Reorder systems are not really a part of the conventional lean toolset, but they are pull systems.[71] It is particularly useful for ship-to-stock situations. The system reorders to reach an inventory limit. Reordering happens either periodically with the reorder period method, or—better—when the inventory reaches a minimum at the reorder point method.

8.1 Fundamentals

The reorder point approach is simple. You track your inventory, separately for every part. **Whenever your inventory for a part type falls below a**

---

[71] Except the abominable fixed time fixed quantity approach, which, fortunately, I have never seen implemented in reality.

lower limit (the reorder point), you reorder to fill up the inventory again to the maximum (the inventory limit).

The reorder point is also sometimes called the *minimum*. Please do not confuse this with the similar-named minimum in a supermarket, as described in Chapter 5.3.2.2. The kanban supermarket minimum results in emergency actions to prevent a stock-out, and is reached only seldomly. The reorder point is reached regularly. You do not want to have chaotic firefighting with every order. Instead, you want to order without time pressure using the normal ordering processes.

Hence, the reorder point should reliably give you enough time to reorder. If your delivery time is zero, you could theoretically set the reorder point to zero parts too. However, in reality there is an order delay, and the reorder point has to be above zero. An idealized system with no delivery delay but still with a reorder point above zero is shown in Figure 134.

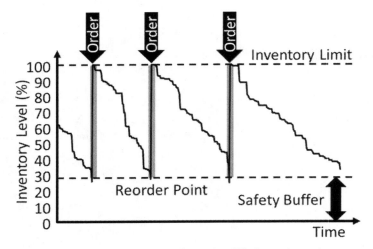

Figure 134: Inventory over time for a simplified reorder point system with no delay for the delivery of an order (Image Roser)

However, since in most cases your delivery time is NOT zero, it would be wise to order more parts before you run out. Hence, the reorder point is usually not zero. This delay is visualized in Figure 135. See how close the actual inventory sometimes gets to being empty. This would actually be too close for my comfort, and I would raise the reorder point a bit.

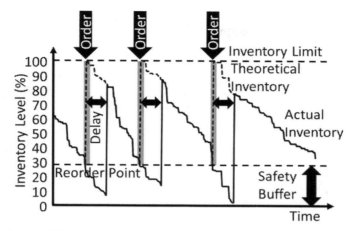

Figure 135: Inventory over time for a reorder point system with a delivery delay (Image Roser)

Please note that you have to track the theoretical inventory (i.e., the combined inventory that is already available or ordered). If this theoretical inventory falls below the reorder point, an order is issued. The actual inventory may drop even further during the delivery delay. However, do not order even more just because your physical inventory is still below the reorder point. Otherwise, you will get multiple orders a bit later and your inventory will exceed the inventory limit. Only **the sum of the physically available inventory and the ordered-but-not-yet-arrived inventory is relevant**.

The reorder point is very similar to a triangle kanban, as described in Chapter 5.2.3. You reorder only if you reach the reorder point. **The reorder point is based on the worst-case expected consumption during the delay between issuing the order and having the ordered items ready for use.**

The delta between the reorder point and the inventory limit depends on how often you want to order or how many items you want to order in one order. The delta could be as little as zero, in which case you order one part whenever one part is consumed. The inventory limit equals the reorder point. Every time you order one item, you drop below your reorder point and reorder one item back to the inventory limit. This system now behaves like a kanban system.

In most cases, however, this delta is much larger to reduce the frequency of orders. But please be aware that **infrequent and large orders increase both your inventory and your fluctuations**.

The difference between a larger and a smaller inventory limit is visualized in Figure 136. The left graph has an inventory limit of 100 and a reorder point at 30. This generated three orders in this example. The right graph has the same customer demand, but the inventory limit is now half of the previous. The reorder point remains at 30. Effectively, the delta was reduced from 70 (inventory limit of 100 minus reorder point at 30) to 20 (inventory limit of 50 minus reorder point at 30). The number of orders increased to 12. Hence, this reduction of the delta to approximately one-quarter resulted in an approximately fourfold increase in the number of orders.

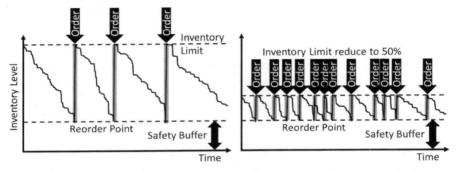

Figure 136: Inventory over time for a large and a small inventory limit (Image Roser)

More generally, **a decrease in the delta between the reorder point and the inventory limit leads to a proportional increase in the number of orders and a reduction in inventory**. Reorder points are often used for purchasing or logistics. They may also be used in manufacturing, especially for systems with large changeover times. In other manufacturing systems, however, frequent and small orders are recommended to better match the production of smaller lot sizes.

8.2 Variants

There are a couple of variants of the reorder point approach. The original reorder point method is usually the best, although the reorder period method can also be used if you want to order regularly.

8.2.1 Reorder Periods

Similar to reorder points, it is possible to have reorder periods. With reorder points, you filled up your inventory to the target limit when you reached a lower limit. **With reorder periods, you reorder every fixed time interval,** as shown in Figure 137.

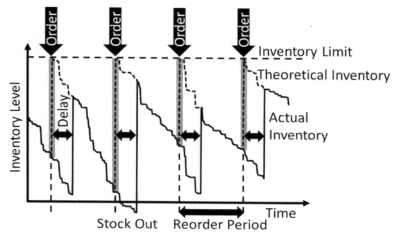

Figure 137: Inventory over time for a reorder period system. There is a stock-out after the second order. (Image Roser)

For example, every Tuesday you order enough parts to fill up your inventory to the maximum inventory limit. This makes ordering easier and more regular, and it is easier to manage your ordering process since you can distribute your orders for different parts over time. In other words, on Mondays you reorder all parts of category A, on Tuesdays you reorder category B, and so on.

Please do not confuse this benefit with the human tendency to prefer ordering at the end of the week, month, or year. If everybody does this, it will again create problems for suppliers. Within some suppliers it is well known that customer orders always peak at the end of the month, making it difficult to run a lean production.

Reorder point methods can always order a similar quantity. Reorder period methods have **a different quantity with each order.** Reorder periods also **require higher quantities of inventory** to avoid a stock-out while still risking a stock-out. If the demand within an order period exceeds the inventory, you will run out of stock. This also happened after the second order in Figure 137. Reorder points react faster. With reorder periods, you react only at given fixed intervals. Hence, reorder points are usually the smarter approach.

8.2.2 Reorder Point and Period Combination

It is possible to combine the reorder point and reorder period into one system. Most orders would follow the reorder period approach and happen regularly. Only if excessive demand causes the theoretical inventory to reach the reorder point is an additional order created following the reorder point method, as shown in Figure 138.

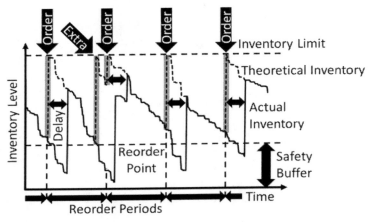

Figure 138: Inventory over time for a combined reorder point and period system. There is an additional order between the first and the second period due to reaching the reorder point. (Image Roser)

This allows you to still have the (marginal) benefit of regular orders of the reorder period, with the safeguard of the reorder point if the customer orders more than usual. However, in my opinion, the benefit is not worth the additional effort.

8.2.3 Fixed-Time, Fixed-Quantity Reorder (Not a Pull System!)

For completeness' sake, I would like to point out yet another variant that is associated with reorder systems. In this method you order at fixed intervals similar to reorder periods, but you **always order the same quantity**. No matter if the customer ordered a lot or only a little, you order the same quantity every interval, as shown in Figure 139. **This is very inflexible! This is a terrible system! It is also not pull, since the inventory can grow very large or shrink to zero over time. I strongly advise you against this method!**

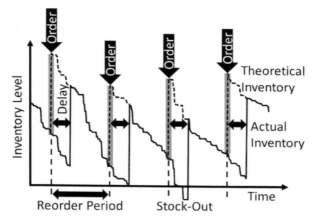

Figure 139: Inventory over time for a fixed-time, fixed-quantity reorder approach. I strongly advise you not to use this! (Image Roser)

8.3 Elements

The reorder systems have very few elements that need to be determined. You need to determine your **inventory limit** (maximum inventory). You need to determine your **reorder point** (minimum inventory) for the reorder point method. And, if you go for a method that uses a reorder period, you will need to decide the **duration of the reorder period**.

Other than that, you just have your normal inventory and ordering processes that need to be tracked. ERP systems are very well suited to assist with such tasks. If you trust the ERP system enough, you can even have the ERP system order more parts automatically.

8.4 Calculation

For the reorder point method, we need to calculate the reorder point and the inventory limit. For the less recommended reorder period method, you would need to decide on the reorder period and calculate the inventory limit. The underlying approaches are actually very similar.

8.4.1 Reorder Point Method Calculation

For the reorder point method, we need to calculate two parts. First, we calculate the **reorder point** inventory, also known as the minimum inventory or sometimes the safety buffer. In the second step, we calculate the **delta** between the reorder point and the inventory limit. Combined, this will give us the inventory limit, as shown in Figure 140. This reorder point calculation uses many similar elements to the calculation of the production or transport kanban. Similarly, as the production kanban calculation is just an estimation, so is the reorder point calculation.

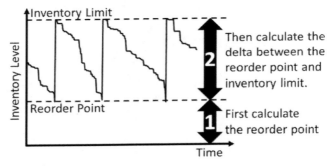

Figure 140: The two steps to calculate the reorder point method illustrated with a simplified example (Image Roser)

8.4.1.1 Elements

For the reorder point calculation, we need a number of elements. These are similar to the elements of kanban, as shown in Table 2 for production systems and Table 3 for transport and purchasing. See Chapter 5.3 with the description of these elements in the kanban calculation for more details. Most of these are elements for the replenishment time. The replenishment time for the reorder point or reorder period method is the delay between reaching the reorder point and having the reordered goods ready for use. **The replenishment time is the sum of the information transport time and the lead time.** Note that if there is a delay in issuing the order, it needs to be included in the calculation.

For the **lead time**, include all delays until the goods are ready for use. This can include waiting for completion of a truckload and waiting in the queue for shipping. However, if you are ordering from a supplier, you may see only the overall lead time, similar to a transport kanban. Be aware that having the truck with the goods drive through your front gate does not mean the goods are already available. There may be the inbound processes, unloading, quality control, internal logistics, and other steps until the goods are truly ready for consumption.

Additionally, you must include fluctuations. Since reorder systems are used for ship-to-stock and sometimes also for make-to-stock, there is usually a high expectation on material availability. You should not only have material in stock **usually**, but preferably **always**. Hence, we need to include the fluctuations. We would need to cover **breakdowns and disruptions** in the ordering and shipping process. What is the worst additional delay that we still want to cover between ordering items and having these items ready for use? This is usually estimated as an additional time on top of the lead time.

On the customer side, the **maximum order size** also has to be included in the calculation. We may also have a higher than expected demand. Of interest is the **peak demand**. As with kanban, the peak demand is the difference between the average and the maximum demand within the replenishment time. This peak demand is also best used as a quantity. If it is a seasonal peak demand, you may choose to temporarily change the reorder point quantity, rather than keeping extra safety stock on hand all year round.

Similar to other calculations, there may be a **safety factor**. If your replenishment time is conservative and includes larger fluctuations, you may need a smaller safety factor and vice versa. Finally, if your system has some unusual **other elements** that either increase the replenishment time or the fluctuations, you may have to include these too. However, the elements shown in Table 20 usually suffice for almost all reorder systems.

Group	Element	Unit	Usually Part Specific	Usually Relevant?	Variable
Replenishment Time	Information Transport Time	Time	Maybe	Maybe	TI
Replenishment Time	Lead Time	Time	Maybe	Yes	LT
Replenishment Time	Breakdown and Disruptions	Time	Maybe	Yes	BD
Customer	Peak Customer Demand	Quantity	Yes	Yes	PD
Customer	Large Customer Order	Quantity	Yes	Yes	OS
Other	Safety Factor	Quantity	Yes	Yes	S
Other	Other Elements	???	???	No	n/a

Table 20: Overview of variables contributing to the reorder point

8.4.1.2   Reorder Point Calculation

For reorder point methods, we start with the minimum inventory, the reorder point. At which inventory level should you reorder? The level should be large enough so that you are unlikely to run out of stock during the delivery delay. Hence, **the reorder point depends on the customer demand and the replenishment time**. Both are fluctuating, and **it is highly recommended to use conservative values and include the fluctuations**.

All times from Table 20 need to be converted into a quantity. The quantities in Table 20 are simply summed up. We combine the information flow time with the lead time and the time for breakdown and disruptions. We convert this time into a quantity by dividing it with the customer takt.

The customer takt, however, differs slightly from the customer takt of production systems. In production systems, the customer takt looks only at periods where the system is actually running, and you divide the working time by the demand that has to be produced within this working time. Purchasing systems, however, may have different working times than production systems. You could use the working time of the inbound warehouse, or also a *24-hour round-the-clock* approach. Make sure you use a consistent working time throughout the calculation.

Next, we add the largest expected order size for this part type minus one and the peak customer demand. Together with a bit of safety we get the reorder point, or the minimum inventory level at which a reorder is initiated. The entire formula is shown in Equation 32. If you order in packaging units of multiple items, it is not strictly necessary but often helpful to adjust the reorder point to a multiple of this packing unit.

$$I_{Min,n} = \frac{TI + LT + BD}{TT_n} + \left(OS_{Max,n} - 1\right) + PD_n + S$$

Equation 32: Calculating the reorder point

The variables for Equation 32 are as follows:

BD   Additional time to cover breakdowns and disruptions (time)
$I_{Min,n}$ Minimum inventory of part type n (quantity)
LT   Lead time (time)
$OS_{Max,n}$ Largest expected order size for part type n (quantity)
PD_n Peak customer demand for part type n (quantity)
S   Safety factor (quantity)
TI   Time for the transport of information (time)
TT_n Customer takt for part type n (time per quantity)

The reorder point should be large enough so that you are unlikely to run out of parts, even if a higher demand happens at the same time as a slower delivery. But please **do not try to cover all eventualities**. If you want to be prepared for all eventualities, your reorder point and therefore your inventory would be infinite.

Think about which situations you want to cover, and when you will decide that it is cheaper to have a stock-out. If you decide to use a worst-case customer demand and delivery delay, you probably won't need much safety factor. On the other hand, if both the customer takt and the delivery times are averages, feel free to add a good safety factor to reduce the likelihood of stock-outs.

Usually, I am a fan of estimations in calculating pull systems. However, for the reorder point you usually have a better understanding of the replenishment time and its fluctuations. Hence, here it may be better to calculate rather than estimate.

8.4.1.3 Economic Order Quantity Inventory Limit

Next, we look at the inventory limit. We do not calculate the inventory limit directly, but the delta between the reorder point and the inventory limit as visualized in Figure 140. This delta is usually the size of your order. It also determines the frequency of orders. This delta is influenced by the customer demand, how often we want to order, and how much inventory limit we want to have. **The delta is not related to the replenishment time.**

Assuming that the customer demand is given, you can make a trade-off between number of orders and inventory. **The more frequently you order, the smaller your delta and the lower your inventory. If you want to order less frequently, your delta and your inventory go up.**

For the reorder point calculation above, we used conservative values, including fluctuations. **For the delta calculation, we just take the averages.** The beauty of the reorder point method is that if demand is higher, we automatically order more often. If the demand is lower, we automatically order less frequently. Hence, there is no need to include fluctuations, worst-case scenarios, or a safety factor for the delta to the inventory limit.

The traditional way to calculate this in the classical cost accounting approach is called "economic order quantity". This is shown in Equation 33. The formula assumes that with the typical zigzag curve of ordering, you have on average half of the order quantity in stock. The order quantity (the delta) is a trade-off between the cost of ordering and the cost of the inventory.

$$I_{\Delta,n} = \sqrt{\frac{2 \cdot CO_n}{TT_n \cdot HC_n}}$$

Equation 33: The economic order quantity formula

The variables for Equation 33 and Equation 34 are as follows:

CO_n Cost of one order of part type n (monetary)

HC_n Holding cost of one part of type n for a given time (monetary per time and quantity)

$I_{Max,n}$ Inventory limit of part type n (quantity)

$I_{Min,n}$ Minimum inventory of part type n (quantity)

$I_{\Delta,n}$ Delta inventory of part type n (quantity)

TT_n Customer takt for part type n (time per quantity)

The formula itself is good, and from a mathematical point of view even beautiful. The problem is the data that goes into the formula. Traditional **cost accounting usually vastly underestimates the cost of having**

inventory. It simply uses the cost of the tied-up capital, and possibly also the warehouse cost. It completely ignores all the other factors where inventory can mess up your production. Items may become obsolete, or you find a defect and need to repair all inventory. It will also take longer to find a defect since more inventory means more delay until the subsequent processes may notice a problem. There are many factors that drive up cost of holding inventory that cannot be calculated well by cost accounting. Hence, **the economic order quantity formula often gives way-too-large values for the order quantity**.

Depending on your circumstances, your inventory can easily cost you between 30% and 65% of the product cost per year.[72] If you still want to use this formula, I recommend taking any number you get from cost accounting for the holding cost, and **multiplying the holding cost by three** before plugging it into the economic order quantity!

If you order in packing units of multiple items, it is also highly recommended to adjust the delta to a multiple of your packing units. Having calculated the reorder point in Equation 32 and the delta in Equation 33, we simply sum these up to get our inventory limit, as shown in Equation 34.

$$I_{Max,n} = I_{Min,n} + I_{\Delta,n}$$

Equation 34: The inventory limit for the reorder point method

8.4.1.4 Inventory Limit Estimation

Like with kanban and CONWIP, I am a fan of estimating values for pull production. You can do this here, too, for the delta between the reorder point and the inventory limit. The aim is to decrease the inventory delta as much as possible by increasing the number of orders until it starts to hurt and then go back a bit. How often do you dare to order without breaking your purchasing department? Once per week per item? Twice per week per item?

Hence, try to order as often as possible. However, you can treat different parts differently. Not all parts need to be maxed out with the number of

---

[72] Helen Richardson, *Control Your Costs—Then Cut Them, Transportation & Distribution* 36, no. 12 December 1995: 94.

orders. It may make sense to relax the number of orders on some parts and instead order even more frequently on others. Of particular interest are **large or expensive parts**, or **parts that often have quality problems**. These you want to order as often as possible to take up less space, tie up less money, and find problems faster. On the other hand, **small, cheap, and trouble-free parts** can be ordered less frequently to give your purchasing department some breathing room. Order a bucket of screws once per month instead of a handful every three days, but order the expensive engine blocks frequently and in small quantities.

8.4.1.5 Example Reorder Point Calculation

For the reorder point calculation example, let's use the same example demand as for the transport kanban in Chapter 5.4.3. The logistic system, however, is different in this example. I will again first summarize the data, and then the calculations. This allows you to calculate the values yourself first and compare them with my results. Since we again have assumptions, your values may look somewhat different from mine. Try to understand and learn from these differences.

8.4.1.5.1 Reorder System Data

We are again ordering wheels for wooden toy cars in yellow, red, and blue for our own production line. We order wheels in boxes of 40. Table 21 shows again the overview data with the expected monthly demand, as well as the excess peak demand for all colors. Defects and scrap are small enough and can be ignored.

Color	Expected Monthly Demand (Wheels)	Peak Demand (Wheels)
Red	40 000	1300
Blue	16 000	680
Yellow	800	70
Total	56 800	n/a

Table 21: Overview of parameters for the example calculation of the reorder point

Information for new orders is transmitted digitally, although the paperwork beforehand takes up to five hours. Trucks from the supplier can drive any time, including weekends. It takes about four days for an order to be delivered. Based on prior experience, management wants to cover up to three additional days' delay.

Additionally, accounting informs you that the cost of one order is €25 regardless of the color of the wheels. Furthermore, the holding cost of one wheel is approximated as €0.30 per wheel and year, based on the cost of capital and the storage cost. This is also the same regardless of the color of the wheel. The supplier ships the wheels in boxes of 40 wheels of one color.

8.4.1.5.2 Reorder Point Calculation

Based on this data, we first calculate the **customer takt**. Please note that since trucks can drive any time, we now will take the entire time under consideration, not only the working hours. We assume a month has on average 30 days with 24 hours, which would be 2 592 000 seconds per month. Dividing this time by the demand gives us the customer takt, as shown in Table 22. Please note the difference to the customer takt in Table 11, which was based on a working time with one shift only.

Color	Expected Monthly Demand (Wheels)	Customer Takt (Second/Wheel)
Red	40 000	64.8
Blue	16 000	162.0
Yellow	800	3240
Total	56 800	45.6

Table 22: Customer takt times for the reorder point example

The **information transport time** is five hours in the worst case for preparing the (digital) paperwork. The **lead time** is already given as four days and does not need to be constructed based on its individual elements like the waiting for truckload or similar. An additional three days are required to cover **breakdown and disruptions**. The **peak customer demand** is a quantity that depends on the part type, as shown in Table 21. Since we are supplying our own assembly lines, we do not have **large customer orders**. Our maximum customer order size is one box of 40 wheels. We could ignore this as it is insignificant compared to the other values, but for didactic purposes I kept it in the calculation. There are also no **other elements** that would affect this replenishment time and its fluctuations. An overview of these values is shown in Table 23.

Element	Unit	Red Wheels	Blue Wheels	Yellow Wheels	Variable
Information Transport Time	Hours (Seconds)	5 (18 000)	5 (18 000)	5 (18 000)	TI
Lead Time	Days (Seconds)	4 (345 600)	4 (345 600)	4 (345 600)	LT
Breakdown and Disruptions	Days (Seconds)	3 (259 200)	3 (259 200)	3 (259 200)	BD
Peak Customer Demand	Wheels	1300	680	70	PD
Large Customer Order	Wheels	40	40	40	OS
Other Elements	???	n/a	n/a	n/a	n/a

Table 23: Overview of variables contributing to the reorder point and the inventory limit

Now we can calculate the reorder point. Make sure to use the same time unit both for the times and for the customer takt. The example calculation for the red wheels is shown in Equation 35. The overview for all wheels is shown in Table 24. The safety here is simply a generous rounding up, albeit with a proportionally slightly larger safety for the less common wheel colors. We also made sure that the reorder point is a multiple of 40, since we order wheels in boxes of 40.

$$I_{Min,Red} = \frac{TI + LT + BD}{TT_{Red}} + \left(OS_{Max,Red} - 1\right) + PD_{Red} + S =$$

$$= \frac{18\,000s + 345\,600s + 259\,200s}{64.8\frac{s}{wheel}} +$$

$$+(40\ wheel - 1\ wheel) + 1300\ wheels + S =$$

$$= 10\,950\ wheels + S$$

Equation 35: Calculating the reorder point for red wheels

Color	Reorder Point without Safety (Wheels)	Safety (Wheels)	Reorder Point with Safety (Wheels)	Safety (Percent)
Red	10 950	570	11 520	4.9%
Blue	4563	437	5000	8.7%
Yellow	301	59	360	16.3%

Table 24: Reorder point example with and without safety

8.4.1.5.3 Inventory Limit Calculation

To calculate the inventory limit, we would first need the delta to the inventory limit. We know that the cost of one order is €25 and the holding cost is €0.30 per wheel and year, regardless of the color. We could now use the economic order quantity formula to calculate the order size. The customer takt is still based on a "round-the-clock" approach. Make sure to either convert the holding cost to € per second or the customer takt to years per piece so as not to mess up the units. The calculation is shown for the red wheel in Equation 36 and the overview in Table 25. You would have to adjust the economic order quantity to a multiple of 40 wheels, since we order boxes of 40 wheels.

$$I_{\Delta,Red} = \sqrt{\frac{2 \cdot CO_{Red}}{TT_{Red} \cdot HC_{Red}}} =$$

$$= \sqrt{\frac{2 \cdot €25 \cdot 31\,536\,000\,\frac{s}{year}}{64.8\,\frac{s}{wheel} \cdot 0.3\,\frac{€}{wheel \cdot year}}} = 9006 \text{ wheels}$$

Equation 36: The economic order quantity formula example for red wheels

Color	Economic Order Quantity (Wheels)	Orders per Year
Red	9006	53.3
Blue	5696	33.7
Yellow	1274	7.5

Table 25: Economic order quantity example with no adjustments. The table also shows the expected number of orders per year.

However, the holding cost given from the accounting department included only the storage and capital cost. It misses out on many more additional costs caused by excess inventory. Therefore, I recommend **multiplying the holding cost by three**. In this case, the economic order quantity would be as shown in Table 26. The economic order quantity is reduced to almost half, while the number of orders double. Note that here, too, you would have to adjust the economic order quantity to a multiple of 40.

Color	Adjusted Economic Order Quantity (Wheels)	Orders per Year
Red	5200	92.3
Blue	3289	58.4
Yellow	735	13.1

Table 26: Economic order quantity example with a tripled holding cost

Finally, you could also simply define how many orders you want to do within one year. Let's assume you want to do 100 orders per year for red wheels, 60 for blue wheels, and 20 for yellow wheels. The order size would be the annual demand divided by the number of orders per year, as shown in Table 27. By coincidence, all order sizes are already a multiple of 40.

Color	Orders per Year (Wheels)	Order Size (Wheels)
Red	100	4800
Blue	60	3200
Yellow	20	480

Table 27: Order size based on a defined number of orders per year

My advice is that whichever approach you use, go with the smaller order size (i.e., the more frequent order). **Do not add a safety to this delta or to the inventory limit!** If anything, adjust the order quantity downward. If necessary, adjust the order size to the packaging size offered to you by the supplier. In our example, the delta should be divisible by 40, since we order wheels in packs of 40.

For the calculation of the inventory limit, we will use the delta based on the target orders per year from Table 27. Since our supplier ships the wheels in boxes of 40 and the results in Table 27 are all divisible by 40, we can use these values without adjustments. The overview of the reorder point, the delta to the inventory limit, and the inventory limit is given in Table 28.

Color	Reorder Point (Wheels)	Delta to Target Inventory (Wheels)	Inventory Limit (Wheels)
Red	11 520	4800	16 320
Blue	5000	3200	8200
Yellow	360	480	840

Table 28: Reorder point calculation example results overview

8.4.2 Reorder Period Method Calculation

The reorder period calculation is needed only if you use the reorder period, which I would advise against. The inventory limit has to cover the **demand during the reorder period,** as well as the **demand during the replenishment** time in addition to the **safety factor. Both should be conservative worst-case estimate including fluctuations.** Therefore, the resulting inventory limit is usually larger than with the reorder point method for a similar number of orders per year. A visualization is shown in Figure 141.

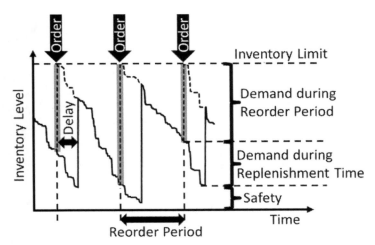

Figure 141: Representation of the elements contributing to the inventory limit for the reorder period. Please note that this is only a momentary view of fluctuating values. (Image Roser)

8.4.2.1 Reorder Period Elements

The reorder period calculation has very similar elements to the reorder point calculation. The replenishment time consists of the **information**

transport time and the **lead time**. Similarly, we have to cover for **breakdowns and disruptions**.

On the customer side, we need to include the fluctuations due to the **peak customer demand** and **large customer orders**. For kanban and the reorder point method, we applied this to the replenishment time. However, for the reorder period we also have to apply this to the reorder period itself. Since these periods are fixed, we cannot order more frequently if there is a higher demand, but instead need additional inventory to cover for this. Hence, since the peak demand now covers a longer time, **the peak demand is usually larger than with the reorder point method**. This can make quite some difference to the total inventory needed.

There is one more element, however: the **reorder period**. This is the duration between orders. The inventory limit has to have enough inventory to cover the demand of the customer during this **reorder period AND the replenishment time—including fluctuations**. You pick how often you want to order and calculate the worst-case demand during the combined reorder period and replenishment time.

You could also use the economic order quantity formula from Equation 33 to determine a good economic order size—but make sure you have realistic holding costs. Or you could just take the shortest period/most frequent orders/smallest inventory that you are comfortable with.

Group	Element	Unit	Usually Part Specific?	Usually Relevant?	Variable
Replenishment Time	Information Transport Time	Time	Maybe	No	TI
	Lead Time	Time	Maybe	Yes	LT
	Breakdown and Disruptions	Time	Maybe	Yes	BD
Customer	Large Customer Order	Quantity	Yes	Yes	OS
	Peak Customer Demand	Quantity	Yes	Yes	PD
Other	Safety Factor	Quantity	Yes	Yes	S
	Reorder Period	Time	Yes	Yes	RP
	Other Elements	???	???	No	n/a

Table 29: Overview of variables contributing to the reorder period

Whichever approach you use, you need to **define a reorder period**. We also have our usual **safety factor**. The table also lists the rarely needed **other elements** if you have a system that is highly unusual and has additional factors. An overview of these elements is given in Table 29.

8.4.2.2 Inventory Limit Calculation

The inventory limit is the sum of the elements from Table 29. The information transport time, the lead time, the reorder period, and the time for breakdown and disruptions are added and converted into a quantity using the customer takt. We also add the largest order size minus one, the peak demand, and a safety. This is shown in Equation 37.

$$I_{Max,n} = \frac{TI + LT + BD + RP_n}{TT_n} + (OS_{Max,n} - 1) + PD_n + S$$

Equation 37: Calculation of the reorder period

The variables in Equation 37 are as follows:

BD   Additional time to cover breakdowns and disruptions (time)
$I_{Max,n}$ Inventory limit of part type n (quantity)
LT   Lead time (time)
$OS_{Max,n}$ Largest expected order size for part type n (quantity)
PD_n Peak customer demand for part type n (quantity)
RP_n Reorder period for part type n (time)
S   Safety factor (quantity)
TI   Time for the transport of information (time)
TT_n Customer takt for part type n (time per quantity)

Compare Equation 37 to Equation 32. The main new element is the reorder period. Please note that **the peak demand is larger than with the reorder point method**, since it now also needs to cover the reorder period in addition to the replenishment time.

With Equation 37, you can play with the order period or the order quantity to find a sweet spot that gives you a nice trade-off between the inventory and the number of orders.

8.4.2.3 Example Reorder Period Calculation

For comparison purposes, we will use the same example as for the reorder point method above. For further comparison, we will use order periods that give us approximately the same number of orders per year as with the reorder point method in Table 27. However, since we now also need to cover the fluctuations during the reorder period, **we need to cover a larger peak demand compared to the reorder point method**. This will significantly increase the overall inventory. Table 30 also shows the expected demand and the customer takt as calculated with the reorder period.

Color	Expected Monthly Demand (Wheels)	Order Period (Days)	Orders per Year	Customer Takt (Second/Wheel)
Red	40 000	4	91.3	64.8
Blue	16 000	6	60.8	162.0
Yellow	800	18	20.3	3240

Table 30: Part-specific data for the reorder point calculation example

The calculation of most elements is also identical to the reorder point method. Please look at the reorder point method on how to calculate these values. However, peak demand is larger than with the reorder point method, as it now also covers the reorder period. The reorder period itself is also a new element compared to the reorder point method. An overview is shown in Table 31.

Element	Unit	Red Wheels	Blue Wheels	Yellow Wheels	Variable
Information Transport Time	Hours (Seconds)	5 (18 000)	5 (18 000)	5 (18 000)	TI
Lead Time	Days (Seconds)	4 (345 600)	4 (345 600)	4 (345 600)	LT
Breakdown and Disruptions	Days (Seconds)	3 (259 200)	3 (259 200)	3 (259 200)	BD
Peak Customer Demand	Wheels	2600	1400	200	PD
Large Customer Order	Wheels	40	40	40	OS
Reorder Period	Days (Seconds)	4 (345 600)	6 (518 400)	18 (1 555 200)	RP
Other Elements	???	n/a	n/a	n/a	n/a

Table 31: Overview of variables for the reorder period example

Using these values, we can now calculate the reorder period inventory limit. This is shown in Equation 38 for the red wheels. Make sure not to mix up the units.

$$I_{Max,Red} = \frac{TI + LT + BD + RP_{Red}}{TT_{Red}} + \left(OS_{Max,Red} - 1\right) + PD_{Red} + S =$$

$$= \frac{18\ 000s + 345\ 600s + 259\ 200s + 345\ 600s}{64.8\dfrac{s}{wheel}} +$$

$$+(40\ \text{wheels} - 1\ \text{wheel}) + 2\ 600\ \text{wheels} + S = 17\ 583\ \text{wheels} + S$$

Equation 38: Calculation of the reorder period example for the red wheels

Table 32 shows the overview of the target inventory without the safety. I added some safety inventory to get the final inventory limit. Since we order wheels in packs of 40, the inventory limit is best a multiple of 40. Since the reorder period method is much more sensitive to fluctuations, I could have added even more safety. But even with this small amount of safety, all reorder period target inventories are larger than the target inventories of the reorder point.

Color	Inventory Limit without Safety (Wheels)	Safety (Wheels)	Inventory Limit with Safety (Wheels)	Safety (Percent)
Red	17 583	817	18 400	4.4%
Blue	8483	717	9200	7.8%
Yellow	911	169	1080	15.6%

Table 32: Reorder period calculation example results overview

In this example, the reorder period inventories are much larger than the reorder point inventories, even with a probably too-small safety buffer for the reorder period calculation. For the high runners of red and blue wheels, we have about 12% more parts comparable to the reorder point method. For the exotic yellow wheels, we need almost 30% more inventory. An overview is shown in Table 33.

Color	Reorder Point Inventory Limit with Safety (Wheels)	Reorder Period Inventory Limit with Safety (Wheels)	Difference (Percent)
Red	16 320	18 400	12.7%
Blue	8200	9200	12.2%
Yellow	840	1080	28.6%

Table 33: Comparing the reorder point and reorder period results for the example.

The difference is that in the reorder point method, only the fluctuations of the replenishment time need to be buffered by inventory. The fluctuations during the time between orders are decoupled in the reorder point method simply by varying the time between orders. The reorder period method, on the other hand, has a fixed order period, and hence the fluctuations during this period also need to be covered. This larger inventory, or a higher risk of stock-outs, or both is the main reason why **I much prefer the reorder point method over the reorder period method**.

8.4.3 Caveats for Combining Reorder Point and Period

If against my advice you decide to go for a system combining reorder point and reorder period, the respective calculations above still hold true. However, the reorder period and the inventory limit should be set so you usually don't reach the reorder point. If your combined system reaches the reorder point frequently, then you lose the (minor) advantage of a reorder point while still having all the effort of maintaining a double system. Hence, your calculation of the reorder period should include a very generous safety factor. This would increase your inventory even more. Again, **avoid such a combined system if you can.**

8.5 Advantages

The advantage of this system is simple. Compared to a kanban system, you usually order much less frequently. Hence, you have much **less reordering effort** though fewer orders. Of course, this depends on your chosen values for the reorder point and the inventory limit, and you can have a reorder point system showing the same behavior as a kanban system.

Another advantage is that it is a **relatively simple system**. You do not need a kanban box, or to print kanban, move kanban around, create sequencing, and all the other things needed for kanban, CONWIP, or POLCA. You just monitor the inventory and order when appropriate. This is well suited for ERP systems.

8.6 Disadvantages

There are a few disadvantages of the reorder point and related methods. However, **all of these disadvantages can be mitigated by adjusting the inventory limit down and ordering more frequently.**

8.6.1 Possibly Larger Inventory

This reduced ordering effort comes at a price. Most significantly, it can **increase the inventory**. The increase depends on the frequency of the orders, or the gap between the reorder point and the inventory limit. Naturally, if you set your reorder point to the inventory limit, you reorder as soon as one part is consumed. In this case, the system would work similarly to a kanban system with a lot size of one part. Yet, **as you order less frequently, your inventory goes up**.

This increased inventory causes several subsequent disadvantages. You have the **inventory cost**. You have the **increased lead time** until a part gets used. Parts may age and degrade. Effectively, all the disadvantages of inventory are there.

8.6.2 Possibly Slower Information Flow

Since you wait before ordering, you also **slow down the information flow**. With kanban, the supplier is informed immediately whenever the customer consumes, and hence the demand information from the customer is forwarded quickly. With reorder systems, however, the replenishment information sits around until the reorder point (or period) is reached. Only then is the information forwarded to the supplier.

8.6.3 Possibly Increased Fluctuations

The system can also **increase fluctuation**. Assume you have a perfect customer with no fluctuations, ordering like clockwork one part every takt. If you have a large inventory limit, your supplier gets a much more fluctuating signal. No orders for four days, and then all the orders at the same time. Hence, reorder systems can increase fluctuations if the order size is large or if the order is infrequent. Please note that **all of these disadvantages can be mitigated by adjusting the inventory limit down**.

8.7 Frequently Asked Questions

8.7.1 When Should I Use Reorder Systems?

Since reorder point fills up inventory of the same part, it is only suited for make/ship-to-stock situations. It is not suited at all for make/ship-to-order. A common usage is ship-to-stock of standard items. Reorder systems increase fluctuation in the value chain. Hence, it is best suited to situations where an increase in fluctuation is acceptable or even desired. Take for example stationery supplies. Your order of 500 blue pens at the same time probably won't bring your office supplier into problems, as they have these on stock by the thousands anyway.

Due to the "bulking" of the order, it is usually not recommended to control production systems that produce in small lot sizes, unless your reorder system also has a small order size (i.e., a small delta between the reorder point and the inventory limit). If your reorder system slows the information flow to make large orders, your supplying production system will now have extra effort to level its production again and to undo this bulking into large orders. However, this problem can be avoided by smaller and more frequent orders.

The exceptions are production systems that by themselves have large lot sizes, usually due to large changeover times. Such systems actually want large orders to reduce the time lost for changeover. In this case, the delta between the reorder point and the inventory limit should match the desired lot size for this part. Nevertheless, consider a reduction in the changeover time and a subsequent reduction in the lot size first.

Since reorder systems usually also use computer systems, it helps if your inventory and your orders are tracked digitally. Reorder systems can also increase inventory if you order infrequently. This is not good, especially for large, expensive, or trouble-prone items. Yet, even here, you can use reorder systems as long as you order frequently enough. **The more frequently you order, the lower your inventory.**

8.7.2 Which Reorder System Should I Use?

Here **my clear preference is the reorder point method**. This system adjusts flexibly to changes in demand by adapting the frequency of the orders. If you really want to use reorder periods, it is possible, but this is a clear second choice for me. Avoid the combined systems. Absolutely stay away from the fixed-time, fixed-quantity system, as this is terrible and not even a pull system.

8.7.3 What If I Keep Having Stock-Outs?

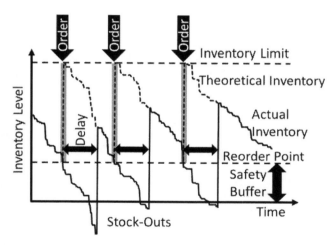

Figure 142: Reorder system with a too-small reorder point (Image Roser)

If you regularly run out of inventory, as shown in Figure 142, then your reorder point is set too low. Increase your reorder point (and correspondingly the inventory limit). Alternatively, you can try to figure out why the delay of the delivery is so large, and try to reduce the delivery delay. The latter is of course more difficult and time consuming. Either approach also works for reorder periods, although for reorder periods you can also increase the frequency of orders and reduce the reorder period duration.

8.7.4 Can I Just Track the Total of All of My Part Types?

Definitely NOT! **You need to calculate and track all part types separately.** Only then do you know which part type to order. Under no circumstances can you do the reorder calculations just for the sum of your entire inventory, while ignoring the part type variety. This will not work! You will run out of some parts while having way too many other parts.

8.7.5 Should I Reorder at My Reorder Point or Below?

There are two possibilities. You can reorder when your tracked inventory reaches at least the value of the reorder point (inventory ≤ reorder point), or you can reorder when it goes below the reorder point (inventory < reorder point). This choice usually makes only a slight difference for the calculation of the reorder point and the inventory limit. I recommend ordering when you have reached the reorder point, as this is more intuitive for the human operators, and also more robust in case of confusing the two options. But both are absolutely feasible.

Chapter 9
Drum-Buffer-Rope

Drum-buffer-rope (or DBR in short) originated with the famous book by Goldratt, *The Goal*[73], although it got its name only later in *The Race*.[74] In *The Goal*, Goldratt manages the unlikely task of combining management science with a romance novel. As a romance novel, the story is mediocre. As a science book, it is a nice collection of general wisdoms and good suggestions. In combination, it was a bestseller, since it is one of the few management science books that almost everybody can understand. However, if you are looking for a production management novel, in my opinion a much better book is *The Gold Mine: A Novel of Lean Turnaround*[75] by Freddy and Michael Balle. If you are looking for a technical explanation of drum-buffer-rope in more detail than this book, I recommend *Goldratt's*

---

[73] Eliyahu M. Goldratt and Jeff Cox, *The Goal: A Process of Ongoing Improvement*, 2nd revised ed. North River Press, 1992, ISBN 0-88427-178-1.

[74] Eliyahu M. Goldratt and Robert E. Fox, *The Race* Croton-on-Hudson, New York, USA: North River Press Inc., 1986, ISBN 978-0-88427-062-1.

[75] Freddy Balle and Michael Balle, *The Gold Mine: A Novel of Lean Turnaround* Brookline, Massachusetts, USA: Lean Enterprises Inst Inc, 2005, ISBN 978-0-9743225-6-8.

Theory of Constraints[76] or the *Theory of Constraints Handbook*[77], although the latter is not an easy read.

9.1 Fundamentals

The drum-buffer-rope method has a lot of similarities to CONWIP, although **the bottleneck takes a central role in drum-buffer-rope**. Drum-buffer-rope is best used for make-to-order. It can be applied to make-to-stock, but this is not a good match. The basic elements are shown in Figure 143.

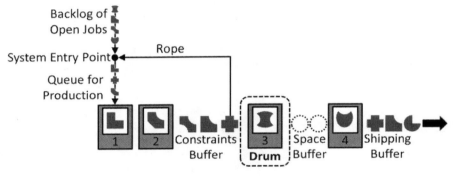

Figure 143: Example of a drum-buffer-rope system (Image Roser)

A very illustrative example of drum-buffer-rope in *The Goal* was how the protagonist of the book manages a Boy Scout outing, especially how to keep the group together while different boys walked at different speeds. The initial solution was to put the slowest Boy Scout, Herbie, at the front and to prohibit all others from overtaking him. Additionally, he lightens Herbie's backpack so he can walk faster.

Later, it turned out that it would be better for Herbie not to walk at the front. Hence, a rope was added from the first person in line to Herbie, preventing the people in front of Herbie from walking too far away and hence

---

[76] H. William Dettmer, *Goldratt's Theory of Constraints: A Systems Approach to Continuous Improvement* Milwaukee, Wisconsin, USA: McGraw-Hill Professional, 1998, ISBN 978-0-87389-370-1.

[77] James F. Cox and John G. Schleier, *Theory of Constraints Handbook* McGraw-Hill Professional, 2010, ISBN 0-07-166554-4.

preventing the group from being separated. The people behind Herbie were also forbidden from overtaking him. This is illustrated in Figure 144.

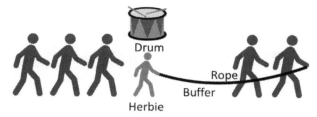

Figure 144: The original drum-buffer-rope example in The Goal (Image Roser)

Taking these Boy Scouts as an analogy for a factory created the drum-buffer-rope method. The drum is the bottleneck, defining the overall speed of the system. The system cannot go faster than the drum.

The drum is the slowest person. The rope extends to the first person in the line, which cannot walk faster than the drum. The buffer is the free space between the drum or bottleneck and the next person in front of him. This allows the bottleneck to walk, even if the next person is temporarily slowed down, for example, to tie their shoelaces.

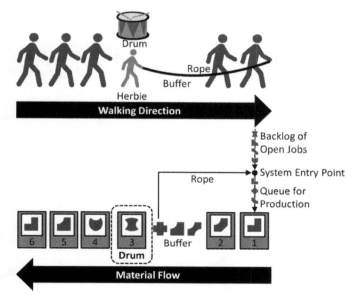

Figure 145: The original drum-buffer-rope example overlapping with a material flow in manufacturing (Image Roser)

This may work for people, but it needs a fair bit of imagination to extend this version of drum-buffer-rope to manufacturing systems. You have to remember that the people in this example are the processes, not the parts. The parts are actually the ground covered. In Figure 144 the people walk from left to right, but the ground covered (the parts) would move from right to left. Hence, the material flow looks more like Figure 145.

Let's orient the material flow from the left to the right as it is custom in manufacturing. This is shown in Figure 146. In manufacturing, the drum is still the bottleneck. The buffer is the material upstream of the bottleneck and has to make sure that the drum is never starved. The rope is a signal or information from the buffer in front of the bottleneck to the beginning of the line. If the drum processes parts, the buffer moves forward. The rope is a signal when material is processed at the bottleneck. This creates information to release the next job in the backlog of open jobs into the queue for production.

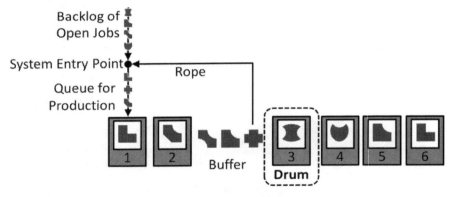

Figure 146: Drum-buffer-rope with a material flow from the left to the right, the reverse of the people example (Image Roser)

Signal when material is taken out… information to release next job… I have heard something very similar before: CONWIP! Yes, drum-buffer-rope is similar to CONWIP, where the last inventory is before the bottleneck. Whenever a part is taken out of the inventory, a signal is sent via the rope to the beginning of the line to release the next job in the queue for production. A drum-buffer-rope system as shown in Figure 146 is very similar to a CONWIP system as shown in Figure 147, although drum-buffer-rope manages only the processes upstream of the bottleneck. Processes downstream of and including the bottleneck are no longer managed by pull. The fundamental problem with drum-buffer-rope is that it assumes a bottleneck that does not shift. In reality, however, most bottlenecks shift!

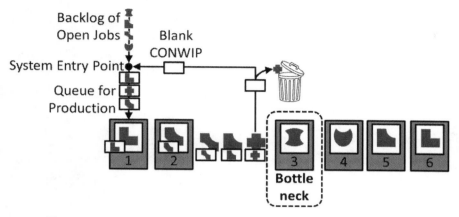

Figure 147: Equivalent of a CONWIP system for a drum-buffer-rope system (Image Roser)

9.2 Variants

I know only one variant of drum-buffer-rope. This variant is called **simplified drum-buffer-rope**, and is very similar to the normal drum-buffer-rope. The key to simplifying the approach is the assumption that the market or the customer is the largest bottleneck and hence the drum. The assumption is that, on average, your system always has enough capacity to satisfy demand. The rope then spans the entire length of the system. This is shown in Figure 148.

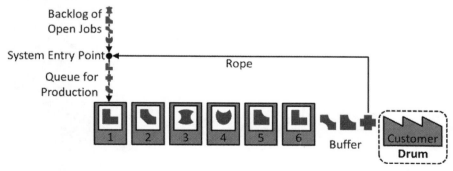

Figure 148: Example of a simplified drum-buffer-rope system, assuming the customer is the bottleneck (Image Roser)

This may solve the problem with the bottleneck, as long as the assumption that the customer is always the bottleneck is true. However, it shares the similar disadvantages with the normal drum-buffer-rope system in assuming that the bottleneck is fixed—which it rarely is. Also, making only one big loop across your value stream is risky. I often find it easier to break it into multiple smaller CONWIP loops, as described in Chapter 11.

9.3 Elements

The key elements of drum-buffer-rope are shown in Figure 143. Naturally, there is the drum, the buffer, and the rope that give the system its name. But there is also a backlog of open jobs and a system entry point (often called the "Material Release Point") similar to CONWIP.

9.3.1 Drum

The drum is the bottleneck in the system (i.e., the process that constrains the flow of material the most). This sounds simple enough. However, there are two problems with this. First, where is your bottleneck? **It is simple if the bottleneck does not shift. Unfortunately, in reality the bottleneck almost always shifts**. This brings us to our second problem: what to do with shifting bottlenecks. Let's first define bottlenecks:

> Bottlenecks are processes that influence the throughput of the entire system. The larger the influence, the more significant the bottleneck.[78]

Finding shifting bottlenecks is tricky. Since this is one of my areas of research, I have developed two methods that actually work and are used in industry. The **Active Period Method** looks at the period of processes between waiting times (blocked or starved processes). The process with the

---

[78] Christoph Roser et al., *Bottleneck Prediction Using the Active Period Method in Combination with Buffer Inventories*, in *Proceedings of the International Conference on the Advances in Production Management System* International Conference on the Advances in Production Management System, Hamburg, Germany, 2017.

longest active period is the current bottleneck. This may also change over time.[79] The Active Period Method is very precise but requires a lot of data.

The second method is the **Bottleneck Walk**, which is still accurate but requires very little data. In fact, it can be done with no math or stopwatch just by walking along the line. A process that is waiting for material points toward a bottleneck upstream. A process that is blocked points to a bottleneck downstream. Similarly, relatively full inventories point to a bottleneck downstream, and relatively empty inventories point to a bottleneck upstream. With enough pointing you will find the bottleneck.[80]

The problem remains that **handling the shifting bottlenecks would require moving the drum frequently**. This would require a frequent change in the layout of the drum-buffer-rope information flow. I believe this is not feasible. Goldratt simply claims that this is not a problem, although I do not believe him.

9.3.2 Buffer

There are actually three relevant buffers. First, there is the buffer in front of the drum. This is called the **constraints buffer** since it protects the drum from running empty. Since this buffer is usually full, it is also called a time buffer since it adds to the lead time of the system.

Second, there is the buffer after the drum. This is called the **space buffer** since it is usually empty. Some sources omit this buffer, but it is also relevant to prevent the drum from being blocked by downstream processes.

Finally, there is the buffer before the customer. This is called the **shipping buffer**. This buffer also buffers against disruptions in the flow. All buffers do what buffers usually do and decouple fluctuations. The placement of the buffers before and after the drum protects in particular the drum. However,

---

[79] Christoph Roser, *Mathematically Accurate Bottleneck Detection 1 – The Average Active Period Method*, in *Collected Blog Posts of AllAboutLean.Com 2014*, Collected Blog Posts of AllAboutLean.Com 2 Offenbach, Germany: AllAboutLean Publishing, 2020, 133–36, ISBN 978-3-96382-010-6.

[80] Christoph Roser, *The Bottleneck Walk – Practical Bottleneck Detection Part 1*, in *Collected Blog Posts of AllAboutLean.Com 2014*, Collected Blog Posts of AllAboutLean.Com 2 Offenbach, Germany: AllAboutLean Publishing, 2020, 142–48, ISBN 978-3-96382-010-6.

I would also recommend adding smaller buffers throughout your value chain to protect against smaller disruptions at other locations that can build up to a bigger disruption that the constraint and space buffer can no longer handle.

9.3.3 Rope

The rope is a mechanism that is used to control the flow. Its principle is very similar to kanban or CONWIP, except that it does not track a quantity, but **tracks the work content**. It is much easier to track quantity, but tracking work content is more accurate. However, in my opinion, the benefit is not that great, and the effort is significant, hence I usually go with tracking quantity.

Anyway, the rope is some type of system, often digital, that tracks how much work content is currently contained in the system between the start of the system and the drum. Whenever a completed job leaves the drum, the corresponding work content becomes available again. The system adds the newly available work content to its pool of available work content. If the available work content in the pool is enough to start the next open job in the backlog of open jobs, then this job is released for production. As such, it is very similar to CONWIP using work content, as shown in Chapter 6.2.6.

9.3.4 Backlog of Open Jobs

The backlog of open jobs is a prioritized list of jobs waiting for production capacity. In its function, it is virtually identical to the backlog of open jobs for CONWIP as described in Chapter 6.3.4, including its prioritization. The only additional element is that the work content for the open jobs needs to be known so it can be matched with the available work content coming through the rope. If you use drum-buffer-rope for make-to-stock, you will need to manage the make-to-stock quantities separately. Hence, drum-buffer-rope is easier for make-to-order.

9.3.5 System Entry Point

The system entry point is very similar to the system entry point in CONWIP, as described in Chapter 6.3.6. This is where the decision is made to release a job for production. The job should have all the required materials, or it should be expected that the materials arrive in time. **The first job in the queue is released as soon as the available free work capacity exceeds the work capacity needed for the job.** With the release, the required work capacity is removed from the free capacity and assigned to this job. Upon completion of the job, this work capacity becomes available again.

9.4 Calculation

Drum-buffer-rope has similar goals as CONWIP. It wants to **keep the system well utilized without the material spiraling out of control**. Hence, the mathematics behind it is somewhat similar to CONWIP in Chapter 6.4. The main difference is that you do not limit the number of jobs, but the workload in the system. Similar to CONWIP, I also recommend an estimation rather than a detailed mathematical calculation.

9.5 Advantages

Like all pull systems, drum-buffer-rope **limits the inventory** and aims to prevent an overloading of the system. This is combined with a **signal to release the next job**. As such, it is a pull system like kanban or CONWIP, and hence drum-buffer-rope is superior to the traditional push systems, at least for the part of the value stream that is covered by the rope.

Another good thing about drum-buffer-rope is that **it measures the work in the system not in pieces, but in workload**. Depending on how many hours' worth of work are in the system, the rope may release another part in the system. In comparison, a kanban or CONWIP system usually only counts pieces.

In my view, counting pieces is fine if the pieces are similar, as in mass production. On the other hand, limiting the workload may be beneficial if the items to produce have vastly different work content, as for example in a job shop. However, measuring time is also more difficult, as you need to determine the time for each product rather than merely counting it. In any case, kanban and CONWIP systems can be adapted to measure workload if needed, resulting in the same benefits and complexity as a drum-buffer-rope system.

9.6 Disadvantages

Drum-buffer-rope has in my view quite a few disadvantages. Unless you are already using it successfully, I would not recommend drum-buffer-rope.

9.6.1 Assumes a Fixed and Known Bottleneck

One of the major underlying assumptions of drum-buffer-rope is the **assumption of a fixed bottleneck**, combined with a second **assumption that the location of the bottleneck is known**. In my experience, finding the bottleneck is often difficult, and even if you have correctly identified the bottleneck, it is shifting frequently to other processes. If the bottleneck shifts, then the drum is in a different place at different times. The entire drum-buffer-rope system would have to be recalculated and set up again every time the bottleneck shifts. This is illustrated in Figure 149. Obviously, this is not feasible for frequently shifting bottlenecks.

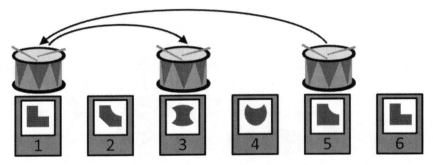

Figure 149: Shifting bottlenecks would shift drums in drum-buffer-rope.
(Image Roser)

Goldratt claimed that in his experience this was not a problem in practice. However, Goldratt was often less than stringent in actually proving his claims, and there are many doubts about the performance of his methods.[81, 82, 83, 84, 85]

In my experience, shifting bottlenecks are not the exception but the norm in most manufacturing systems. Simply assuming a fixed bottleneck will lead to problems. The Theory of Constraints also does not offer any good approach to find the bottleneck. Of course, increasing buffer sizes will lead to less shifting, but it will also lead to a larger inventory, which in turn will lead to a lot of other unpleasant side effects.

9.6.2 May Ignore Blocking of the Bottleneck

Drum-buffer-rope explicitly places a buffer in front of the drum to prevent starving (i.e., the buffer prevents the drum from running out of material). However, many sources completely **omit the possibility of the drum being blocked** by a downstream process, which may equally lead to bottleneck downtime. While the buffer after the bottleneck is usually near empty, it is necessary to provide the space in case a downstream process makes problems and blocks the bottleneck. If you use drum-buffer-rope, make sure that there is also adequate buffer downstream of the bottleneck.

[81] Alexandre Linhares, *Theory of Constraints and the Combinatorial Complexity of the Product-Mix Decision, International Journal of Production Economics,* Modelling and Control of Productive Systems: Concepts and Applications, 121, no. 1 September 1, 2009: 121–29.

[82] Dan Trietsch, *Why a Critical Path by Any Other Name Would Smell Less Sweet? Towards a Holistic Approach to PERT/CPM, Project Management Journal* 36 2005: 27–36.

[83] Christoph Roser, *"Faster, Better, Cheaper" in the History of Manufacturing: From the Stone Age to Lean Manufacturing and Beyond,* 1st ed. Productivity Press, 2016, ISBN 978-1-4987-5630-3.

[84] Dan Trietsch, *From Management by Constraints (MBC) to Management by Criticalities (MBC II), Human Systems Management* 24 January 1, 2005: 105–15.

[85] Adam Lazarski, *Limitations of the Theory of Constraints and Goldratt Concept in Optimizing Project Portfolios, ODiTK,* 2010, https://www.akademiacontrollingu.pl/article/limitations-of-the-theory-of-constraints-and-goldratt-concept-in-optimizing-project-portfolios/.

9.6.3 May Pull Only Part of the Value Stream

Drum-buffer-rope controls not only the buffer in front of the drum, but also the entire inventory upstream of the bottleneck. **However, little or no consideration is given for the value stream after the bottleneck.** This is not only the buffer immediately afterwards, but the entire value chain to the customer. Hence, the inventory is not limited and — while usually empty — under the wrong circumstances can still lead to overproduction. Combined with shifting bottlenecks it is quite possible that the downstream inventory will at least temporarily spiral out of control.

9.6.4 Only One Pull Loop by Default

Drum-buffer-rope **has only one major loop between the bottleneck and the first process.** However, there are many good reasons why you may want to use more than one loop, as for example differences in cycle time, merging or splitting material flows, or system boundaries. See Chapter 11 for details.

Overall, drum-buffer-rope has been shown to perform worse than other pull systems.[86, 87, 88] Hence, kanban or CONWIP systems are more flexible and better controlled compared to drum-buffer-rope.

9.7 Frequently Asked Questions

9.7.1 Should You Use Drum-Buffer-Rope?

Very good question. I personally find it **inferior to kanban or CONWIP,** even though it measures the actual workload rather than simply the

---

[86] Mabel Qiu, Lawrence Fredendall, and Zhiwei Zhu, *TOC or LP?*, *Manufacturing Engineer* 81, no. 4 August 1, 2002: 190–95.

[87] Alexandre Linhares, *Theory of Constraints and the Combinatorial Complexity of the Product-Mix Decision, International Journal of Production Economics*, Modelling and Control of Productive Systems: Concepts and Applications, 121, no. 1 September 1, 2009: 121–29.

[88] Dan Trietsch, *From Management by Constraints (MBC) to Management by Criticalities (MBC II), Human Systems Management* 24 January 1, 2005: 105–15.

quantity. However, the limitation on the bottleneck is very restrictive, especially if the bottleneck shifts a lot—and in my experience, almost all production systems have shifting bottlenecks.

On the other hand, drum-buffer-rope as part of the Theory of Constraints is used in industry, and many users claim that it really helped them and improved their production system performance. Hence my recommendation is: **If you already use drum-buffer-rope and it works for you, keep on using it!** However, ignore the limitation of having only one loop that also only ends in front of the bottleneck, as this significantly decreases the performance of the system. **If you are not (yet) using drum-buffer-rope, stick to kanban or CONWIP**, which will also work and improve your production system if implemented correctly.

9.7.2 Can I Fix My Bottleneck?

One problem of drum-buffer-rope is the shifting bottleneck. In theory, you could avoid that by having one process significantly slower than the rest. This would force one process to be almost always the bottleneck. In turn, this would simplify drum-buffer-rope since the bottleneck no longer shifts.

However, this would also generate large inefficiencies. The processes before the bottleneck would always have to wait for the bottleneck before moving their material forward. The processes after the bottleneck would always have to wait for the bottleneck to get material. Overall, the line would be intentionally unbalanced, with lots of waiting of the processes except for the exaggerated bottleneck. **I would be very hesitant to intentionally create such an imbalanced production system that introduces so much waste.**

There may be some exception where the bottleneck is the largest and most expensive machine, and management puts a premium on utilizing this expensive equipment. Common examples are paper plants or foundries, where the huge primary machine often dwarfs any other process both in size and in investment. But for most systems, I believe that with forcing a large bottleneck, the cure is worse than the disease.

9.7.3 Is It Really a Pull System?

I have listed drum-buffer-rope as a pull system. This is sort of true. Instead of limiting the inventory, it limits the work content, which has the same effect. Combined with a signal to release the next job, this makes drum-buffer-rope into a pull system. However, depending on the type of drum-buffer-rope, the pull loop extends only from the bottleneck (the drum) upstream. Any processes downstream of the drum no longer have an inventory limit. Therefore, drum-buffer-rope is only a pull system upstream of the drum.

Downstream of the drum it is a push system, and material can accumulate. If the drum is truly the bottleneck, then this is unlikely to happen, as all processes downstream of the bottleneck will always be starved for material by the bottleneck anyway. However, shifting bottlenecks or changes in the system that are not reflected by a move of the drum can cause material to accumulate downstream of the drum. Therefore drum-buffer-rope is only a partial pull system, as the work content is only limited upstream of the drum.

Chapter 10
Pull Systems Outside of Manufacturing

This book describes pull systems with a particular focus on manufacturing. However, **pull is not limited to manufacturing**. There are many more systems where pull can be applied, as for example healthcare, administration, development, and many more. This chapter will give you inspiration on how to apply pull to areas outside of manufacturing, although it is not intended to be a comprehensive coverage.

All non-manufacturing systems that require materials can use pull to supply any order-to-stock material. Any kind of kanban or reorder point method is well suited to supply your regularly used materials. Custom-ordered material is not controlled by pull, but merely ordered as needed, similar to manufacturing systems.

Here are some ideas and examples on how pull could look in different areas. It may be helpful for you to also read the sections on other areas, as often these ideas can help with similar problems in widely different industries.

10.1 Healthcare

The flow of material and patients in hospitals can also be managed through pull systems. As stated in Chapter 2.2, pull is a limit on the number of items or patients in the system, combined with a signal for replenishment or release.

10.1.1 Single-Use Items

The consumables you regularly need for healthcare—medications, bandages, protective equipment, disinfectant, wipes, single-use instruments, and many more—can easily be managed using kanban or reorder points. Distributing items from a central storage to the different departments can be done using transport kanban with milk runs. Be extra careful with the margin of safety, as a stock-out on a critical medication can cause the death of a patient. It is again a trade-off between the cost of the inventory and the consequences of a stock-out, with the consequences being potentially deadly.

Healthcare also has processes similar to manufacturing. Some medications and other items are prepared on demand for the patient. Some doctors like to have their customized kit of tools for the operating room, which is put together beforehand. Other tools have to be sterilized between use. Such items could be make-to-stock or make-to-order. Here, too, conventional manufacturing pull systems for make-to-order and make-to-stock can be used. Depending on the severity of a missing item, make sure to **bias availability over the cost of inventory for make-to-stock items**. Similarly, **bias the lead time over the utilization for make-to-order items**.

10.1.2 Multi-Use Items

Healthcare also has unusual processes where the product keeps on moving in a loop. Some instruments are reusable, but need to be sterilized, cleaned, wrapped, recharged, or otherwise prepared after every use. These could be surgical instruments, endoscopes, bedsheets, respirators, or many other multi-use products. These have the benefit that they are automatically a pull system. The inventory limit within this pull system is... drumroll... the number of items in the loop. **The number of hemostat clamps you have is the number of hemostat clamps you have.** The item is effectively a kanban.

An additional benefit is that such **multi-use items are usually make-to-stock**, which helps with their management.

However, designing the pull loops may be a bit difficult. Let's take again the hemostat clamps. You may have a central sterilization department with an autoclave, supplying the different sections (e.g., operating rooms) of your hospital. A sterilized clamp is the equivalent of your part with an attached kanban, and a dirty clamp is your kanban coming back to start replenishment.

There are different approaches available. You could establish separate loops for both the sterilization and the different operating rooms. However, for this to work you would hand out sterilized clamps only in exchange for a returned used clamp, which is impractical. This not-so-good example is visualized in Figure 150.

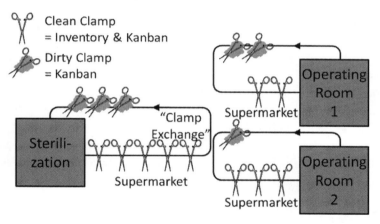

Figure 150: Flawed example of hospital clamp supply example with separate loops for all departments (Image Roser)

Another inferior possibility would be to have completely separate loops for every final destination department. This is visualized in Figure 151. However, this solution is also not good, since every clamp is now assigned to one department only. This is inflexible.

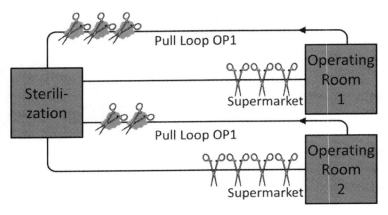

Figure 151: Flawed example of hospital clamp supply example with separate loops for the final destinations (Image Roser)

Probably the best approach are nested loops. Each department has its own loop, including its own supermarket, similar to a transport kanban. This loop should have an inventory limit of clamps high enough to ensure a good availability. The sterilization department itself does not have an explicit loop. All clamps that are returned are sterilized and added to an inventory of ready-to-use clamps. This inventory, however, is NOT a supermarket. If a clamp is removed, it does not generate a signal to replenish. Hence, without a signal it is not a supermarket, but only "almost a supermarket". Nevertheless, the signal in the form of a used clamp will come back eventually, but only after passing through one of the subsequent loops. This nested system is visualized in Figure 152.

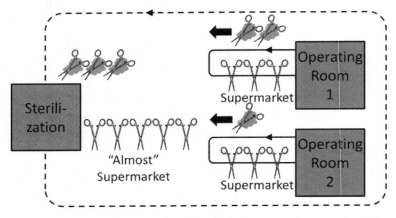

Figure 152: Feasible example of hospital clamp supply example with nested loops (Image Roser)

Nevertheless, the system is limited by the total number of clamps. It also has a signal to replenish, although it is somewhat unconventional. Hence, it is a pull system. Between the sterilization and all end customers, the inventory limit is the number of clamps. Any dirty clamp coming back is a signal to clean (replenish) the clamp.

Furthermore, for organizational ease, it makes sense for the operating rooms to always fill up their supermarket inventory to the maximum, regardless of how many clamps have been consumed. Whenever a clamp is taken out of the supermarket, the resupply of a fresh clamp should be issued. This could be done, for example, through transport kanban using a milk run. Otherwise, a clamp could only be moved into the supermarket if a dirty clamp is returned, which again limits the flexibility.

Overall, the inventory needs to be limited within the reuse loop. It also has a signal to replenish. Otherwise, material may accumulate in certain locations, while other locations run out of items.

Make sure to have enough clamps to fill all supermarkets, have clamps in the return loop, and have time to sterilize them. Both the supermarkets at the operating room and the total number of clamps need to be defined. You also need to occasionally check the number of clamps in the system to see if any are missing. This is similar to the check for missing kanbans, as explained in Chapter 13.1.

10.1.3 Patients

Patients in hospitals are a special situation. They are both the product and the customer. Effectively, it is more of a service, where the patients are served by the doctors. There are multiple complications with having patients in a pull system. **It is difficult to limit the number of patients arriving.** This is the main factor which makes pull a bit more difficult for patients, as described in Chapter 2.6.1.

Second, **while parts have no problem waiting indefinitely, patients are much less... well... patient.** Let them wait for too long, and they will complain, their health may worsen, and they may even die. If you call them in for a second appointment, they may miss it. Multiple visits instead of a single appointment may be an undue burden on the patient. Hence, the needs on timeliness for the patients are also very important.

However, here, too, pull can be used. You need to decouple the flow of incoming patients from the rest of the system. In effect, you let (some of) your patients wait. However, not all patients can wait. You must prioritize your patients according to urgency. For manufacturing, I do not recommend more than two levels of priority (*urgent* and *normal*). Healthcare is the exception, and multiple levels of priority are highly recommended. This is called triage, from French *trier*, which means to separate or select. Figure 153 shows an example of such a triage system with four levels, although other hospitals may use a different number or definition of levels.[89]

	1 Red Rescuscitaton 0 min	2 Orange Urgent 15 min	3 Yellow Less Urgent 60 min	4 Green Not Urgent 180 min
Breathing	Obstructed airway Stridor	Threatened airway		
SpO₂ Oxygen Saturation	< 80	80-89	90-94	≥ 95
Respiratory Rate	<8 or >35	31-35	26-30	8-25
Heart Rate	>130	<40 or 121-130	40-49 or 111-120	50-110
Blood Pressure Systolic	<80	80-89		
Glasgow Coma Score	<8	9-13	14	15
Temperature		<32 or >40	32-34 or 38.1-40	34.1-38

Figure 153: Hospital triage prioritization system with clear standards and multiple levels of priority. Based on Barfod et al.[90] Use original source for medical purposes! (Image Roser)

Another complication with most healthcare providers is that **patients flow through the system similar to a job shop**. Some healthcare service providers may be more like a flow shop, particularly if they are specializing in a certain type of treatment, like eye lasering or cosmetic surgery. But

---

[89] Inevitably, this will get you complaints from Karen's that they are *"waiting over two hours now with their migraine while the guy that just came in leaking body fluids all over the place gets treated right away!"*

[90] Charlotte Barfod et al., *Abnormal Vital Signs Are Strong Predictors for Intensive Care Unit Admission and In-Hospital Mortality in Adults Triaged in the Emergency Department - a Prospective Cohort Study, Scandinavian Journal of Trauma, Resuscitation and Emergency Medicine* 20, no. 1 April 10, 2012: 28.

especially for larger hospitals, patients move between different departments within a hospital with little repetition. An example is given in Figure 154. Job shops are generally more difficult to manage than flow shops.

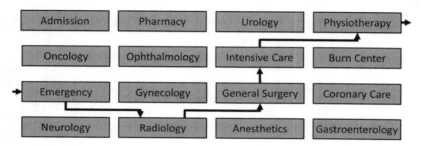

Figure 154: Example path of a patient through the different departments of a hospital. This is effectively a job shop. (Image Roser)

Furthermore, the path of a patient through the hospital is often difficult to determine and plan beforehand. There is similar uncertainty regarding the time a patient remains in each department. As the patient is diagnosed, different departments may be added or removed from the schedule for this patient. In the worst case, death cancels all future appointments but will now keep the morgue busy.

Also, **patients are always a make-to-order type of situation.** It is almost a cliché to say "every patient is different", but it is true. Even with a high level of specialization that many doctors nowadays have, the many different factors of a patient from age, weight, gender, medical history, etc. make standardized treatment difficult. Even if this is possible, you can't do a couple of appendectomies beforehand just so you have them on stock when a patient comes.

Finally, in manufacturing, operators are (somewhat) used to following orders that come down from management. Not so in medicine. **Doctors often have very strong opinions on how the hospital should be run.** Ordering "demigods in white" around is asking for trouble. It is much more effort to convince them. For example, the assignment of limited resources like operating rooms is often much more a political power issue than based on factual needs. Some hospitals had success with strictly separating the management of the patient flow from the medical treatment. The patient flow is arranged by pull, and the medical treatment is whatever the doctor thinks is best.

Grappling with all these problems makes patient management challenging. In some cases, you have an automatic pull system as your number of patients are limited by the number of spaces, like hospital beds, intensive care beds, operating rooms, and other single patient equipment. You cannot have more patients than beds. Fewer beds make a better utilization, but more beds can handle peak demands better. Whenever a bed becomes available again, a new patient can be admitted.

Actually, good "bed management" is important to assign the patients to their best locations. A patient ending up in the wrong ward happens more often than hospitals would like to admit. I once shared a room in a Japanese hospital with nine elderly women for a night, simply because they mistakenly assigned the wrong gender to me on the admission form. While the mistake cleared up quickly once they took a look at me, the men's room was already full, making for an awkward night for me and even more so for the nine women.

Different from inpatient care, in ambulatory or outpatient care your patients are waiting at home or in waiting rooms. There is not really any limit for the healthcare provider on how many patients are waiting at home for an appointment. This often creates very long lead times at the cost of time and suffering to the patient. Reducing the lead time would reduce suffering and improve the patients' health.

Overall, scheduling patients is a difficult task similar to job shop scheduling, but with additional complications. There is plenty of literature focusing on healthcare, which would exceed the scope of this book.[91, 92] I also enjoyed the success story of Virginia Mason Medical in Seattle, Washington, USA.[93]

[91] Mark Graban, *Lean Hospitals: Improving Quality, Patient Safety, and Employee Engagement, Second Edition*, 2nd edition New York, USA: Productivity Press, 2011, ISBN 978-1-4398-7043-3.

[92] Marc Baker, Ian Taylor, and Alan Mitchell, *Making Hospitals Work: How to Improve Patient Care While Saving Everyone's Time and Hospitals' Resources*, 1.1 Edition Lean Enterprise Academy Limited, 2011, ISBN 978-0-9551473-2-6.

[93] Charles Kenney and Donald M. Berwick, *Transforming Health Care: Virginia Mason Medical Center's Pursuit of the Perfect Patient Experience*, 1st edition Boca Raton, Florida, USA: CRC Press, 2010, ISBN 978-1-56327-375-9.

10.2 Project Management and Development

Project management also benefits from lean. In software development, a popular method is Agile Software Development, which overlaps a lot with the ideas of lean manufacturing. Lean product development also often includes methods like "design for manufacturing and assembly" (DFMA).

Projects in general are **make-to-order**, often in a **job shop** type of project flow. As with all make-to-order systems, **the number of projects is a trade-off between the lead time and the utilization**. There are, however, a few differences between manufacturing of parts and development of projects.

In manufacturing, only one process can work at one part at a time. In development, however, **multiple developers or programmers can work on the same project simultaneously**, often on different subcomponents, sub-programs, or sub-aspects of the project. Often, while the developers wait for information on one project, they work on another project.

Another difference is that in manufacturing, the utilization goes up with the inventory. One hundred percent utilization would in theory require an infinite inventory. **With project management both the lead time and the utilization will be worse if there are too many projects**. Developers and other project related people usually need to coordinate with their colleagues. In product design, mechanical engineers, electrical engineers, and programmers are often involved in the same project. Depending on your product, you may also need chemists, biologists, mathematicians, and others to take part in the development. Similarly, software development often involves many different programmers.

The people involved need to coordinate, which takes time. **The more projects a developer has, the more time is needed for coordination.** I have seen departments where developers were in charge of ten projects or more. After all the coordination meetings, there was almost no time left for actual development. The developers subsequently focused on the one or two projects that they felt most important and ditched the rest (although they communicated it more diplomatically to their management). Since eight out of ten projects were not worked on at all, the lead time went through the roof while the actual productive output suffered.

Hence, you need to carefully decide the **number of projects for one person** to get the most out of your project teams. Keep in mind that often **many**

projects depend on a few key people, who then will have a very high project work load again. The ideal number of projects for a person is subject to much debate. Often, around three simultaneous projects for one person is seen as a good workload, although it depends on your situation.

Similarly, the **total number of projects under development** should also be limited. The number of projects depends on the number of people you have, and how many projects they can work on simultaneously. This is very similar to a CONWIP system. You can limit the total number of projects, or you can limit the workload of these projects. In the latter case, a smaller project requiring fewer people would have a lower demand on the development capacity, but would require an estimation of this workload. Often, simply limiting the number of simultaneous projects is easiest.

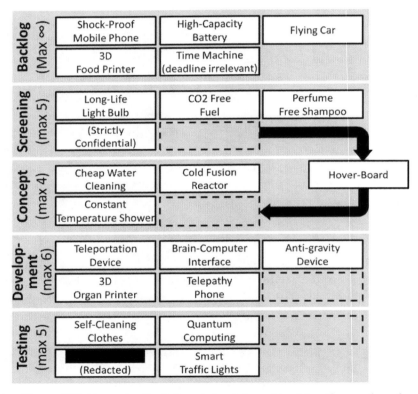

Figure 155: Example of a fictional simple board tracking the number of development projects across different stages (Image Roser)

You can also track and limit the number of projects for different stages of the development process. For example, software development often moves from planning to analysis, design, development, testing, and implementation. For product development, it is often from screening of ideas to concept analysis, development, and testing. If you work in development, you surely have divided the overall process into similar sub-steps.

Figure 155 shows a fictional example of a simple board for tracking and limiting the number of simultaneous projects in different stages of product development. A completed project can move forward only if a slot is available in the next stage. The backlog of open projects is prioritized, and the highest-priority project takes the first available slot in the first stage.

10.3 Administration

Administration can have many different aspects. You could have highly repetitive tasks with few variations, or you could have highly specialized tasks where every new task is quite different. Similar to manufacturing, many administrative processes probably have a spectrum ranging from highly repetitive tasks to exotic assignments. The exotic tasks are probably much less frequent than the highly repetitive tasks.

However, even the highly repetitive tasks are usually not "on stock", but are make-to-order. Only highly unusual offices keep an "inventory of completed administrative tasks" on hand in case a customer needs one. For most offices, even though the processing may be very similar, the task itself is unique. Hence, it is a make-to-order situation, and the goal is a trade-off between lead time and utilization.

Hence, CONWIP or its variants would be the right approach to establish pull systems in an office. The backlog of open tasks may also be prioritized. For the frequent and repetitive tasks, you may even consider establishing a flow line if the tasks have to go through multiple administrative staff.

In any case, even though the implementation may look different from manufacturing, the basics are the same. Limit the number of tasks to improve the lead time. Whenever a task leaves the system, it should give a signal to start the next task.

10.4 Construction Industry

Most of the material required for the construction industry can be provided using conventional pull systems. However, there are some materials with a very short life span between preparation and consumption. Examples are hot asphalt or concrete in mixing trucks. Wait too long, and the asphalt is getting cold or the concrete will start to set.

Let's take the example of hot asphalt. You can easily establish a pull system using trucks supplying hot asphalt from the asphalt plant to the road works. The number of kanbans would be the number of trucks in the loop. You would need enough trucks to ensure a good asphalt availability, so the paving machine does not run out of asphalt. Effectively, one truck represents one kanban for a truckload of hot asphalt.

The number of trucks depends on the replenishment time. The longer the drive, the more trucks you need. This should also cover fluctuations. However, since these fluctuations happen both on the outbound and the return trip, you may have multiple trucks waiting in front of the paving machine, while the asphalt is cooling down. If the trucks wait too long, the asphalt will no longer be hot enough and has to return to the plant for reheating. This situation is shown in Figure 156.

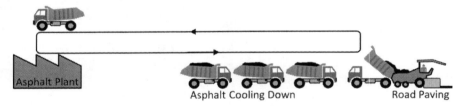

Figure 156: Example of supplying asphalt using a conventional pull loop. The asphalt is cooling down while waiting to be used. (Image Roser)

A slight modification to this asphalt pull system would be an additional signal. The trucks do not wait with asphalt in front of the paving machine. Instead, the empty trucks wait in front of the asphalt plant. A signal comes from the paving machine to release the next truck. This truck fills up with asphalt and transports it to the paving machine. The signal has to be early enough so that the truck has enough time to fill up and drive to the destination, even with fluctuations. This will have most trucks waiting empty, and only a few trucks waiting with hot asphalt. Since there are fewer trucks with asphalt, the asphalt has less time to cool down. This is visualized in Figure 157. Similar systems can easily be imagined for concrete mixer trucks.

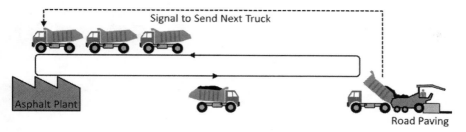

Figure 157: Example of supplying asphalt using a modified pull loop with a signal for release. A separate signal informs the next truck to pick up a shipment of hot asphalt. (Image Roser)

Chapter 11
Pull System Layout

Pull production creates a feedback loop from the departure of an item or job back to the beginning where new items are produced or ordered or jobs are released. Departure of an item creates a signal to replenish or to start the next job. The inventory within these loops is limited. Together, this makes each loop a pull system. One key question for pull is therefore the range of these loops. **Where should your loops start and end?** Should you split one big loop into multiple smaller loops? Should you merge smaller loops? Let me help you with that.

11.1 Loop Sizes

A critical distinction for your loop is if you have a **flow shop** (much easier), a branching flow shop (a bit more difficult), or a **job shop** (much more difficult). There are also many intermediate stages where part of your system is a flow shop and other parts are a messier job shop. It could even be different for different products. Some products flow easily along the flow line. Other products may skip parts of the flow line. Others may go at one point to a process outside of the flow line, or even loop back to be processed again at a previous process in the flow line. **The more exceptions and irregularities you have in your material flow, the more difficult it becomes to make nice loops.**

11.1.1 One Single All-Encompassing Loop

It is always possible is to make a **single all-encompassing loop**. This is easiest for straight flow shops, but also possible for branched flow shops or job shops, as shown in Figure 158.

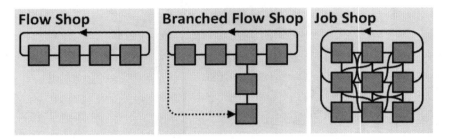

Figure 158: Illustration of a flow shop, a branched flow shop, and a job shop with a single pull loop. (Image Roser)

If there are incoming branches (e.g., if the product needs subcomponents), then the loop would have to initiate the production or shipping of these subcomponents too. Whenever a material or job leaves the system, the information to replenish needs to go not only to the beginning of the main branch but also to the beginning of every sub-branch that feeds into the main branch. The start of the work on the subcomponent may be timed to start at the same time, later, or even earlier than the work on the main component. You just have to ensure that the component is ready when it is needed.

A well-known example is the manufacturing of seats for cars, where in most cases each seat is made explicitly for a single car. The order of a car has not only to start the production of the car but also the production of the seat. The seat also has to arrive just-in-sequence to avoid mix-ups. If a delivery just-in-sequence is not possible, the buffer inventory between the last process of the branch and the next process of the main line needs to be able to readjust the sequence for make-to-order items.

If the system is a job shop, the routing is different for different products, and the final route may not even be known in advance. Here it is also possible to have a single all-encompassing loop. Whenever a job leaves the job shop, a new job can be started. However, this system would need additional information about the path of a product (i.e., the process sequence for each job needs to be known beforehand or determined in process).

11.1.2 Loops for Different Segments

It is also possible to make **loops for different segments** or groups of processes. The challenge here is to manage the transition from one loop to the next loop. The output of the preceding loop is now the input for the next loop. This is visualized in Figure 159.

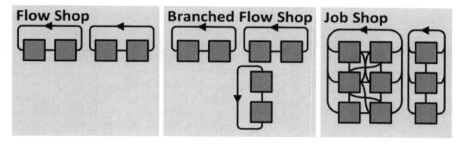

Figure 159: Illustration of a flow shop, a branched flow shop, and a job shop with different smaller segments of pull loops (Image Roser)

This is extra work. Hence, you should not do this just because it is possible, but only if there is a valid reason for it. Please see the next section, 11.2, for more details on where to split into different loops. For job shops in particular, it may be difficult to find a good spot to divide the job shop into segments.

11.1.3 Loops for Individual Processes

Finally, you can have **separate loops for every single process**. This is the most complex solution that requires the largest effort to set up and maintain. On the other hand, it gives you the finest level of individual workload of the processes and allows frequent re-prioritization. The POLCA method presented in Chapter 7 actually uses these type of loops by default. Figure 160 shows examples of individual loops.

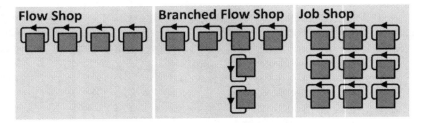

Figure 160: Illustration of a flow shop, a branched flow shop, and a job shop with individual pull loops for every process (Image Roser)

11.1.4 Single Loop for Splits in Material Flow

The easiest way to do a split in the material flow is after a single loop, as shown in Figure 161. If it is a make-to-stock pull system, the inventory at the end of the loop is a supermarket, and the subsequent processes take whatever they need. If it is a make-to-order system, the job is moved to the next process after the loop, as per the rules of the subsequent process. The entire inventory limit should be able to fit in the buffer to avoid blocking.

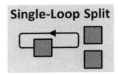

Figure 161: Illustration of a split within a single loop (Image Roser)

11.1.5 Multiple Loops for Splits in Material Flow

Another option is to have separate loops for every direction that the material flow can take in a split. This is illustrated in Figure 162 for two subsequent processes. The number of loops goes up with the number of processes. This is the default approach of POLCA.

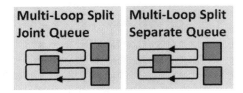

Figure 162: Illustration of a split with multiple loops for both a joint queue for production and separate queues for production (Image Roser)

For this to work, **the entire inventory or workload limit of each loop must fit into the inventory at the end of the respective loop**. Otherwise, a full loop in one direction may again block the first process. The sequence of cards returning to the first process also needs some consideration. Since there are cards returning from multiple loops, **the first process needs to decide which card should be processed first**. All possible jobs, regardless for which loop, should be prioritized.

The returning information from different loops could go into a combined queue for production on a first-come-first-serve basis, as shown in Figure 162 on the left. You could also have separate queues for production for each loop, as shown in Figure 162 on the right. In this case, the first process needs a clear standard on when to serve which queue for production. Care should be taken that when the loop splits, the material is moved in the correct direction. Make sure the information regarding the respective loop is well visible on the cards.

Even if there are multiple processes within the loop, such a **multi-loop split is easier to understand** compared to a single-loop split. On the other hand, a **multi-loop split drastically increases your number of pull loops**. It will depend on the situation in your system if it is better to have fewer but more complicated loops or more but easier loops. **If in doubt, use a single-loop split.**

11.1.6 Separate Loops for Every Possible Path

Literature sometimes suggests in particular for CONWIP a separate loop for every possible path of the material flow. This is called m-CONWIP for "multiple CONWIP" loops.[94] While academically interesting, it quickly becomes very messy in reality. Figure 163 shows an example with three different routings through nine processes.

[94] Remco Germs and Jan Riezebos, *Workload Balancing Capability of Pull Systems in MTO Production, International Journal of Production Research* 48, no. 8 April 15, 2010: 2345–60.

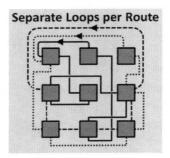

Figure 163: Example job shop with three separate loops through nine processes for the possible routings (Image Roser)

Even though there are only three different routings, it already becomes confusing and difficult to manage. The operators have to take constant care to make sure each card stays on its intended route, which is confusing, and frequent mistakes can be expected. I strongly **advise against such a separate-loop type of routing**. It may be usable if there are only very few different routes that by itself differ little, as for example the multi-loop splits shown in Figure 162. But avoid this if it becomes complex, which it quickly will. POLCA uses separate loops for every possible path, but a loop covers only the gap between two processes.

11.1.7 Serial Loop Types

It is possible to combine different types of pull production (and sometimes even push if it cannot be helped) for your value stream. One or more kanban loops that feed into supermarkets can easily supply one or more CONWIP loops. Similar can also be done with many other pull methods. An example is shown in Figure 164.

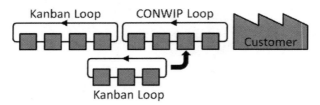

Figure 164: Sequence of kanban and CONWIP loops (Image Roser)

Figure 165 gives you an overview of the possible combinations. Which type of pull system (or push) can feed into which other type of pull system (or push). There is a lot of compatibility, with only a few restrictions.

😊 Good
😐 Possible
☹️ Bad

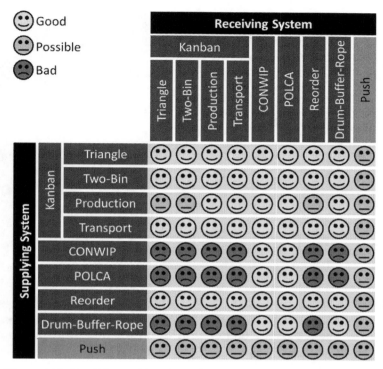

Figure 165: Possible combinations of loop control type sequence (Image Roser)

First, **avoid transitions from make-to-order to make-to-stock**. Systems suited for make-to-stock production like kanban or reorder systems can easily feed into systems suited to make-to-order production like CONWIP, or POLCA. However, the other direction of make-to-order feeding into make-to-stock is not suitable. If a CONWIP system supplies a kanban system, then you will have custom-made parts supplying make-to-stock products. Since the make-to-order part is only produced if there is a demand, the lead time for the entire system would be excessive. Hence, I advise against such combinations. Fortunately, it is rare to have a make-to-order system feeding into a make-to-stock system, as this usually makes no sense technically.

A second, smaller limitation tries to avoid **infrequent large orders for a preceding system that is set up for production of small quantities**. In particular, **reorder systems** may have large orders to refill the entire stock back to the target level, but **triangle kanban** and **two-bin kanban** systems can also batch demand into larger orders.

Those systems do not convey the information of their demand until they reach the minimum inventory. Once they reach the minimum, they demand everything at the same time. It is possible to have a supply system that produces frequent small quantities for a receiving system that has infrequent but large orders. However, you need additional inventory to decouple these fluctuations. Hence, it may be better to have small orders from the receiving system.

Altogether, to avoid large buffer inventories, it may be better to have another kanban system following the first kanban system instead of a reorder system. Yet, if the delta between the minimum level and the target level of the receiving reorder point system is small enough, it can work.

Finally, **all combinations involving push are marked neutral**, since pull is almost always superior to push. It is possible to have a push-pull combination in both directions if set up carefully. Push-pull boundaries can happen if a transition from push to pull has not yet transformed the entire value stream, or if some segments of your value stream are unsuitable for pull production as described in Chapter 2.5. Still, go for pull if possible, and see push as a temporary situation until you have time to change it into a pull system. Such combinations along serial loop types can be from push to pull as well as from pull to push.

11.1.8 Overlapping and Intersecting Loops

It is possible to have **loops of different types overlap**. If you plan to do this, consider in particular combinations of kanban and CONWIP, as shown in Figure 166. As explained in Chapter 6.2.1, kanban and CONWIP can be combined well in the same loop. It is important that **every part type is clearly assigned to one loop only** wherever it is in the value stream. If there is some ambiguity which loop a part in the system belongs to, then there will be mistakes and problems. It is important that there is always a **clear standard as to which part to make at every process**. Ideally, the first process needs to have a standard to decide which loop to serve, and all subsequent processes merely work in FIFO sequence. See Chapter 6.2.3 and 6.2.4 for more details. Due to different control approaches, avoid combinations including drum-buffer-rope, POLCA, and reorder point.

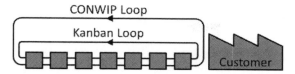

Figure 166: Common example of a CONWIP loop overlapping with a kanban loop (Image Roser)

Another approach often mentioned is a **combination of push and pull** within the same segment of the value stream. Some parts, often the make-to-stock items, are controlled with an inventory limit using a pull system. Other parts, usually the make-to-order items, are simply pushed into the system whenever needed.

An example of such a hybrid push-pull system using kanban is shown in Figure 167. This is possible, but I find it troublesome. It can work, but only if the share of push-type items is significantly smaller than the share of pull-type items. Even then, there is a risk of a high demand of push-type items leading to delays and stock-outs of pull-type items. Due to the pull aspect, the overall inventory in the segment can also spin out of control if too much is pushed into the system simultaneously. I would much rather prefer also to control the "push" items with a CONWIP system or other pull system.

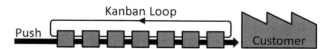

Figure 167: Example of a not recommended hybrid push-pull system using kanban (Image Roser)

It is also possible, but more complicated, to have **overlapping loops of different sizes**. Figure 168 shows a feasible example, where two kanban loops for the make-to-stock items overlap with a single CONWIP loop for the make-to-order items. Processes may have two possible inputs, one from each loop. It is important that there is always a **clear standard as to which part to make at every process**. For example, the first processes for each kanban loop in Figure 168 could have the rule to always make any CONWIP part first before making a kanban part. All other processes may follow FIFO and simply make the next part that comes down the line. Especially the two processes at the kanban loop transition also need to have very clear standards regarding which information flow to initiate when. Mistakes in this information flow will create chaos for the entire system. I usually find this risk too high, and would **advise against such a loop structure**.

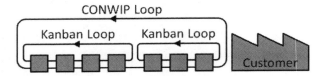

Figure 168: Feasible but not recommended example of a CONWIP loop overlapping with two kanban loops (Image Roser)

Figure 169 shows an example, which at first glance is very similar to Figure 168, but much more of a headache to implement. The CONWIP loop starts one process later than the kanban loop. Where does the CONWIP material come from? If it comes from the kanban material, then kanbans will be taken out of the loop somewhere in the middle of the loop, which is not good. Even if you have a good material supply, it is an extra hassle to decide which part to make, particularly at the second process.

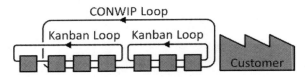

Figure 169: Poor example of a CONWIP loop partially overlapping and intersecting with two kanban loops (Image Roser)

In sum, I **recommend avoiding partially overlapping loops**. This will reduce a potential source of ambiguity and errors. I **strongly recommend avoiding intersecting loops**. It is easiest and often better if the loops for all parts start at the same process or inventory and also end at the same process or inventory. In Chapter 11.2 I will go into more details on when to break the value stream into different pull loops.

Please also **avoid combinations of push and pull within the same pull loop**. The key feature and benefit of pull is to restrict the number of parts within the pull loop, including a signal to replenish. If an overlapping push system can push material into the pull loop unrestricted, you will end up not with a partial pull system but only with a push system. The push element can stuff the pull loop with material until the pull system loses its benefit of limited inventory. **Try to avoid push within a pull loop whenever possible**.

11.1.9 On the Hand-Over

Regarding the hand-over of the material, there are two options visualized in Figure 170. You could consider **completed parts outside of the previous loop**, and the pull information is sent back as soon as the part is completed at the last process within the loop. This is sometimes called a "push gap", as the material in between is no longer controlled by pull. Hence it is push. You can also have the **completed parts within the previous loop**. In this case, all material is controlled by pull.

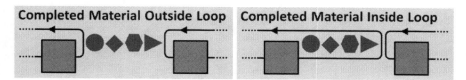

Figure 170: Completed material can be outside of the loop or inside of the loop. The latter is usually better. (Image Roser)

We have to distinguish between make-to-stock and make-to-order. Make-to-stock controls the finished-goods inventory within the loop. Hence, **it is essential for make-to-stock to keep completed parts within the pull loop until they are moved to the next loop**. The pull loop information stays attached with the parts in the loop. It is removed only when the subsequent process or customer actually takes the part. In the worst case, the card is removed if the part is scrapped or disassembled. Make-to-stock parts always should be in a loop. Otherwise, you risk overproduction, and your system is no longer pull. Material between two loops could accumulate, and you would lose all the benefits of pull production.

If it is a **make-to-order system like CONWIP, both options are possible**. The goal of make-to-order is not material availability, but a trade-off between utilization and inventory. Here we can usually assume that the customer wants the products as soon as possible, and not much material will accumulate anyway. But even then, keeping all material within the loop is a safer approach. See also Chapter 6.7.1 for this question on CONWIP systems.

11.2 When to Break Loops

Usually, good lean manufacturing systems are often divided into different pull loops. This makes the system more manageable, and can also improve its speed. The big question, however, is: Where do you break the value stream into separate loops? Figure 171 shows the four possibilities for three processes.

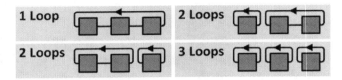

Figure 171: Four options to split a system with three processes into different loops (Image Roser)

Between processes you always have two options. It could be a transition between loops. For make-to-stock, this would be a supermarket. If it is not a transition between loops, it should be a limited-buffer inventory, ideally a FIFO. You can make a single big loop over all three processes, split the processes into two loops, or even split the processes into three separate loops with one loop for each process.

As a general rule, **use a FIFO whenever there is no reason against it**. A FIFO is much easier to control and manage. Establishing a pull loop usually requires more work to both implement and keep it running smoothly. Hence, unless there is a good reason against it, use FIFO by default.

At Toyota, this is called "flow where you can, pull where you can't". However, this can confuse, since the material definitely also flows within a pull system. What Toyota means by "pull" here is a supermarket in the case of kanban, or—more generally—a break between pull loops. Hence, the material "flows" between supermarkets or general breaks between loops, and is "pulled" from the supermarket. The message, however, is good and I fully agree. Use FIFO ("flow") whenever you can, and break loops ("pull") where you can't.

Therefore, **make your pull loops as big as possible unless there is a reason not to**. What follows are my reasons for breaking a system into two pull loops. Most of these reasons are not absolute musts, but suggestions. You always have to **make the trade-off between the efforts of creating two separate loops versus the benefit of it**.

11.2.1 Break Loops for Lot Size Differences

It may be necessary to break into different loops if the lot sizes are different. This can be avoided by simply using the same lot size throughout the value stream. However, sometimes processes either outright require a certain lot size or at least benefit from a certain lot size. For example, an oven may fit only a certain number of parts, or a time-consuming changeover benefits from larger lot sizes. If the processes in your value stream have different lot size requirements, it may be necessary to break into different pull loops.

To the best of my knowledge, this may be the only situation where breaking a loop may be absolutely necessary. All other reasons are only suggestions of varying emphasis. Figure 172 shows a few examples of different lot sizes for a simple pull loop with two processes.

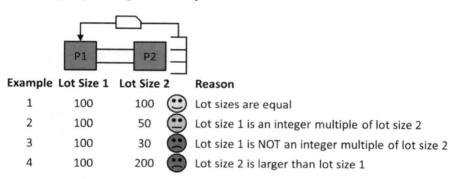

Example	Lot Size 1	Lot Size 2		Reason
1	100	100	🙂	Lot sizes are equal
2	100	50	😐	Lot size 1 is an integer multiple of lot size 2
3	100	30	🙁	Lot size 1 is NOT an integer multiple of lot size 2
4	100	200	😠	Lot size 2 is larger than lot size 1

Figure 172: Example for processes with different lot sizes (Image Roser)

If the **lot sizes are equal,** as in example 1 in Figure 172, then there is no problem whatsoever. It is not necessary to break the system into separate pull loops. This is the ideal lot size situation.

If the **previous lot size is an integer multiple of the subsequent lot size**, then it is also not a problem. Example 2 in Figure 172 has a lot size of 100 at P1, which constitutes exactly two lots of 50 at P2. In effect, P2 is forced to have the same lot size as P1 by repeating two lots of 50 each.

If the **previous lot size is *not* an integer multiple of the subsequent lot size**, then you may have a problem. Example 3 in Figure 172 shows such a situation where P1 has a lot size of 100 and P2 has a lot size of 30. You can no longer split the previous lot size in an integer number of subsequent lot sizes anymore, as in example 2. If you need to use exactly a lot size of 30 every time for P2, then there will be either 10 parts at P2 left uncompleted, or one lot size of P2 will be short by 20 parts. If the **lot sizes are fixed**, and you don't want to rearrange parts in the FIFO, then the only option is to have three lots at P1 (300 parts) followed by 10 lots at P2 (also 300 parts). However, this is different if the **lot sizes are not fixed but only a minimum**. If the lot size at P2 is not fixed at 30 but flexible with *at least 30*, a lot of 100 would work for P2 since it has at least 30 parts.

Finally, if the **subsequent lot size is larger than the previous one**, then there is a risk of not completing a full lot at the subsequent process. In example 4 in Figure 172, P1 may complete 100 parts, but P2 requires 200 parts to make a full lot. Hence, P2 may come up short since P1 is already producing other items. You would always have to make two lots at P1 to satisfy the lot size requirement at P2.

Overall, try to **keep the same lot size for one batch throughout the entire loop** whenever possible. Changing lot sizes within a loop is always a hassle. In any case, this rule can easily be avoided by adjusting lot sizes throughout the process. I find this rarely to be an issue on the shop floor.

Please note that this does not mean that all product types that go through the system need the same lot size. It does not even apply to different batches of the same product. Just **avoid changing the lot size for one batch within a pull loop**. For example, you can easily have a system where your high-runner product A has a lot size of 100 throughout the pull loop, but an exotic product C has only a lot size of 30. You can even have a lot size of 100 for product A, and later a different batch of the same product A with a lot size of 80. This is not an issue and is commonly done in many production systems. It is only a problem if you have a lot of 100 of product A that changes to 80 for this very lot at some point within the same pull loop.

11.2.2 Break Loops in Front of the Customer

In almost all cases, it is strongly recommended to end a pull loop in front of the customer. In other words, the last process or inventory in your organization should also be the end of the pull loop, as shown in Figure 173. Otherwise, the pull loop would extend to your customer, which means that the information to start the next work in your pull loop would have to flow through your customer too.

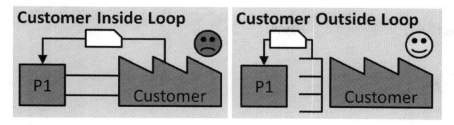

Figure 173: Example of pull loops with the customer inside and outside of the loop (Image Roser)

The customer would issue your replenishment orders directly. This is not necessarily impossible. However, the customer would also control the inventory of your pull loop. It would also make it difficult to follow the rule that the supplying process controls the supermarket. Can you control the inventory at your customer? Does the customer control your production process? The customer will have to give you feedback if the parts leave the pull loop at the customer. This is tricky. If the customer forgets to give you the information, your system utilization will go down, your lead time may increase, you may run out of stock, and the deliveries to the customer may be late. Overall, **it is usually best to keep your pull loops and the pull loops of your customer separate**. Similar also applies if you are the customer for your suppliers.

There are a few exceptions. You can use a transport kanban or reorder point loop between the supplier and the customer. In this case, the loop is controlled by the customer (i.e., the customer controls the shipments). It is unusual for the customer to control production! If you do just-in-sequence production, it is possible for the customer to control the last loop of your production. The common example is again the seat suppliers for automotive, where the seats usually arrive just-in-sequence for the assembly line.

Even if you have a transport kanban or just-in-sequence between the supplier and the customer, the responsibility for this loop should be in one hand only. For example, the customer could use a transport kanban loop to order items from you. When you receive a transport kanban, you then send it back with the parts. The loop, however, is managed by the customer, and your last loop should end where the customer's transport kanban loop starts.

11.2.3 Break Loops for Splitting Material Flows

Another reason to decouple the material flow using separate pull loops is a splitting material flow. If some parts go in one direction and others in another direction, using two loops can make it easier for you. Three possible situations are shown in Figure 174, with the split either after the FIFO or before the FIFO, or separate loops altogether.

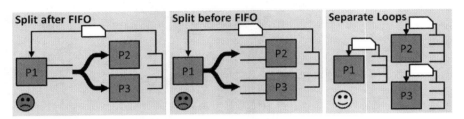

Figure 174: Examples for splitting material flows (Image Roser)

Such **a split can be managed within the same pull loop**. This is especially true if the two **subsequent paths can both handle any part**. If a part leaving P1 in Figure 174 could be processed either by P2 or by P3, then you can use the same pull loop, although your sequence may no longer be FIFO. In this case, a split after the FIFO would be easier.

However, if the **part must go through only one subsequent path but not the other**, then using the same loop may be problematic. Assume in Figure 174 parts A have to go to P2 and parts B have to go to P3. In effect you would have to break FIFO to rearrange the sequence. Even with a perfect ABAB... sequence in the FIFO, a subsequent process may have to wait due to other reasons, leading to a block. It is possible, but I usually recommend against it. It is much better to have separate loops, and the subsequent pull loops pick whichever part they need from the inventory at the end of the preceding loop. See Chapter 4.6.2 for more details. Overall, having separate loops may be easier. See also Chapter 11.1.5.

11.2.4 Break Loops for Merging of Material Flows

Similarly, using separate loops may also be helpful for merging material flows. This situation is often combined with splitting material flows, where the material splits into parallel processes and then merges again. Figure 175 shows examples with one larger loop and two separate loops.

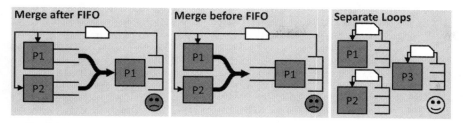

Figure 175: Examples for merging material flows within a pull loop or for separate loops (Image Roser)

There are a few possibilities. **Does the subsequent process assemble a product using components from the two (or more) preceding processes?** If it is only one big loop, a just-in-sequence production is necessary to ensure no mix-ups during a product change. If there are separate pull loops, it is not necessary to do just-in-sequence production. Instead, the subsequent process picks whatever it needs from the inventories after the preceding processes. Hence, separate loops may be easier.

Does the subsequent process work on parts from the preceding processes individually? In this case, the sequence is relevant. In the example in Figure 175, the sequence of parts leaving P1 and the sequence of parts leaving P2 have to be merged into a sequence of parts arriving at P3. If you leave it up to the operators of P3, they may prefer parts from one process over the other. Maybe because some parts are closer or are easier to do, maybe it is habit, but there may be some imbalance in the part consumption. If you have a rule of alternating usage of parts from P1 and P2, it may also go out of control if in the long-term one preceding process is faster than the other. It may be best to always take parts from the preceding process with the most completed parts, but even then, you may have issues.

Nevertheless, it is possible. For example, Toyota uses two merging FIFO when installing seats in cars. Whenever a car comes down the assembly line, the matching seat has to be at the end of the merging FIFO for seats. With Toyota, there are just too many seat variants to justify a supermarket. But in many other cases, **it may be easier to simply split the system into separate pull loops**.

11.2.5 Break Loops Between Very Different Cycle Times

A break in loops is also possible if two processes have very different cycle times. Coupling processes with different cycle times using a FIFO will lead to a lot of waiting time for the faster process. On the other hand, if the process would be decoupled, then the faster process may work on other products for other processes in the meantime. Alternatively, the faster process could work fewer shifts. Hence, if it is okay for the faster process to have lots of short idle times, then it can be in the same pull loop. This is common for automatic processes, but should be avoided for manual processes.

11.2.6 Break Loops Between Different Shift Patterns

Similar to different cycle times, it is possible to decouple the material flow for processes with different shift patterns. For example, if one process works one shift per day and the other process works two shifts per day, then **a break in the loops may make things easier**. In any case, the first process has to stockpile enough material to get the second process through the second shift. This material is required regardless of whether you use one or two loops.

The advantage of a break, however, is flexibility. If problems pop up during the second shift, an inventory in between may provide an alternative material. A FIFO on the other hand is stuck with the FIFO sequence—unless, of course, you manually override the FIFO principle and pull parts out of the middle of the FIFO. Overall, a break in the loop may give you more flexibility here compared to a FIFO.

11.2.7 Break Loops When Creating Different Variants

A break in the pull loops may also be advisable if the subsequent process creates different variants of the product. This is common in industry, especially with a change from make-to-stock parts into a make-to-order product.

Assume the first process makes standard blanks and the second process customizes these blanks into different variants, as visualized in Figure 176. Hence, the second process creates variants from the material received from the first process.

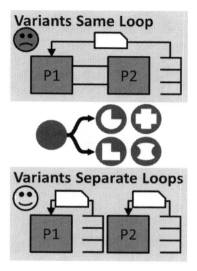

Figure 176: Example for creating 4 variants at the second process from one blank stock at the first process, either in the same loop or in separate loops (Image Roser)

In a FIFO, the process knows what to produce through the parts coming down the FIFO. However, when differentiating into variants, the information about which variant to be produced needs to be assigned beforehand to the generic parts in the preceding process. Second, this information has to be carried all the way from the beginning of the pull loop to the actual process where the differentiation happens. Hence, all parts coming down the pull loop are already earmarked for a certain variant from the start, even though the process physically does not require it yet.

It can be done, but especially for make-to-stock production, a supermarket may be an easier option here. **A break in the pull loop avoids the complexity of conveying additional information along the FIFO. Additionally, you have the flexibility to use a part in the supermarket for any variant you choose.** You do not have to assign a part to a product variant long before it becomes physically necessary. This allows for a later decision making, a shorter turnaround time for the customer order, and hence more flexibility.

11.2.8 Break Loops for a Large Distance Between Processes

FIFO work very well with processes in close proximity to each other. However, over longer distance, it requires more effort to keep things in FIFO and to know what is coming down the FIFO. Hence, **for longer distances it may be better to use separate loops**. For make-to-stock production loops, **the supermarket should be near the end of the supplying loop**, and the consuming loop picks up the material at the supermarket. This helps the visual management at the supplying processes and reduces the lead time.

For larger distances, it may even be sensible to insert a third loop between two loops merely for the shipping process. In kanban, this would be another transport kanban instead of a production kanban. These examples are visualized in Figure 177. For make-to-order, this is less common, and the custom parts are simply shipped to the destination.

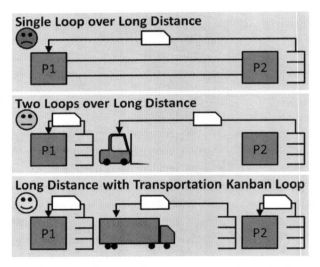

Figure 177: Example of a single loop over long distance broken into two loops or even three loops with a transport kanban in between (Image Roser)

For very long distances, it may even be possible to have a **sequence of transport pull loops**. You could use one transport kanban loop from the supplier in China to the central warehouse in the USA. You establish a second transport kanban loop from the central warehouse to the inbound warehouse in the plant. The third transport kanban goes from the inbound warehouse to the small supermarket supplying the production line.

Granted, you can also make a FIFO over longer distances, but in my experience, it often complicates things. This is more relevant the larger the distance is. Having parts shipped from one end of the plant to the other may still be doable by FIFO. However, if you import parts from China to the USA, I strongly recommend not using FIFO.

Besides the effort necessary to keep FIFO alive over longer distances, the time needed for transport is also an important factor. Separate loops keep you more flexible than a FIFO, and you can easily change from one product to the next in the following processes.

11.2.9 Break Loops to Save Space in Manufacturing

Another possible reason to break a loop is to save space. This is common in manufacturing, especially in assembly processes. Manufacturing processes can work more efficiently if they are close together. This often leaves little space between and around the processes. Assembly processes especially need many different parts. To save the valuable space around the manufacturing processes, it is common to have a separate pull loop between a central warehouse—where space is less tight than around assembly—and the manufacturing processes. Often, a transport kanban is established using a milk run to reduce the quantity of material and hence the space needed around the assembly processes.

11.2.10 Break Loops for Flexibility

The wider the span of a loop, the fewer loops you have to manage. However, a wide span also increases the lead time. It takes longer from the time of the signal to replenish or produce is sent out until the completed product comes back.

Therefore, if you need a system that reacts quickly, it may be better to make the loops not too big. Especially for make-to-stock feeding into a make-to-order system, smaller loops can react quicker to changing customer demand. This may be especially important if you have many low-runner products that you don't keep in stock and produce only as needed. If the pull system is set up correctly, this is most relevant for the last loop.

11.2.11 Break Loops for Change of Responsibility

The final reason to break a loop into two instead of continuing using a FIFO is if there is a change in responsibility. If the material flow leaves one department and enters other departments, a break may make things easier.

Using a logical view of the material and information flow, this would not be necessary. However, whenever there are people involved, things are not always logical. A break of the pull loops can keep responsibilities more separate. This has nothing to do with hard facts but everything to do with things like "my turf" and "your fault".

If there are FIFO across department boundaries, there is a risk of the first department carelessly throwing things over the wall and the second department equally carelessly throwing information back. Neither will help the overall operations of your plant. Both sides may blame each other for the problems, spending significant time, energy, and resources to show that the other side is at fault.

A break in the loops can keep these systems more separate and assign clear responsibilities. Again, from a purely logical point of view, this may not be necessary, but I have seen many plants where such blame games were a major part of everyday life. Judge for yourself if this may be a factor worth considering with your plant.

11.3 Effect on Inventory

My master's student Denis Wiesse did a detailed comparative analysis of supermarkets and FIFO and the effect on the inventory and the delivery performance.[95, 96] We compared a simple kanban system with two processes using either one kanban loop using a FIFO or two kanban loops using a

[95] Denis Wiesse, *Analyse des Umlaufbestandes von Verbrauchssteuerungen in Abhängigkeit von der Nutzung von Supermärkten und FiFo-Strecken* Master Thesis, Karlsruhe, Germany, Karlsruhe University of Applied Sciences, 2015.

[96] Denis Wiesse and Christoph Roser, *Supermarkets vs. FIFO Lanes – A Comparison of Work-in-Process Inventories and Delivery Performance*, in *Proceedings of the International Conference on the Advances in Production Management System* International Conference on the Advances in Production Management System, Iguassu Falls, Brazil, 2016.

supermarket between the two processes. This is shown in Figure 178. The goal was to see which system needs fewer kanban and hence less inventory for the same delivery performance.

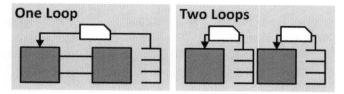

Figure 178: Two processes using either one big loop or two smaller loops (Image Roser)

The system was tested for many different cycle times and utilizations. We also compared the system for different numbers of kanbans and FIFO capacity. We even used different random distributions to see if this also has an effect. Out of the data gathered from thousands of simulations, we always looked for the best combination of inventory and delivery performance. Figure 179 shows you the best possible trade-offs between inventory and delivery performance for both a single-loop and a double-loop system.

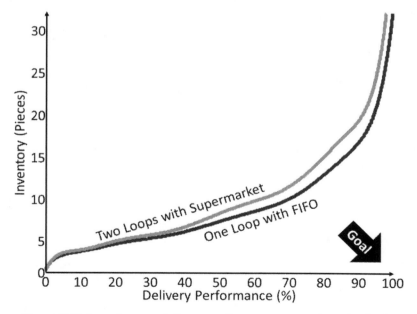

Figure 179: Inventory vs. delivery performance comparison for single- and double-loop systems (Image Roser, based on data from Wiesse)

These two lines are close together. Wiesse also calculated confidence intervals and did statistical hypothesis testing to verify that this difference is not just a random fluke. The difference is statistically significant for delivery performances above 50% — which is where most factories are.

No matter which system we simulated, the results were very similar. In all cases, the single-loop system needed slightly less inventory than the double-loop system for the same delivery performance. Or the other way around, you always got a slightly better delivery performance in a single loop for the same number of kanbans. Hence, our conclusion is that **a single larger loop needs less inventory for the same delivery performance than multiple smaller loops,** all other things being equal. However, the result is small for lower delivery performances. For higher delivery performances, the inventory difference may be more significant.

In a single larger loop, the inventory flow clusters in the supermarket, creating imbalanced and unleveled inventory. Hence for me the main trade-off is still the effort of establishing and maintaining two pull loops versus the benefit of splitting it into two loops. The benefit of a single loop having less inventory or better delivery performance should not really have a large influence on this decision. You should make large loops with FIFO anyway, unless there is a good reason to break loops as listed above.

Chapter 12
Pull System Ramp-Up

Designing a pull system on paper is much easier than implementing it on the shop floor. In this chapter, I will discuss the steps needed to actually implement the system. Most of the following explanation will be for general pull systems. Please note, however, that a lot also depends on your type of system. For example, if I talk about adding cards, then this would not apply to reorder point systems that have no cards. If any of the suggestions below seem odd to you, use your common sense and adjust.

12.1 The Big Picture—Where to Start?

It is likely that you are in charge of more than one value stream. Even if it is only one value stream, it may be longer than what you want to fit into one pull loop. As we discussed in the previous chapter, it may make sense to break your system into multiple pull loops. **Do not try to implement all pull loops at the same time!** This will have a high risk of major disruptions of your production system.

Instead, start with one loop. You could even start with a single product type within one loop. However, the benefit will only materialize if the majority or all of the part types in the loop have been converted to pull. Only after successfully implementing all product types within a single loop should you move on to the next loop. For the second pull loop, also use the experience gained from the first loop to make it even better. Lean manufacturing is mostly about lots of smaller steps, and implementing one loop is already a challenge. Implementing multiple loops at the same time is likely to cause you—and maybe your career—to stumble and fall. **Hence, implement only one loop at a time!**

The questions are now: Where should I start? Which loop should be implemented first? There are different schools of thought about this. You can **implement the easiest-to-implement pull loop first**. With an easy loop, the chances of success are much better. This will give you and your people a valuable learning experience, and your people the confidence that the newest fad from upper management may actually work for a change! In fact, just for training purposes, I love to create a kanban system for the coffee corner or the stationary in the office. Using triangle or two-bin kanban, you can teach your people about kanban in a risk-free environment. However, these are only the learner's steps, and if you also want to impress your boss, you should pick an easy pull loop in the actual value stream. Often, **flow shops are easier than job shops. Few numbers of variants are easier than large numbers of variants. Stable systems are easier than chaotic ones. Loops over a shorter distance are easier than long-distance loops. Finally, reorder point systems are easier than others**.

A second approach would be to **implement the pull loop with the biggest benefits first**. Which pull loop would give your system the biggest benefit? Where do you generate the most value? Where is material missing most often? Implement the pull loop in the segment that causes this lack of material to improve material availability. Where is the biggest chaos? Implement the pull loop in the segment that is most chaotic to improve efficiency. This will be most beneficial to your shop floor, but may also be more challenging.

Finally, there is the approach to **implement the pull loop with the largest management attention first**. This is often the final assembly. Management attention is usually focused more on one system than the others. This is often the high-value final assemblies. Improving these is likely to get the attention of management, and may be helpful to your career—if the pull system works. I am not saying that this is the most important criteria. But it may be a smart career move. My experience is that final assemblies are usually among the first to be converted to pull, or in fact the first for any kind of improvement projects.

So, there you have it. You should **implement pull in the loop that is easy, has big benefits, and the attention of the management**. Maybe you have a possible loop that fits all criteria. However, it is more likely that you do not have a loop that fits all three criteria. Start to make trade-offs and select a pull loop that fits your needs best. Although, at least at the beginning, I would definitely stay away from the difficult to implement pull loops. Failing with your first pull loop will make both the operators and your managers unhappy, and all subsequent changes more difficult.

12.2 Preparation

Before you implement your pull system, figure out what kind of pull system you want. This was the focus of the previous chapters in the book. Decide which type of pull systems you want to have, and where you want the pull loops to start and end. This could be a value stream design of the new system, or more generally a plan on how the material and information should flow in the new pull system.

Do the necessary calculations or estimations. For kanban, this would be the number of kanbans, similar for CONWIP, POLCA, and drum-buffer-rope. For reorder points, this would be the reorder point and target stock levels.

If you use kanban or other cards, define how this card will look. Is it paper? Is it digital? What information goes on the card and where? What type of sleeve will the paper card be in? What type of box if it goes on a box? If it is a digital system, see what the system can already do, and where you need a programmer.

The entire process should be **in coordination with and support from the people actually using the pull system**. The more you involve the people on the shop floor from the beginning, the more they can add their knowledge and experience to the system. This also means they are more likely to accept the new system. It also means that the system is more likely to work at all. If the shop floor rejects a new idea, it will be very difficult to implement against their resistance.

The following description assumes that you already have a production system in place, as this seems to be the majority of pull implementations. If you are in a greenfield situation and there is no production system yet, a lot of the tasks below become more difficult but have to be done regardless.

12.3 Timeline

You should think about the timeline. There are some tasks you can do while the old system is still running. Some other tasks can be done only after the new system is started again. And finally, some tasks can be done only when the system is stopped. You want to minimize the stoppage of your production system. Similar to changeover processes, try to do as much before and after, and keep the actual stop to a minimum. This is shown schematically in Figure 180.

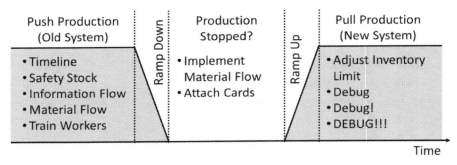

Figure 180: Possible sequence of steps for implementing a pull system. Minimize the stop of production during the implementation. (Image Roser)

A good approach is to schedule the stop of production to implement pull during a period where the system is either little utilized or completely idle, anyway. This may be, for example, a weekend or a night shift. If you can wait longer, you could plan it for a seasonal period of low demand when you don't need much material anyway. For example, if you produce ice cream, don't tinker with the system during the hottest days of the summer! Depending on your relationship with the customer, you may also inform the customer about the temporary disruption of production.

12.4 Safety Stocks and Capacity for Implementation Downtime

Depending on the extent of your changes, implementing your pull system may temporarily disrupt production. For example, you probably have to stop production to attach the cards to the inventory. If something goes wrong, you may also need more time than expected. Try to mitigate the negative effects of this stoppage and try to keep the customer supplied with the ordered items.

For make-to-stock, the most common way to cover an upcoming disruption is to **build up some buffer stock** before the implementation to avoid stock-outs. The additional buffer inventory should cover the expected downtime of the system with some safety. This buffer inventory should be on top of your normal inventory, otherwise you run out of parts by the time the system starts working again. You may have to store the goods elsewhere to have the space to install a supermarket or a FIFO and make other changes if needed.

It is a bit more difficult for make-to-order items, as these cannot be stocked up beforehand. Sometimes it may be possible to **provide additional capacity** to additional processes to produce around the shut-down part of the system. In the worst case, there may be a delay in deliveries. Try to keep the shutdowns short.

12.5 Prepare Information Flow

Now we will look at the information flow in the pull loop. The information flow of all pull systems aims to signal replenishment. This could be the flow of physical or digital cards, or the digital side of a reorder point system. Depending on your choice of pull system, it may look very different.

12.5.1 The Cards

If you have some type of cards, like kanban or CONWIP cards, prepare them beforehand. Print out the necessary cards, and insert them into their covers or prepare them for attachment to the boxes.

Pro tip: Print a few more cards and put them aside. If for some reason you estimated too few cards for your system, you can simply pull some more cards out of the drawer and bring them into circulation. You also may need them for the ramp-up if you have more material than cards, as shown in Chapter 12.9.2.

12.5.2 The Digital System

If you use some digital system to track and manage the information, then this needs to be prepared too. In most cases, the existing ERP system is expanded to include the needed tools for the pull system. Most ERP systems can create digital kanban and reorder point, and many can do CONWIP. POLCA and drum-buffer-rope are less common.

Many of these pull systems have a printed card or work order. The flow of information from the ERP system onto the paper should work. Do you have printers? Do you need more printers? The same applies for the flow of information back from the paper into the ERP system. Often this involves barcodes, 2D codes, or RFID chips. Do you have the necessary scanners? Do they work seamlessly with your system?

If you are fortunate, an off-the-shelf solution will be available or may be already part of your software package. If you are less fortunate, you need to get your programmers involved. In any case, make sure to plan ample time for any digital changes. **This needs to be tested thoroughly!** The history books are full of companies that messed up a change to their ERP system and lost tons of money or even went bankrupt.

12.5.3 The Flow of the Information Upstream

Prepare the information flow upstream. This is from the finished-goods inventory or supermarket back to the first process, as shown in Figure 181. In the easiest situation, this is simply a card that is physically carried back to the beginning to initiate the next production, but it may also be a box or other container, or a digital information flow.

When parts are taken out of the finished-goods inventory, the card has to go back to the source to get more parts. Walk the way the cards would go back to the source. Don't add any cards yet; we will do that later. Ask yourself the following questions:

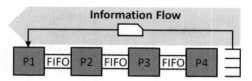

Figure 181: The information flow in a pull system is the flow of the cards.
(Image Roser)

Who would remove the card from the item and when? Where would the cards be stored until they are picked up to be brought back? (For kanban, this would be the kanban box.) Is there a scanning or other digital process involved? Who would do this? What type of hardware and software is needed? If it is already available, does it work? Who would bring the cards back? How often would this happen? Where would the cards be dropped off? Is it clear for the first process which card to use first? (This is especially important if you have pull systems with more than one queue in front of the process.)

Walk this information flow a few times and consider the flow of the information in detail. Involve the shop floor operators. If it involves longer distances as for example shipments between plants or continents, visit both endpoints if possible. Make it as visual and foolproof[97] as you can.

12.5.4 Sequencing

For make-to-stock production, in particular for kanban systems, the arriving cards may be sequenced. You may create lot sizes, or optimize for changeovers, or have other reasons for sequencing. Who does this? Where? How? What are the rules and standards? Can you make it visual? Do you need a card-sorting board, as shown in Figure 73? Do you need other hardware or software? **Involve the operators in the development of the sequencing standard.**

12.5.5 Backlog of Open Jobs

For make-to-order production, you have a backlog of open jobs. How is this information stored? Is it a printout, or a digital entry in your ERP system?

---

97 Or, to be politically correct, "mistake proof". You wouldn't want to call anybody a fool!

For printouts, how do you arrange the papers? What are the rules for creating the priority of the open jobs? Who makes these decisions and creates the sequence? How often? How much has to be sequenced in detail until the sequence is updated again the next time? How do you know if the material is available or will arrive in time? What do you do with jobs that lack material?

12.5.6 System Entry Point

The backlog of open jobs also usually has a system entry point. Who handles the arriving cards or information and releases a job into the production queue for production? When? How is the information from both the pull loop and the details of the job combined? Do you put everything in a plastic folder? Do you have enough folders? Again, make it visual and easy to understand. **Involve the operators in the development of the backlog rules.**

12.5.7 Production Queue

For both make-to-stock and make-to-order production, there is a queue of work waiting for production. How do you organize the production queue? In its easiest form, it could be a FIFO system. The work waiting for production the longest (the first in line) should be processed first. How does this look in reality? How do you arrange the information? Is it easy to see which job is first in line?

If you have a more complex prioritization system in mind with two queues for production: How are they organized? Who does this? Is it clear for the operators which of the two jobs at the front of the two queues has to come first? What is the work standard for prioritization? Often, the make-to-order jobs have their separate queue, being prioritized over the make-to-stock jobs in the second production queue. Again, **use visual management as much as you can**, and **involve the operators**.

12.5.8 The Flow of Information Downstream

Now walk the way from the start of the production or transport back to the supermarket. This is primarily the material flow, but any material flow is also an information flow, as shown in Figure 182.

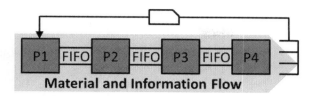

Figure 182: The material and information flow in a pull system is the flow of the cards together with the material. (Image Roser)

How does the information stay with the material? Do you attach the card or information to the part itself, or to the work-piece carrier? Is it in paper form or in digital form? If the information is a box or container, how does this travel downstream?

Again, we don't add any cards yet but merely see how the card would move along the line. The card should stay with the part at all times. Is this possible? If for example the part goes through a tempering oven at 900°C, the paper card won't make it through. Same for coating processes where the card is attached to the part.

When, where, and who attaches the card to the item? Do you have to remove the card from the part for some processes? If you have to remove the card during processing, where would it be put? By whom? Who puts it back and when? How do you handle rework and scrapped parts?

You see, there are tons of little details to take care of. I highly recommend **doing this together with the operators who will handle the cards**, both for the information and the material flow. If it involves longer distances as for example shipments between plants or continents, visit both endpoints if possible. Make it as visual and foolproof as you can.

12.6 Prepare Material Flow

Similar to the information flow, the material flow has to be prepared. If you are already producing, then you have a material flow already. This material flow may have to be tweaked. Some of these tweaks can be done while the system is running, but at other times you may have to switch off the system to install a FIFO. Try to do as much as possible while the system is working normally before stopping the system. **Here, too, you should involve the operators.**

12.6.1 FIFO Inventories

Depending on your initial plan, you may transform some normal inventories between processes into FIFO inventories. Sometimes there may already be a FIFO, but sometimes not. Look at the locations where you want to establish FIFO. What is necessary to implement it? How can you make it foolproof, so that it truly maintains a FIFO sequence? Do you need rolling lanes? How do you limit the space so the operators won't overstuff the FIFO? Is there some digital tracking of the FIFO quantity?

12.6.2 The Supermarket

If you are producing make-to-stock, you may need supermarkets. The supermarket has to be set up depending on the type and quantity of containers that go in there. Ideally, the supermarket should be able to hold all the products for all the kanbans in circulation. If you are really short on space, you may be able to get away with less space for some high runners. However, in this case you need a backup plan for where to put the material if the supermarket is full. See Chapter 5.7.3 for details.

If the container size allows it, consider rolling lanes as described in Chapter 5.3.2.3. You add the material on one side and it rolls or slides down to the other end. This way it is very easy to create a first-in-first-out system for a supermarket.

In any case, you probably would have to get storage equipment to establish a supermarket. There are lots of details that are necessary. Does it fit the material? Does it fit in the available space? Do you need an electrical connection? Is the storage rated for the weight? Are the emergency doors still accessible? The list is endless, and the questions above are only examples of what you may have to keep in mind. Make sure to involve colleagues who are familiar with those kinds of questions, both technically and legally. If you have the equipment for the supermarket already on hand, install it. Otherwise, you have to first order the equipment and then install it. This is easiest if the equipment is already installed and can be reused.

It is also possible to create a virtual supermarket using your ERP system. The computer keeps track of all the items in your "normal" inventory, adding and removing them in a virtual FIFO sequence. This also needs to be installed and tested. Make sure that **any removal of material initiates an**

information flow to replenish the item or to release the next job into the system. No material should be removed without initiating this information flow.

12.6.3 Non-Supermarket Inventories

Especially for make-to-order production and in job shops, you may have inventories that are neither FIFO nor supermarkets. Have a look at these too. Are they up to the task? Is it well visualized? Can you find the materials quickly again? It is possible that the current inventory will also work within a pull system, but do verify this beforehand.

12.7 Training of the Operators

All operators who have to use the new pull system need to be trained in its use. This should be started before the transition to pull, but can be completed afterwards. It is easier to train operators if the system is already set up. However, have some operators already trained before you start the system so that production runs smoothly after start of the new pull system.

If you already have a tool to track skills, like a qualification matrix, update the matrix to include the pull system. In any case, you need to keep track of whom you have already trained, and who still needs to be trained. Train at least some operators well enough so that they can train others. Don't forget to also train the night shift and operators that were absent for other reasons.

A common mistake for operators is to search for work for their process if there is no regular work available in the FIFO or production queue. This should not happen! **If there is no work assigned to the process, the process must stop.** Operators are usually hesitant to stop and may work on parts without cards just to be busy. This is overproduction! Don't do it. Rather, if they run out of parts, they should go to a supervisor or manager. Depending on the situation, they may be temporarily assigned to another workplace until work becomes available again. Again, **no production without a proper permission from the pull system, like a kanban or CONWIP card.**

12.8 Resolve Material Supply Issues

One challenge is that pull assumes a good availability of the necessary raw materials. The pull system is set up under the assumption that the material needed for production is available. If the supplying system is already a functioning pull system, then the material availability is probably good.

However, if the material is supplied by a push system, **you need to ensure that there is a good availability of the material required for production**. This may be especially tricky if a central system uses push for the entire value chain but only one segment is converted to pull. Depending on the software used, it may be difficult to have a seamless integration between push and pull.

12.9 The Switch to Pull

At this point, we are ready and prepared to do the actual switch of the pull system. Now it may be time to stop the system. Go through the system and attach the correct card to every part in the system, including the parts in the supermarket or finished-goods inventory. Attach a card to every part. If you use boxes or other containers as cards, make sure all items are in such a properly labeled box. Similarly, if you use a digital system, assign the digital link between the pull inventory and the parts in the system. **This is best done when the processes are stopped.** Otherwise, you may miss a part that is moved from an area yet to be labeled with cards to another area where you already attached the cards.

It may be necessary to do this while the process is still running. In this case, it is easier if you walk against the material flow, starting from the finished-goods inventory. This way the material comes toward you, and you are less likely to miss a part. Still, it will be easier if the process is stopped.

Attach the cards to the material. When you do that, there are three possibilities. In a perfect world, it turned out that you just have enough cards for all the items in the loop. Neither parts without cards nor cards without parts are left. More likely, however, is a mismatch between the number of cards and the inventory. The easier case is to have more cards than material. If you have more material than cards, it becomes a bit trickier.

12.9.1 More Cards Than Material

If there are cards left over after attaching a card to every part, put them in the loop as if they just returned from the finished-goods inventory. For **make-to-stock** production, they can be added before sequencing if applicable, as shown in Figure 183, or directly into the queue for production if there is no sequencing or lot size formation.

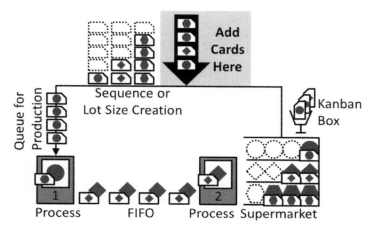

Figure 183: Visualization of a ramp-up with more cards than material (Image Roser)

The sequence of the cards or lot sizes should be mixed rather than having large *clumps* of identical parts. This is very similar to the pattern of one-piece-flow leveling, as visualized in Figure 184. Larger lot sizes would generate a slightly different pattern, but the sequence of lots should be well mixed too.

Figure 184: Visualization example of a good and a bad sequence for additional cards (Image Roser)

For a completely new and empty system without any existing material yet, all cards are mixed according to this pattern. Add these cards in front of the sequencing process. You can (optionally) create a temporary priority that any card coming from the supermarket has priority over cards from the initial sequence that are still not yet produced. This way your production follows demand even closer. But again, this is optional.

For **make-to-order** production, the cards are added before the system entry point. Since the cards are not yet assigned to material, the sequence of the cards is not relevant.

Assume you have make-to-stock cards waiting for sequencing or make-to-order cards waiting for the system entry point. In this case you should create as much sequence as possible according to the sequencing rules, or assign as many jobs from the backlog of open jobs to the cards as possible. In effect, move as many cards into the queue for production as allowed by the rules.

12.9.2 More Material Than Cards

If you have more material than cards after attaching every card to a part or box, you have a bit more work. You have more material than your system should have according to the rules of your pull system. Yet, in a pull system, all material must have a (digital or physical) card associated with it. Hence, you need more (temporary) "extra" cards. Use these extra cards for material left without cards after using up all regular cards. This is shown in Figure 185.

Figure 185: Visualization of a ramp-up with more material than cards and hence using extra cards marked with a "+" (Image Roser)

Doing so will exceed your initially planned inventory limit. This is fine for the temporary transition process to pull. But make sure to mark these as "extra" cards. Pro tip: If you attach the extra cards to material in the supermarket or toward the end of the loop, they can be removed much faster again as material is taken out of the supermarket.

Now that all material has cards, reduce these extra cards again over time to reach the inventory limit. Whenever the customer removes a part from the finished-goods inventory, you get a card without material. If it is a "normal" card, it proceeds normally. An "extra" card is removed out of the system. Over time, all the extra cards are taken out once they are removed from the products, and you end up with only the target number of cards. This is visualized in Figure 186.

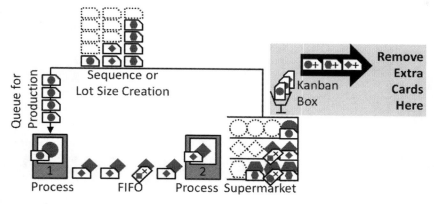

Figure 186: Example of extra cards marked with a "+" being removed after the supermarket (Image Roser)

You theoretically could shut down the line until you have your target number of cards. However, this is not good. In all likelihood, you have multiple part types in production. In this case, you probably have too much material only for a few part types. If you shut down the line, you risk running out of stock of the other part types that you did not have too much material for. It is probably best to reduce the number of cards gradually over time rather than reduce all of them as soon as possible.

It is important to **take out the extra card only when it is not attached to a part and not already sequenced into a lot size or other sequence**. Otherwise, removing the card will cause problems later on. Having marked or labeled these "extra" cards makes it easy to identify them.

12.10 Debugging and PDCA

If you have turned off the system for attaching the parts, it may now be a good time to restart the system again. Make sure the operators know what to do with these new cards in your new pull system.

Wonderful! Now your system is up and running and the cards are circulating. This means you are probably more than halfway done. The second half of debugging, adjusting, and verifying is unfortunately all too often forgotten.

Just because the system is running does not mean that it is running smoothly. There is still **much more work to debug the bugs, fix the kinks, and overcome smaller hurdles**. This will make the difference between a mediocre system and a good one—but it will take quite some time and effort. **Talk with the operators frequently** and see where they have problems. Mentally sort the complaints into those due to the operators not being used to a new system (nobody likes change anyway) and those that are actual problems. Try to fix the latter ones, but don't forget to help the operators to adjust with the former ones.

Be sure to **verify that the operators are following the new standard.** If the operators deviate from the new standard, find out if the operators are wrong or if the standard is flawed. If the standard is flawed, improve the standard until you have a good, robust standard for your pull system. If the operators just stick to the old ways, you have to convince them toward the new standard. Involving the operators from the beginning will significantly improve your odds here.

It is rare but possible that implementing the pull system influences the processes itself. There could be quality issues. For example, due to a shorter waiting time of the parts between the processes, the part may arrive at the next process hotter than before, or a resin had less curing time, etc. If necessary, do perform some quality checks just to make sure that the goods are up to their expectations.

But the main focus is on the correct working of the pull system. Do the cards flow as you wanted them to? Are there any hiccups? Overall, this debugging process will also help you with the Check and Act of the plan-do-check-act (PDCA) sequence shown in Figure 187. If you do this debugging, you will learn if the system actually works and if it is (hopefully) better than what you had before. **Do not take it for granted that just because you changed something, it must be better than before!**

Analyze Gap to Target
Follow-Up PDCA
Determine Next Goals

Define Target
Analyze Problem
Develop Solutions
Choose Best Solution

Verify Results
Check Standards
Improve Standards

Prepare Implementation
Develop Standards
Implement Solution
Train Workers

Figure 187: The PDCA circle (Image Roser)

Just as a refresher, PDCA is one of the key elements in lean manufacturing, or for that matter in any kind of improvement process. It is the most essential framework for any kind of change. **Plan** stands for planning what you want to do. **Doing** is then actually doing and implementing it. This is this chapter with the ramp-up.

Many people believe that they are now done and completely forget the Check and Act part. **Check** if it actually works as intended, and if the goals have been achieved. Check not only right after implementation but also, for example, a month later to see if it still works. You will be surprised how quickly a beautifully thought out system will deteriorate, assuming that it even worked in the first place. **Act** looks at remedies if the new system does not perform as expected. Find out why it does not work (or no longer works) and fix it. **If you omit the Check and Act steps of the PDCA, then all your hard work may be for nothing, and the outcome may be even worse than what it was before.**

Chapter 13
Pull System Maintenance

The maintenance of a pull system consists mainly of two elements. Periodically **check for lost cards** and periodically **update the inventory limit**. Checking for lost cards is easier in digital systems, as you can create a rule that flags any card that has not moved in some time. For reorder point systems it is even easier, as you don't have any cards at all, and only have to adjust your reorder point and your inventory limit occasionally.

13.1 Check for Lost Cards

Losing cards—no matter if digital or physical—is a constant worry for any pull production system except reorder point systems. If the card is lost, the inventory limit in the pull loop shrinks. At one point, it may be no longer enough to cover the replenishment time. For make-to-stock, this can lead to stock-outs and unhappy customers. For make-to-order, this can lead to a lower utilization of your system and unhappy bosses, albeit the lead time will improve.

Even with great care, you will occasionally lose cards. Losing one card out of twenty is normally not a huge problem, as pull systems are usually quite robust. However, losing multiple cards will cause problems in your pull system. This is illustrated in Figure 188. Losing a single card can also cause problems if you have very few cards for that part type, as in a two-bin system. Hence, check now and then if the number of cards in the system you have is still the number of cards you want to have in the system.

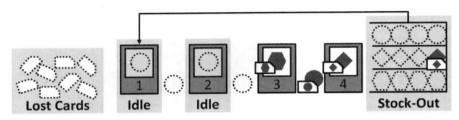

Figure 188: Too many lost cards will make both your shop floor and your customers unhappy. (Image Roser)

When they check for lost cards at Toyota, they sometimes even check the sequence of cards in the system. If the kanbans for one part type started out in sequence 1-2-3-4, but later have a sequence of 1-4-2-3, then something must have gone amiss with the FIFO sequence. At this point, Toyota may start digging for the cause of this change in sequence. However, this is probably too much detail for most production systems outside of Toyota.

13.1.1 Reduce the Likelihood of Losing Cards

You can reduce the likelihood of losing cards through different measures. One way to reduce the likelihood of a card getting lost is through a **sturdy design**. A simple sheet of paper will be damaged and/or lost soon. At a minimum, the card should be in a sturdy plastic sleeve. More robust are metal cards or boxes or other containers to which a card is attached. See Chapter 5.3.1.1 for details.

A curious case of missing cards happened to me in a northern European plant where cards always went missing in winter. As it turns out, the plastic sleeves of these cards were well suited to scratch ice from the windshield of the cars of the employees. A pair of scissors with a zigzag edge from the craft store (called a pinking shear) ended the problem of losing cards in winter. The resulting cards looked similar to the right card in Figure 189.

Figure 189: A card with zigzag edges makes a bad windshield scraper.
(Image Roser)

Another thing you should do for cards in a pull system is to make the system **robust and visual**. Is there a clearly defined place where the cards are attached to the material? Is it attached well, or is it likely to fall off during transport? For example, for larger iron products I had good success with magnetic cards that simply stuck to the part. Is there a defined place, or does the operator have to walk around the larger part to find the cards? Do you have clearly marked cards boxes at the start and end of production? Do you have a visual management to see easily how many cards are where? Your pull system has to be robust to reduce the likelihood of losing cards.

You need to **educate your workforce** so they know and understand the importance of these cards. Cards need to be treated as important information for your production. In fact, the word *kanban* comes from the Japanese word for shop sign, where the sign is not only a sign but also the representation of the honor of the establishment. Hence, you need to train your people about the significance of the cards. Not only the operators handling cards regularly need to know about it. Others that may or may not handle the cards at one point also need to know about it.

13.1.2 Digital Cards

If you have a system that is at least partially digital, checking for lost cards is much easier. You could have a system that prints a new single-use card every time. It could also be a system where a reusable card is scanned or typed into a computer at least once every turn in the loop. In any case, it is usually easy to check in the system when a card was last used or printed.

If the last timestamp of one card is much older than timestamps of other comparable cards, then the likelihood is high that this card was lost somewhere. See if you can find that particular card. If you don't find this card, then you could digitally reset the status of the card to available. However, if the old card for some reason pops up again, you may have two identical cards in the system. It may be easier to invalidate the cards and issue new cards in the system. The exact solution depends on the options you have in your ERP system.

13.1.3 Physical Cards

If you have no digital system but only physical cards, then it will be a bit more time consuming to check for lost cards. You should print out a list of all cards that should be in the loop. Next, go through the entire pull loop, look at all cards in the loop, and cross them off your list. This includes cards attached to the parts; cards waiting in card collection boxes, during lot size creation, or simply waiting for production; as well as cards at the processes where the parts are currently in process. Also, check the rework stations and the desk of the supervisor.

It is much easier if you go against the flow of material and information when physically checking cards. In this case, the cards are flowing toward you, and you are less likely to miss a card because it moved forward. It is much more difficult in a job shop, where the flow is not standardized. In this case, it may be best to check during an off-shift or the weekend when production is stopped and no material or cards move.

Afterwards, check which cards you did not find. These are most likely missing. Print out new cards correspondingly to get the actual number of available cards back to target. It is possible that you missed a card during the Check, and a "missing" card is actually not missing at all. If you printed a new card for the "not-actually-missing" card, you may have one more card in the loop than planned. This is not a big deal, as long as you can distinguish the cards (e.g., through a unique card identification number). Pull systems are very robust, and having one card more or less than intended usually won't break the system. Besides, you may notice an extra card during the next search for lost cards.

For simple, short loops, your "card" may also be a mere object, like a colored washer or colored ball. Since these objects unlike paper cards rarely have their own number, you can't really verify each individual object. In this case, count the number of "cards" for each type, and compare it with the expected number. If your count and your target differ, adjust the number of objects accordingly.

13.1.4 Frequency of Checks

There is no easy answer as to how often you should check the number of cards. You should definitely check them if the people on the shop floor indicate that there may be a problem with too few cards. Otherwise, your check depends on how fast you lose the cards—which of course you know only **after** you have checked it. For an ERP system, you could set up an automatic check that flags cards that have been idle for some time. Simply looking at the number of idle cards over time tells you how many are missing.

For physical cards, you need to get a feeling for how often a check makes sense. If you have other pull systems that you already check, you may know how fast cards disappear, and can use this experience also for the new pull system. For a completely new pull system, I would check a bit more often after implementation, to see if the people can handle the cards properly. Use visual management and add a calendar to the team corner of the group responsible for these audits. This allows tracking if the checks for lost cards have taken place.

Keep in mind that losing one card is usually not an issue for proper pull systems (unless it is the only card out of two cards). Hence, a single missing card probably won't break the system, but you need to act before a lot of missing cards do.

13.2 Adjust the Inventory Limit

The second important step to maintaining your pull system is to adjust the inventory limit periodically. For most systems, this would be the number of cards. For reorder point systems that do not use cards, you would have to adjust the reorder point and the inventory limit. In any case, you would have to redo the calculation or adjust your estimation of your pull system occasionally.

13.2.1 When to Adjust

An adjustment to the number of cards is necessary when the **underlying behavior of your pull system changes**. Does your customer demand change, for example, due to seasonality? Was there a change in a legal framework? Did the world just suffer a global pandemic? Did the government make some cross-border taxation change? Was there a change to the replenishment time (e.g., due to a new machine or a different lot size)? Did you introduce a new product and phase out an older one?

Whenever the basis for your calculation or estimation of the inventory limit changes, it may be necessary to recalculate or estimate this number of cards. It helps that you will know some of these changes beforehand. Seasonality rarely surprises a seasoned production manager (pun intended). Changes to the line or product portfolio also rarely just happen without prior notice.

You may also adjust if **your pull system becomes lopsided**. For make-to-stock, if the inventory levels or the delivery performance change, you may have to check if the number of cards is still adequate. Similarly, for make-to-order, update the number of cards if the utilization or the lead time changes. Often, the people on the shop floor or the sales people will let you know that something is amiss. An angry phone call from your customer due to lack of goods can lead to an adjustment of the number of cards. Please note that not all such changes are due to an incorrect number of cards. For example, if your supplier cuts you short, your delivery performance, inventory, and utilization will go down, but no number of cards can fix that. However, if the problem is the number of cards, then please adjust.

Finally, you **may regularly check the number of cards as a precaution**. Have a look at your pull systems now and then regardless, just to make sure it still works fine. This is particularly true for newly established systems, where your inventory calculation or estimation of the number of cards has a large uncertainty. Of course, common industry practice is to ignore this until it is a problem, but wouldn't it be nice for a change to prevent a problem before you get an angry call from the customer?

If your system makes or ships to stock, or generally a card is permanently assigned to a certain product, it is important to **check for all parts separately**. You cannot look at the total number of cards across all parts, but have to check cards for every single part number separately.

13.2.2 Make-to-Stock: Tracking Delivery Performance

For make-to-stock, a simple way to gauge the system is to track the inventory levels in the finished-goods inventory—usually the supermarket—over time. The key performance indicator to watch is the **delivery performance**, or alternatively the **percentage of the time your supermarket is empty. The percentage of the time your supermarket is empty is a good estimate of your delivery performance.**

However, please note that the supermarket inventory timeline can look very different depending on your system behavior. The replenishment time especially determines what share of your products are in the supermarket, and what share are currently replenished. The longer the replenishment time, the more products are currently replenished in the loop, and the fewer products will be in the supermarket. See Chapter 5.7.3 for a more detailed discussion on the supermarket fill levels.

Take for example the two graphs in Figure 190, showing the supermarket fill level over time for two different systems. Both systems have **a very good delivery performance of around 99%.** However, the system of the top graph has only a single process in the loop. Hence the replenishment time is rather short. The supermarket frequently reaches the inventory limit.

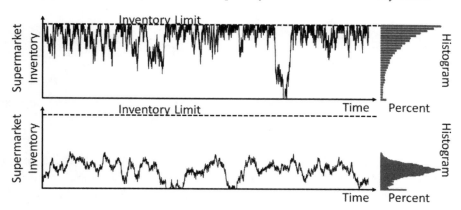

Figure 190: Behavior of the supermarket inventory over time for one product in a good pull system with 99% delivery performance. The top is a system with a short replenishment time, and the bottom a system with a long replenishment time. (Image Roser)

The bottom graph also has a delivery performance of around 99%. However, the loop includes a system with many processes, leading to a lengthy replenishment time. Even though the delivery performance is also 99%, there are at most half of the parts in the supermarket at any given time. The histogram of the supermarket inventory is also shown on the right in Figure 190. Please note that the percentages for the histogram in this and the following graphs are on different scales, but the sum of all bars is always 100%. The histogram bar for the inventory being empty also often looks like it covers a disproportionately large area, but this is only due to the printed width of the bar.

Figure 191 shows the supermarket inventory for comparable systems with **a mediocre delivery performance of only 90%**. Both graphs zero out more frequently. Again, the top system has a short replenishment time, and the bottom system a long replenishment time.

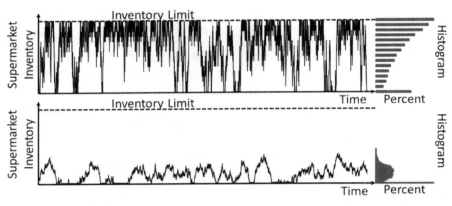

Figure 191: Behavior of supermarket inventory over time for one product in a mediocre pull system with 90% delivery performance. The top is a system with a short replenishment time, and the bottom a system with a long replenishment time. (Image Roser)

Figure 192 shows again comparable systems with **a substandard delivery performance of around 80%**. Both graphs bottom out even more often. However, the top system with the short replenishment time still frequently fills up the supermarket, whereas the bottom system with a long replenishment time never even has 50% of the inventory limit in the supermarket.

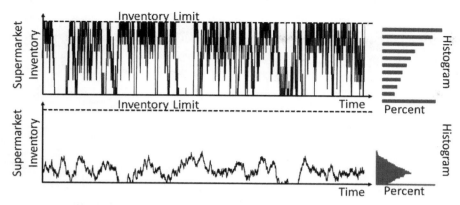

Figure 192: Behavior of the supermarket inventory over time for one product in a substandard pull system with only 80% delivery performance. The top is a system with a short replenishment time, and the bottom a system with a long replenishment time. (Image Roser)

Please note how similar the graphs in Figure 190, Figure 191, and Figure 192 are for the respective systems. It may be difficult to "eyeball" the curves. Calculating the delivery performance or the frequency of stock-outs will give you a much better picture of your system behavior.

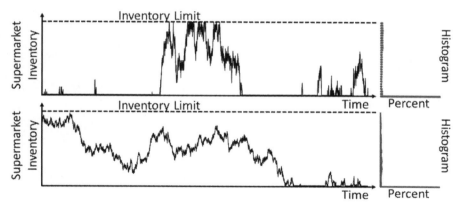

Figure 193: Behavior of the supermarket inventory over time for one product in a pull system with insufficient capacity. The top is a system with a short replenishment time, and the bottom a system with a long replenishment time. (Image Roser)

Figure 193 shows again the inventory of the two example systems. However, in this case, the system has **not enough capacity** to satisfy the customer demand. A pull system cannot help if the capacity is insufficient.

If the customers would wait forever for their parts, the delivery performance would approach zero over time. In the bottom graph the trend is visible, since the system started with a nearly full supermarket. A continuously low-delivery performance may be due to a too-small inventory limit, or insufficient production capacity, or material shortages. More cards will help only if a low inventory limit actually caused the poor delivery performance. You need to determine the root cause of the problem to see which solutions could help.

Finally, Figure 194 shows two systems where **the inventory limit is way too large**. The system with the short replenishment time is always at or near the upper limit. The supermarket never falls below 80% fill level. Similarly, the second system with the long replenishment time also never falls below 60% of the inventory limit. However, it also never reaches 100% fill level due to the long replenishment time. In both cases, the delivery performance is 100%, but the inventory limit is way too big. You probably could reduce the inventory limit in both cases by 60% with little risk, reducing all the expenses associated with keeping inventory.

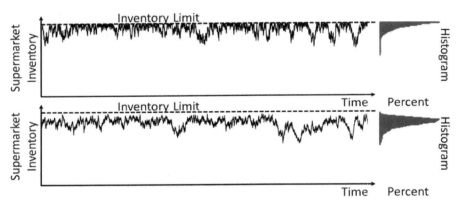

Figure 194: Behavior of the supermarket inventory over time for one product in a pull system with a way-too-large inventory limit. The top is a system with a short replenishment time, and the bottom a system with a long replenishment time. (Image Roser)

Through this observation of supermarket inventories, especially the delivery performance or the frequency of stock-outs, you can adjust your inventory limit. By observing your real system with real data, you can avoid all those rough estimates in the kanban formula. If your delivery performance is insufficient, you could increase the inventory limit—if you are sure that the cause is not insufficient capacity or a lack of material. If your delivery performance is better than required, you may reduce your inventory limit. But be aware that depending on the replenishment time, it may be equally as normal to never have all the parts in the supermarket as it is to frequently have them all.

13.2.3 Make-to-Stock: Predicting Delivery Performance

Tracking the supermarket inventory can help you decide if you want to increase or decrease the inventory limit. The percentage of the time when the supermarket is not empty is often a good estimate of the delivery performance.

A careful analysis of the supermarket data also allows a prediction of the delivery performance for a reduction of the inventory limit. You need a histogram of how many items were in the supermarket for what percentage of the time for a given part number.

Figure 195 shows a histogram of an example supermarket inventory. The data is based on a simulation. The supermarket was empty for 4.95% of the time, had exactly one part for 0.79% of the time, two parts for 1.02% of the time, and so on. The delivery performance of the system was 95.02%. This means that 100% - 95.02% = 4.98% of the customers had to wait for their parts. This correlates very closely with the percentage of the supermarket being empty of 4.95%, which would predict a delivery performance of 100% - 4.95% = 95.05%.

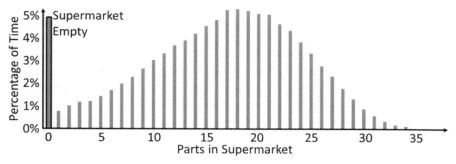

Figure 195: Histogram of an example supermarket with a delivery performance of 95.02% (Image Roser)

This histogram can now be used to predict the delivery performance of a system with a lower inventory limit. Let's assume we want to reduce the inventory limit by two parts. Using this histogram, we can predict the percentage that the supermarket is empty. We add the percentage of the time that the supermarket had exactly one or two parts to the percentage of the time that the supermarket was empty. This is shown in Figure 196.

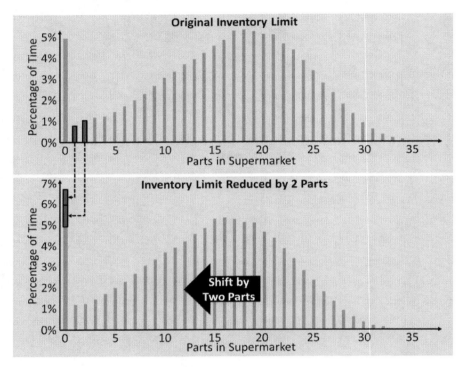

Figure 196: Change in the percentage of time a supermarket is empty if the inventory limit is reduced by two parts (Image Roser)

In this example, the predicted percentage of the time that the supermarket is empty is now 4.95% + 0.79% + 1.02% = 6.76%. This in turn predicts a delivery performance of 100% - 6.76% = 93.24%. The actual measured delivery performance was almost identical of 93.21%. In reality, expect the error to be a bit larger due to random behavior of the system.[98]

---

[98] To improve accuracy, the simulation used the same random seed (i.e., the same random numbers for every simulation). This "eliminated" the randomness between different simulation runs. Of course, in reality the random events will

I tested this method for quite a number of different scenarios. Figure 197 shows a representative example, where both the measured and the predicted delivery performance is shown for a wide range of inventory levels. For the prediction, I used data from a single simulation with a way-too-high inventory level. This resulted in an original delivery performance of 100%. The dot on the right in Figure 197 is this original simulation. Based on this data, I predicted the delivery performance for every inventory limit level down to a single part.

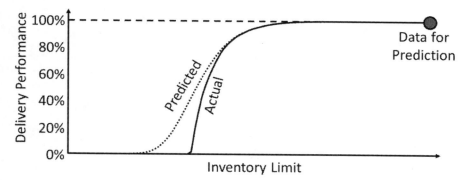

Figure 197: Comparison of the predicted delivery performance with the actual delivery performance based on a single data point (Image Roser)

Overall, the prediction is highly accurate. Especially for delivery performances above 50%, the lines mostly overlap. For mediocre delivery performances there is a larger error, before the lines meet again for delivery performances near zero. Hence, it is quite easy to predict a future delivery performance after a reduction of the inventory limit, especially for delivery performances above 50%. The key data here is a histogram of the supermarket fill levels. But be aware that the prediction is not accurate for low-delivery performances.

Predicting the effect of the reduction of an inventory limit is mathematically straightforward. Prediction of the effect of an increase of the inventory limit, however, is more complicated. The underlying principle is shown in Figure 198.

---

always be different over time. These random events will fluctuate the actual measured performance around the prediction, leading to somewhat larger errors due to the randomness.

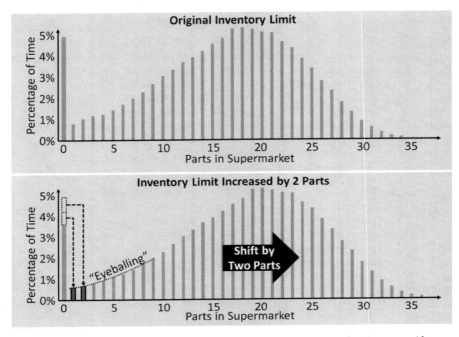

Figure 198: Change in the percentage of time a supermarket is empty if the inventory limit is increased by two parts (Image Roser)

You shift the histogram the desired number of slots to the right, except for the bar where the inventory is empty. Now you add more bars to fill the gap. The height of these added bars is removed from the height of the bar for the empty inventory. Figure 198 shows this for an increase of the inventory limit by two parts. However, there is no easy math to do this. You could either do tricky curve fitting, or... my recommendation... eyeball it!

I also eyeballed the increase in Figure 198. I eyeballed that with two more parts there will be exactly two parts in the supermarket for 0.7% of the time, and exactly one part for 0.65% of the time, with everything else being shifted two parts to the right. Hence, with two more parts 0.7% + 0.65% = 1.35% of the time, the supermarket will no longer be empty. This reduces the percentage of the time the supermarket is empty from 4.95% to roughly 3.6%. This would correspond to a delivery performance of 100 - 3.6% = 96.4%. The actual simulated delivery performance was 96.46%, which again is very close. However, eyeballing may be difficult for larger increases in the inventory limit. Also, here, too, the error may be larger around the "hump", especially if you are on the wrong side of the hump and can't see the hump yet. But overall, **the histogram of the supermarket inventory gives an easy tool to predict future delivery performances**.

Finally, the above model assumes an unchanged system. However, in reality if companies see that they will run out of stock, they start firefighting and reprioritize the production queue to avoid a stock-out. This will of course change the supermarket inventory histogram, and may give slightly different results than the theoretical prediction. Nevertheless, this approach is well suited for a first estimate.

13.2.4 Make-to-Order: Tracking Utilization and Lead Time

Tracking the supermarket is a simple way to judge the health of your pull system with make-to-stock production. Unfortunately, this does not work with make-to-order production, as you usually don't really have much inventory. There are also signals, but they are much more muddled. You could track the utilization of your system. Are your processes and operators busy? If your operators complain about not enough work, then a lack of cards (CONWIP, POLCA, etc.) may be one of the possible reasons for this. Others may be lack of material or simply chaotic organization. If a lack of cards is in fact the reason for the lack of work, you may consider increasing the cards and hence the inventory in the system.

The lead time is also relevant, although in the other direction. If your lead time is too long, you may have too many cards in the system. Consider removing some cards to reduce the inventory and thereby also the lead time.

Hence, not enough work means not enough cards, and too much lead time means too many cards. But the signals are not as clear as with tracking a supermarket inventory. It is quite possible to have your operators complaining about not enough work while your customers complain about too much lead time. But you can't simultaneously increase and reduce the number of cards. Go with your best judgment and make a reasonable trade-off. It is often impossible to make everybody happy.

13.2.5 How Much to Adjust

To determine the inventory limit, you can follow the calculations provided in the corresponding chapters. However, all these calculations are only rough estimations. If you are adjusting an existing pull system, you already have much better data than the assumptions in your calculations—you have data from your real system.

Rather than twiddling with the calculation, update your estimation. If it feels like you have too many cards, remove some. If you feel like there are too few, add some. Use your current situation in your real system as the starting point.

As for the magnitude of the change, here, too, you make a guess. Don't worry too much about high precision, as a pull system is usually quite robust against small offsets from the ideal. **If in doubt, take small steps.** Add or remove a few kanbans, and see how the system changes. If you think you can add or remove even more, do so. If it turns out that it is too much, take a small step in the opposite direction again. Chapter 13.2.3 also shows a (mathematically not-too-complex) method to estimate the delivery performance for make-to-stock systems based on a supermarket histogram.

And again, **do not try to cover all eventualities**. This is not possible, and will only lead to larger and larger inventories. Instead, try to keep a good material availability for make-to-stock or a good lead time and utilization for make-to-order, so that only few problems pop up. If an occasional problem pops up, instead of increasing the inventory level, try to find out if you can eliminate the source of the fluctuation rather than just buffering it with even more inventory.

13.2.6 Adding Cards

Depending on your calculations or estimations, you may want to add cards into the system. This is very similar to the ramp-up in Chapter 12.9.1. You prepare the additional cards if it is a physical card or adjust the number of cards in your ERP system. These cards are then added into the loop.

For **make-to-stock** pull systems, the cards are added before the lot size and sequencing operation, as shown in Figure 199. While there is no particular sequence needed for blank make-to-order cards, the sequence becomes relevant for make-to-stock cards. As shown in Figure 184, create a good mix of the cards. If there are too many cards of the same type after another, it may cause imbalance in the production system. This is especially true if there is no sequencing and the cards go directly in the queue for production. Similarly, if you add a lot of cards, your system may be busy for a while with the new cards, and may not produce any of the other products. You may consider adding cards gradually over time if there are larger changes.

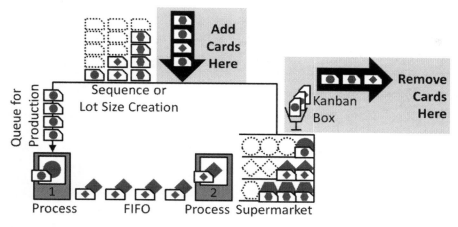

Figure 199: With make-to-stock systems, add cards before the sequence or lot size creation, and remove after the supermarket. (Image Roser)

For **make-to-order** pull systems, the cards are simply added before the system entry point. Unlike make-to-stock, it is not a problem to add a lot of cards at the same time. Since the cards are all blank, no sequence is needed for adding the cards. This is shown in Figure 200.

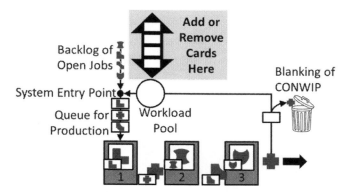

Figure 200: With make-to-order systems, add or remove cards before the system entry point. (Image Roser)

For **reorder point** systems, simply increase the reorder point and/or the inventory limit. If your current inventory including the items already ordered now falls below the reorder point, issue an order to fill up to the inventory limit.

13.2.7 Removing Cards

Removing cards is a bit easier. For **make-to-stock,** you can remove cards anytime as long as they are not attached to a material or part of a sequence or lot. You should not remove cards from the queue for production if that would violate any rule regarding lot size or sequence, or if logistics already started to move material for this product. In the case of doubt, it may be best to take out cards after they are removed from the parts in the supermarket, as shown in Figure 199.

For **make-to-order,** you can remove any card that is blank (i.e., not connected to any open job or part). It is usually easiest to remove them from the workload pool, as shown in Figure 200.

For **reorder point** systems, simply reduce the reorder point and/or inventory limit. If you have material in excess of the inventory limit, simply wait until normal consumption has reached the inventory limit, and eventually the reorder point, at which point you order more items.

Please be careful if you remove many cards at the same time. If you take a lot of cards at the same time, your process may not have any work to do due to a lack of cards arriving. You may have to either plan less work time for your system or remove the cards gradually over time. No matter if adding or removing cards, **gradual small changes are usually better than large adjustments with uncertain outcomes**.

Chapter 14
Summary

Pull systems are one of the powerful tools for lean manufacturing. They help you with make-to-order to maintain a good trade-off between lead time and utilization. They help you with make-to-stock to maintain a good trade-off between material availability and inventory. However, **pull is only a tool, and as with any tool, it depends on how well you use it**.

Pull should be part of an overall continuous improvement *kaizen* strategy. Such an improvement should **always start with the problem you want to solve**. This could be either a difficult problem that creates a lot of trouble for your plant, or a minor problem that is quick and easy to solve and may also raise morale and acceptance of lean manufacturing. It should not be just a random problem that popped up. You probably do not have enough capacity to solve all of your problems, so get the most out of the effort you put in. Hence, **focus on the problems that give you the biggest improvement for the effort invested**.

Second, this should also be **a real problem affecting either safety, quality, cost, or time**. Occasionally managers tell me that their problem is that they "don't have kanban". No, not having kanban is not a problem, nor is having kanban. Kanban—and a pull system in general—are a solution for problems related to lead times, delivery performance, or cost. Hence, don't start out with wanting to have kanban, as another pull system may be an even better solution, and the organization of your production may not even be your biggest problem.

I cannot emphasize this enough: **Always start with a problem, and from there onward work your way to a solution.** You could even conceptualize multiple solutions and then pick the best one. In particular for pull systems, the pull system calculations may show you which aspects have the largest impact on the number of cards or the inventory limit. If you want to reduce inventory or lead time, this will give you valuable clues on where to improve.

Also, you are not done after implementing a solution. **Do not forget the Check and Act steps of PDCA.** After the implementation, thoroughly check to make sure it works, even months later, although the sooner the better. If it doesn't work well enough, find out why. Determine the causes for the unsatisfactory results, and then find out what to do to improve your performance. See Chapter 12.10 for details. The PDCA is a continuous sequence of loops until you have achieved your target, as shown in Figure 201.

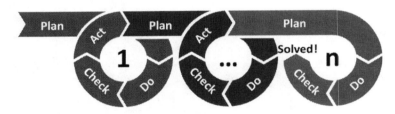

Figure 201: The PDCA is a series of continuous loops until the problem is truly solved. After this, the next problem is tackled. (Image Roser)

Pretty much all companies do improvements. But **excellent companies focus on moving in the right direction, ensure the results are actually achieved, and keep on working in the same direction, until they have finally achieved satisfactory performance**. For example, the changeover time reduction of stamping tools at Toyota, better known as Single Minute Exchange of Die (SMED) was a continuous effort. Throughout three decades, they reduced the changeover time from up to eight hours to less than ten minutes. There was a **continuous support across multiple generations of management pushing the same problem in the same direction for over thirty years.** This is rare in most modern companies.

To improve the chances of success for your company, make sure to pick the relevant problems, select a good solution, and then make sure the solution actually works as intended before moving on to the next problem.

I sincerely hope that this book helps you in this process by giving you a thorough and practical overview of the different challenges and possibilities for pull production systems. Now, **go out, work on your problems, and organize your industry!**

Appendix A
Table of Variables

This list includes all the variables used within this book. Each entry also has a brief description. In the brackets, I give you the unit type that is commonly used with the variable. A time, for example, could be measured in days, hours, minutes, or seconds. Ensure to adjust the unit so all units in one equation have the same type. For example, do not mix hours and seconds in the same equation. Also, please note that many variables are determined slightly differently for make-to-stock and make-to-order systems. For example, the lead time LT includes worst-case elements for make-to-stock systems, but only an average case for make-to-order systems.

BD	Additional time to cover breakdowns and disruptions (time)
CO	Cost of one order (monetary)
CO_n	Cost of one order of part type n (monetary)
D	Demand during a given time period (quantity or job)
D_n	Demand of part type n during a given time period (quantity)
D_{All}	Demand for all part types during a given time period (quantity or job)
DF	Demand frequency (quantity or job per time)
DF_n	Demand frequency for part type n (quantity or job per time)
DF_{All}	Demand frequency across all part types (quantity or job per time)
HC	Holding cost of one part for a given time (monetary per time)
HC_n	Holding cost of one part of type n for a given time (monetary per time and quantity)
I	General inventory (quantity)
$I_{Max,n}$	Inventory limit of part type n (quantity)
$I_{Min,n}$	Minimum inventory of part type n (quantity)
$I_{\Delta,n}$	Delta inventory of part type n (quantity)
KL	Lot size as a number of kanbans (card quantity)
KL_n	Lot size as a number of kanbans for part type n (card quantity)
LT	Lead time (time)
m	Count of all part types in the pull loop (no unit)
n	Generic referrer to a part type (no unit)
NC_{CONWIP}	Number of CONWIP cards (card quantity)
NC_{Kanban}	Number of kanbans (card quantity)

$NC_{Kanban,n}$	Number of kanbans for part type n (card quantity)
NC_{POLCA}	Number of POLCA cards (card quantity)
NPC_n	Number of parts per kanban for part type n (quantity per card)
OS	Order size (quantity)
$OS_{Max,n}$	Largest expected order size for part type n (quantity)
PD	Peak customer demand (quantity)
PD_n	Peak customer demand for part type n (quantity)
PT	Sum of all process times (time)
PT_n	Sum of all process times for part type n (time)
Q	Quantity in general (quantity)
Q_n	Produced quantity of part type n (quantity)
Q_{All}	Quantity across all part types (quantity or jobs)
RP	Reorder period (time)
RP_n	Reorder period for part type n (time)
RT	Replenishment time in general (time)
RT_n	Replenishment time for part type n (time)
$RT_{Max,n}$	Maximum considered replenishment time for part type n (time)
$RT_{\varnothing}$	Average replenishment time (time)
$RT_{\varnothing,n}$	Average replenishment time for part type n (time)
S	Safety factor (quantity, card quantity, or workload depending on usage)
T	Time in general (time)
TI	Time for the transport of information (time)
TI_n	Time for the transport of information of part type n (time)
TL	Line takt (time per quantity or job)
TL_n	Line takt for part type n (time per quantity)
TL_{All}	Line takt across all part types (time per quantity or job)
TP	Throughput (quantity per time)
TP_n	Throughput for part type n (quantity per time)
TP_{All}	Throughput across all part types (quantity or jobs per time)
TT	Customer takt (time per quantity or job)
TT_n	Customer takt for part type n (time per quantity)
TT_{All}	Customer takt across all part types (time per quantity or job)
TW	Working time period of a system (time)
TWT	Sum of all transport and waiting times (time)
TWT_n	Sum of all transport and waiting times for part type n (time)
WB	Waiting time at (kanban, CONWIP, etc.) box (time)
WI	Waiting time in inventory (time)
WL	Workload (workload)
WL_{Max}	Upper workload limit (workload)

WP	Waiting time in queue for production (time)
WP_n	Waiting time in queue for production for part type n (time)
WQ	Waiting time for sequence creation (time)
WQ_n	Waiting time for sequence creation of part type n (time)
WS	Waiting time in shipping queue (time)
WT	Waiting time for a truckload (time)
α	Safety factor (percent)

Appendix B
Value Stream Mapping Symbols

A value stream map (VSM) is a common way to describe the material and information flow in a somewhat standardized manner. Within this book, I often use schematics to explain pull systems, sometimes using value stream symbols. Most of these symbols are easy to guess. Nevertheless, I will give you a brief introduction on the value stream symbols used within this book, although with the assumption that most readers have at least a basic familiarity with value stream mapping. For a deeper look, please check my blog posts[99, 100, 101, 102, 103], or the key source literature.[104] Figure 202 shows examples of the most important value stream symbols.

---

[99] Christoph Roser, *When to Do Value Stream Maps (and When Not!)*, in *Collected Blog Posts of AllAboutLean.Com 2015*, Collected Blog Posts of AllAboutLean.Com 3 Offenbach, Germany: AllAboutLean Publishing, 2020, 212–19, ISBN 978-3-96382-013-7.

[100] Christoph Roser, *Overview of Value Stream Mapping Symbols*, in *Collected Blog Posts of AllAboutLean.Com 2015*, Collected Blog Posts of AllAboutLean.Com 3 Offenbach, Germany: AllAboutLean Publishing, 2020, 220–28, ISBN 978-3-96382-013-7.

[101] Christoph Roser, *Basics of Value Stream Maps*, in *Collected Blog Posts of AllAboutLean.Com 2015*, Collected Blog Posts of AllAboutLean.Com 3 Offenbach, Germany: AllAboutLean Publishing, 2020, 229–36, ISBN 978-3-96382-013-7.

[102] Christoph Roser, *Practical Tips for Value Stream Mapping*, in *Collected Blog Posts of AllAboutLean.Com 2015*, Collected Blog Posts of AllAboutLean.Com 3 Offenbach, Germany: AllAboutLean Publishing, 2020, 237–44, ISBN 978-3-96382-013-7.

[103] Christoph Roser, *Value Stream Mapping – Why to Start at the Customer Side*, in *Collected Blog Posts of AllAboutLean.Com 2013*, Collected Blog Posts of AllAboutLean.Com 1 Offenbach, Germany: AllAboutLean Publishing, 2020, 92–97, ISBN 978-3-96382-007-6.

[104] Mike Rother and John Shook, *Learning to See: Value-Stream Mapping to Create Value and Eliminate Muda: Value Stream Mapping to Add Value and Eliminate Muda* Lean Enterprise Institute, 1999, ISBN 0-9667843-0-8.

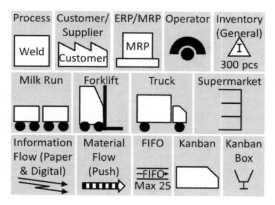

Figure 202: Examples of the most important value stream mapping symbols (Image Roser)

Most important is probably the **process**, a simple box, although often with additional data added into the box. A "factory" symbol is used for the **customer** or **supplier**. A computer symbol stands for the **ERP** system. The **operator** is also represented by a top-down human icon. A triangle stands for **inventory** in general, distinctively NOT a FIFO or supermarket inventory (i.e., not an inventory managed by pull). The inventory may show the number of parts counted when the value stream map was created. Different small icons for transport include a **milk run**, a **forklift**, and a **truck**. A **supermarket** is symbolized by an open box with three lanes. A simple arrow represents **information flow**, occasionally with a zigzag for digital information flow. A more complex striped arrow represents a **push material flow**. A **FIFO** is also included with a symbol, often shown with the maximum capacity. A **kanban** is represented by a square with a missing corner. A **kanban box** (or sometimes also kanban post) is a symbol of a small stand for kanban.

These symbols can be combined into larger value stream maps, as for example shown in Figure 203. While value stream mapping feels like a rigid standard, it is not. There are more symbols in existence than listed here. There is also no fixed canon of recognized value stream mapping symbols. Many organizations use slightly different symbols for the same purpose. Others use the same symbol with different definitions. If you create a value stream map, the goal is not to follow the symbols to the letter. **The goal is to make a representation of the material and information flow that helps you and your team in improving the system.** Feel free to adapt and invent your own symbols as needed, while at the same time trying to keep it simple.

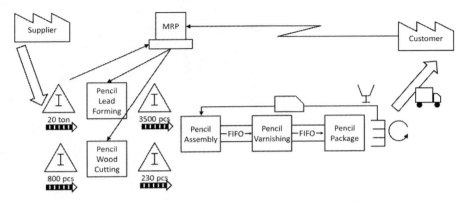

Figure 203: Example of a value stream map (Image Roser)

Appendix C
COBACABANA

The Copacabana is a very nice beach in Rio de Janeiro. Spelled slightly differently, COBACABANA is a pull production control approach. COBACABANA stands for "control of balance by card-based navigation" (sometimes also abbreviated to COBA).

COBACABANA was developed by Martin Land and improved by Matthias Thürer.[105, 106, 107, 108] It aims to help with the management of job shops, especially the task of keeping your processes busy without overloading one process or idling another. This is a daunting task that many have tried but few have succeeded at. Furthermore, it does so using only paper cards. A lot of paper cards, in fact, which also makes the method a bit complex. To my knowledge, there is no real-world implementation of COBACABANA yet. Hence, I have included the method not in the main body of this book, but in the appendix, more out of academic interest. Use this method at your own risk.

C.1 Fundamentals

COBACABANA breaks the flow of a customer order into two main acceptance processes, as shown in Figure 204. The first step is **order acceptance**. The order acceptance tracks the total workload of accepted

---

[105] Martin Land, *Cobacabana (Control of Balance by Card-Based Navigation): A Card-Based System for Job Shop Control, International Journal of Production Economics* 117 2009: 97–103.

[106] Matthias Thürer, Mark Stevenson, and Charles W. Protzman, *COBACABANA (Control of Balance by Card Based Navigation): An Alternative to Kanban in the Pure Flow Shop?, International Journal of Production Economics* 166 August 1, 2015: 143–51.

[107] Matthias Thürer, *Card-Based Control Systems for a Lean Work Design: The Fundamentals of Kanban, ConWIP, POLCA, and COBACABANA* Productivity Press, 2017, ISBN 978-1-138-43790-6.

[108] Matthias Thürer, Nuno O. Fernandes, and Mark Stevenson, *Material Flow Control in High-Variety Make-to-Order Shops: Combining COBACABANA and POLCA, Production and Operations Management* 29, no. 9 2020: 2138–52.

orders in the backlog of open orders. Whenever a new customer order arrives, the order acceptance checks how much work this order represents for the different processes, versus how much work there is already in the backlog of open orders. This is used to estimate feasible due dates, where the due date is the sum of the workload in the order acceptance, plus the workload in the order release, plus some safety.

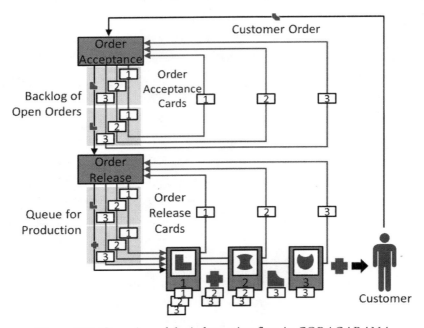

Figure 204: Overview of the information flow in COBACABANA (Image Roser)

An order is accepted by attaching **order acceptance cards** representing the workload to the order. At least one card is attached for every process of the order. When the order is released for production in the next step, these cards return to the order acceptance station.

A second, similar process is the **order release**. This also tracks the workload in the system for every process. However, the order release also limits the workload. An order is not released until there is enough available capacity. Whenever there is enough free capacity for all needed processes, the open order from the backlog is released into the queue for production. **Order release cards** representing the workload for each process of the order are attached to the order. After a process completes its work, the corresponding order release cards for this process are returned.

A push system would simply release these open jobs into the factory. A pull system, however, controls and limits the amount of work on the shop floor. COBACABANA is a pull system, as the total number of work in the production system is limited by the order release cards. An additional backlog of open orders can theoretically be limited by the order acceptance card, although this is not recommended. As you can probably see in Figure 204, COBACABANA is more complicated than CONWIP or POLCA.

C.2 Variants

Since the method was originally presented by Land in 2009, it has been adjusted a bit. Quite a bit actually. While it has the same name, consider it COBACABANA 2.0 (or even 3.0).

Normally, COBACABANA uses cards of standard size representing similar workloads. For example, each order release card could represent two hours' worth of work. If the order takes six hours, three cards are attached to the order. To avoid the inflationary large number of cards for different orders, Thürer recommends instead using only a **single custom card per order and a workstation whose size (i.e., length) represents the workload for this station**. This significantly cuts down on the number of cards, but requires the cutting of custom-sized cards for every order.

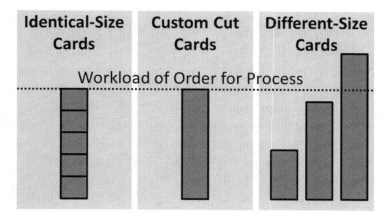

Figure 205: Representation of workload in COBACABANA using identical-sized cards (the original approach), custom-cut cards, and cards with different standard sizes (Image Roser)

Since this update to the method, they have figured out that cutting cards is cumbersome, and now recommend **cards in different standard sizes**. Here it seems three sizes (small, medium, and large) are good enough in terms of accuracy. You simply pick the card whose size matches your workload best for each process and add them to the accepted or released order. This is visualized in Figure 205.

In another modification to COBACABANA, a single **pool card** per open order in the backlog of open orders is created. The acceptance cards from above are given to the salesperson. The height of the stack of acceptance cards gives the salesperson an estimate on how long the delay of orders in the backlog will be. The pool card stays with the open order.

On the shop floor side, an **operation card** was added to the order release cards. The release card is cut to the correct size and stays with the planner. The height of the stack of release cards represents the workload. New orders are released only if there is enough space in the stack for them. The operation card travels with the order to the processes. After completion, the operation card returns to the planner, who then also releases the release card back into the stack.

Literature describes a use of these cards to **estimate a due date** based on the data from the backlog of open orders under the assumption that the lead time on the shop floor is relatively stable. Depending on the number of order release cards in front of an order, the due date could be estimated. However, like all of COBACABANA, this is a theoretical idea that has not yet been tested in reality. Due to the highly chaotic nature of job shops, I am a bit doubtful how well this approach works.

They also changed the order acceptance process and the order release process. In the original version explained in the next subchapter, a card in the order acceptance process or order release process represents available capacity, and the empty space represents the used capacity. This is shown in Figure 206 and Figure 207. In 2014, they turned this around, and the **cards represent available capacity**, whereas the empty space represents used capacity. However, for this approach you need every card twice, once for the order acceptance process or order release process board, and a duplicate card to go with the actual order to the shop floor. This will increase the already large number of cards even more.

C.3 Elements

The two main elements of COBACABANA are the order acceptance stack for the order acceptance process, and the order release stack for the order release process. Additional elements are surely needed to handle the paper cards, although these are not detailed in the original literature. These would be probably very similar to the elements of kanban and CONWIP.

C.3.1 The Order Acceptance Process

A customer orders an item. This item would need to be processed at different processes within the system. The time needed for this order is estimated for every process. Assume an order of parts would need six hours of milling, eight hours of hardening, and four hours of grinding. This order first goes into the **backlog of open orders** before being released for production.

To keep an overview of the workload, each process has a set of **order acceptance cards** representing a certain workload. Cards available represent available capacity, whereas cards attached to an order are tied-up capacity. This is shown in Figure 206. In this example, each card represents two hours of work. There are already open orders in the backlog of open orders equivalent to ten hours of milling, hence five cards of milling representing ten hours' worth of work have been removed. Similarly, the open orders already include eighteen hours of hardening and eight hours of grinding, hence nine cards for hardening and four for grinding have been removed. For easier visualization, each process in Figure 206 has its own color.

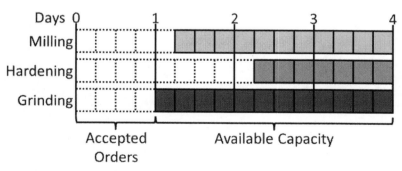

Figure 206: COBACABANA acceptance stack before accepting a new order (Image Roser)

With the new order, we need another six hours of milling, eight hours of hardening, and four hours of grinding. Hence, we remove three cards (six hours) from milling, four cards (eight hours) from hardening, and two cards (four hours) from grinding. These nine cards are attached to the open order in the backlog, as shown in Figure 207.

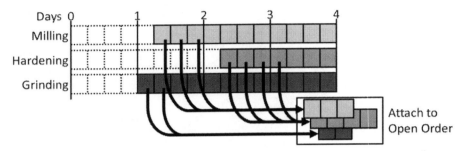

Figure 207: COBACABANA removing order acceptance cards from acceptance stack during the acceptance of a new order (Image Roser)

Afterwards, the acceptance cards stack should look like Figure 208. Hence, the person managing the stack always has a good overview of the work that is already committed to the customer but not yet released.

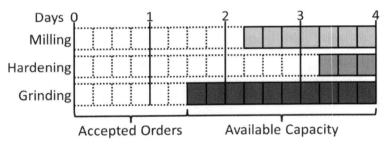

Figure 208: COBACABANA acceptance stack after accepting a new order (Image Roser)

C.3.2 The Order Release Process

A similar method is used for the release of the orders. The backbone of every pull system is to limit the work in the system. Most pull systems merely count the number of orders, but COBACABANA actually measures the workload. Orders are released from the backlog of open orders into the queue for production only if the processes have enough capacity to handle the workload. The approach is similar to the backlog of open orders above.

These cards are called **order release cards**. The total number of cards represents the maximum amount of work you want to put into the system at the same time.

An example is shown in Figure 209. Each card represents a certain amount of work. In this example, each card is also the equivalent of two hours' worth of work (although the original author suggested 1% of the desired maximum workload—in which case you would end up with one hundred cards for every process).

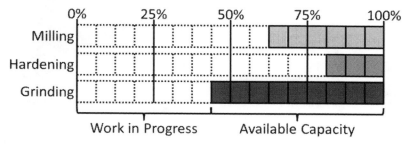

Figure 209: COBACABANA release stack before releasing an order for production (Image Roser)

When releasing an order from the backlog to the shop floor, the acceptance cards go back to the order acceptance. The release cards are removed from the release stack and attached to the open order. You must have enough release cards to release the order; otherwise, the order cannot be released and has to wait in the backlog of open orders. The orders are released according to their planned release date, with the hope that the most urgent order will be the next one in line for the shop floor.

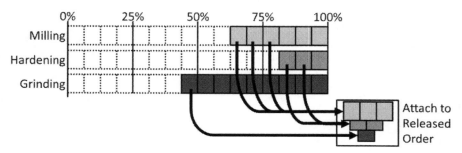

Figure 210: COBACABANA removing order release cards from the release stack during the release of an order from the backlog for production (Image Roser)

In our example, we barely had enough cards for hardening to release the order to the shop floor, as shown in Figure 210. The release stack afterwards is shown in Figure 211. Hence, the order release always has a good overview of the current workload of each station, although again at the cost of quite a lot of cards. Once the order is completed, the release cards go back to the release stack to be available for the next orders to be released.

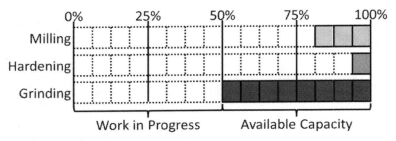

Figure 211: COBACABANA release stack after the release of an order (Image Roser)

C.4 Calculation

There are no details in the original literature on the calculation of the number of order release cards. Similar to CONWIP, the goal of the order release cards is to keep the system well utilized without clogging it up and increasing the lead time. This is difficult to calculate, and it is probably best to use an estimate. Also, be aware that due to different workloads of different orders for different processes, not all order release cards may be in the system at any given time despite a backlog of open orders.

The number of order acceptance cards is not a limit, but serves only for the estimation of the delivery time. Hence, you do not need to calculate the order acceptance cards, but just have plenty around and add more if you run out.

C.5 Advantages

The major advantage of COBACABANA is that it is all based on cards. Hence, the system is very visual and easy to track. It is also much easier to adjust or improve compared to a computer-based system that always needs programmers—which are hopefully good at programming but often understand little of the needs of the shop floor.

I do like the focus on a purely paper-based system without a complex ERP system. In that aspect, COBACABANA is quite unique. It is the only purely paper-based method I know that manages the workload of a job shop. In any case, there seems to be an ongoing stream of publications on the topic, mostly by Thürer, and maybe in the future there will be more updates and changes to make the system easier to use.

C.6 Disadvantages

Overall, the approach is so far **rather theoretical**, even though one of the co-inventors, Professor Thürer, has a highly respected German *meister* degree that comes with lots of shop floor experience. Anyway, to my knowledge, there is not yet any functioning real-world application. Not all kinks and issues of the method have yet been fully debugged, although there is ongoing research to improve the methods.

The **number of cards (or the cutting of custom card sizes) and its complexity** is an issue for me, albeit in my opinion there simply are no good *and* easy solutions for job shop control. However, COBACABANA uses many more cards than other pull systems, making a real-world implementation daunting.

C.7 Frequently Asked Questions

C.7.1 Can I Do This Digitally?

In theory, it should be possible to implement COBACABANA digitally. However, the authors developed COBACABANA with the explicit goal to make a card-based system. Yet, this is so far also only a theory without a real-world implementation. Therefore, if you choose to do COBACABANA, you should also be able to do it digitally if you wish—although I estimate that the implementation effort will be much higher due to the lack of COBACABANA software.

C.7.2 Can I Use This for Delivery Time Estimation?

According to the authors, COBACABANA can be used for delivery time estimation.[109] Based on the number of order acceptance cards and order release cards, the lead time and hence the delivery time is estimated. The problem is that these cards exist for every process in the system separately, and would need to be consolidated into a joint lead time. Anyway, like the entire COBACABANA method, this delivery time estimation is a theoretical assumption that is not yet validated in industry.

---

[109] Matthias Thürer, *Card-Based Control Systems for a Lean Work Design: The Fundamentals of Kanban, ConWIP, POLCA, and COBACABANA* Productivity Press, 2017, ISBN 978-1-138-43790-6.

Appendix D
Recommended Reading

There are many books available on lean, pull, kanban, and other related topics. Here are a few sources that I think stand out (with no claim to completeness). If you like my style of writing, I can also recommend my blog AllAboutLean.com at https://www.allaboutlean.com/, although you may have guessed this already from the many references I have to my own blog posts.

Baudin, Michel. *Working with Machines: The Nuts and Bolts of Lean Operations with Jidoka*. 1st ed. New York: Productivity Press, 2007. ISBN 978-1-56327-329-2. (Very hands-on and easy-to-read author. Two more of his books are below.)

Baudin, Michel. *Lean Assembly: The Nuts and Bolts of Making Assembly Operations Flow*. 1st ed. New York: Productivity Press, 2002. ISBN 978-1-56327-263-9.

Baudin, Michel. *Lean Logistics: The Nuts and Bolts of Delivering Materials and Goods*. New York, USA: Taylor & Francis Inc, 2005. ISBN 978-1-56327-296-7.

Dettmer, H. William. *Goldratt's Theory of Constraints: A Systems Approach to Continuous Improvement*. Milwaukee, Wisconsin, USA: McGraw-Hill Professional, 1998. ISBN 978-0-87389-370-1.

Lödding, Hermann. *Handbook of Manufacturing Control: Fundamentals, Description, Configuration*. Translated by Rett Rossi. New York, USA: Springer, 2011. ISBN 978-3-642-24457-5. (A bit academic, but very thorough. See below for updated German version.)

Lödding, Hermann. *Verfahren der Fertigungssteuerung: Grundlagen, Beschreibung, Konfiguration*. 3. Aufl. 2016. Berlin Heidelberg, Germany: Springer Vieweg, 2016. ISBN 978-3-662-48458-6. (Updated German version of the *Handbook of Manufacturing Control*.)

Suri, Rajan. *Quick Response Manufacturing: A Companywide Approach to Reducing Lead Times*. Portland, Oregon, USA: Taylor & Francis Inc, 1998. ISBN 978-1-56327-201-1. (First book on POLCA. For another, newer book by the same author see below.)

Suri, Rajan. *The Practitioner's Guide to POLCA: The Production Control System for High-Mix, Low-Volume and Custom Products.* Productivity Press, 2018. ISBN 978-1-138-21064-6. (THE book on POLCA)

Thürer, Matthias. *Card-Based Control Systems for a Lean Work Design: The Fundamentals of Kanban, ConWIP, POLCA, and COBACABANA.* Productivity Press, 2017. ISBN 978-1-138-43790-6. (Good overview of pull systems using paper cards rather than digital ERP systems, with a focus on COBACABANA)

Bibliography

I explain a lot of the lean techniques and fundamentals in detail on my blog AllAboutLean.com. Hence, I frequently refer to my blog for further details that would be beyond the scope of this work. I also contribute to the body of knowledge through my own original research together with my students.

Baker, Marc, Ian Taylor, and Alan Mitchell. *Making Hospitals Work: How to Improve Patient Care While Saving Everyone's Time and Hospitals' Resources*. 1.1 Edition. Lean Enterprise Academy Limited, 2011. ISBN 978-0-9551473-2-6.

Balle, Freddy, and Michael Balle. *The Gold Mine: A Novel of Lean Turnaround*. Brookline, Massachusetts, USA: Lean Enterprises Inst Inc, 2005. ISBN 978-0-9743225-6-8.

Barfod, Charlotte, Marlene Mauson Pankoke Lauritzen, Jakob Klim Danker, György Sölétormos, Jakob Lundager Forberg, Peter Anthony Berlac, Freddy Lippert, Lars Hyldborg Lundstrøm, Kristian Antonsen, and Kai Henrik Wiborg Lange. *Abnormal Vital Signs Are Strong Predictors for Intensive Care Unit Admission and In-Hospital Mortality in Adults Triaged in the Emergency Department - a Prospective Cohort Study*. Scandinavian Journal of Trauma, Resuscitation and Emergency Medicine 20, no. 1, April 10, 2012: 28.

Breithaupt, Jan-Wilhelm, Martin Land, and Peter Nyhuis. *The Workload Control Concept: Theory and Practical Extensions of Load Oriented Order Release*. Production Planning & Control 13, no. 7, October 1, 2002: 625–38.

Chen, Hong, Murray Z. Frank, and Owen Q. Wu. *What Actually Happened to the Inventories of American Companies Between 1981 and 2000?* Management Science, July 1, 2005.

Cox, James F., and John G. Schleier. *Theory of Constraints Handbook*. McGraw-Hill Professional, 2010. ISBN 0-07-166554-4.

Dettmer, H. William. *Goldratt's Theory of Constraints: A Systems Approach to Continuous Improvement*. Milwaukee, Wisconsin, USA: McGraw-Hill Professional, 1998. ISBN 978-0-87389-370-1.

Duenyas, Izak. *A Simple Release Policy for Networks of Queues with Controllable Inputs*. Operations Research 42, no. 6, December 1, 1994: 1162–71.

Fredendall, Lawrence D., Divesh Ojha, and J. Wayne Patterson. *Concerning the Theory of Workload Control. European Journal of Operational Research* 201, no. 1, February 16, 2010: 99–111.

Germs, Remco, and Jan Riezebos. *Workload Balancing Capability of Pull Systems in MTO Production. International Journal of Production Research* 48, no. 8, April 15, 2010: 2345–60.

Goldratt, Eliyahu M., and Jeff Cox. *The Goal: A Process of Ongoing Improvement.* 2nd revised ed. North River Press, 1992. ISBN 0-88427-178-1.

Goldratt, Eliyahu M., and Robert E. Fox. *The Race.* Croton-on-Hudson, New York, USA: North River Press Inc., 1986. ISBN 978-0-88427-062-1.

Graban, Mark. *Lean Hospitals: Improving Quality, Patient Safety, and Employee Engagement, Second Edition.* 2nd edition. New York, USA: Productivity Press, 2011. ISBN 978-1-4398-7043-3.

Hopp, Wallace J., and Mark L. Spearman. *Factory Physics.* 3rd Edition. New York, NY: Waveland, 2011. ISBN 978-1-57766-739-1.

Hopp, Wallace J., and Mark L. Spearman. *To Pull or Not to Pull: What Is the Question? Manufacturing & Service Operations Management* 6, no. 2, April 1, 2004: 133–48.

Jäger, Yannic. *Einfluss von Priorisierung auf das Verhalten eines Produktionssystems.* Master Thesis, Karlsruhe University of Applied Sciences, 2017.

Jäger, Yannic, and Christoph Roser. *Effect of Prioritization on the Waiting Time.* In *Proceedings of the International Conference on the Advances in Production Management System.* Seoul, Korea, 2018.

Kenney, Charles, and Donald M. Berwick. *Transforming Health Care: Virginia Mason Medical Center's Pursuit of the Perfect Patient Experience.* 1st edition. Boca Raton, Florida, USA: CRC Press, 2010. ISBN 978-1-56327-375-9.

Land, Martin. *Cobacabana (Control of Balance by Card-Based Navigation): A Card-Based System for Job Shop Control. International Journal of Production Economics* 117, 2009: 97–103.

Lazarski, Adam. *Limitations of the Theory of Constraints and Goldratt Concept in Optimizing Project Portfolios. ODiTK,* 2010. https://www.akademiacontrollingu.pl/article/limitations-of-the-

theory-of-constraints-and-goldratt-concept-in-optimizing-project-portfolios/.

Linhares, Alexandre. *Theory of Constraints and the Combinatorial Complexity of the Product-Mix Decision. International Journal of Production Economics*, Modelling and Control of Productive Systems: Concepts and Applications, 121, no. 1, September 1, 2009: 121–29.

Little, John D. C. *A Proof for the Queuing Formula: L = ΛW. Operations Research* 9, no. 3, June 1961: 383–87.

Nyhuis, Peter, and Hans-Peter Wiendahl. *Logistische Kennlinien: Grundlagen, Werkzeuge und Anwendungen*. 3. Aufl. 2012 Edition. Berlin Heidelberg Dordrecht London New York: Springer, 2012. ISBN 978-3-540-92838-6.

Oosterman, Bas, Martin Land, and Gerard Gaalman. *The Influence of Shop Characteristics on Workload Control. International Journal of Production Economics* 68, no. 1, October 30, 2000: 107–19.

Pound, Edward S., Jeffrey H. Bell, and Mark L. Spearman. *Factory Physics for Managers: How Leaders Improve Performance in a Post-Lean Six Sigma World*. New York: McGraw-Hill Education Ltd., 2014. ISBN 978-0-07-182250-3.

Qiu, Mabel, Lawrence Fredendall, and Zhiwei Zhu. *TOC or LP? Manufacturing Engineer* 81, no. 4, August 1, 2002: 190–95.

Richardson, Helen. *Control Your Costs–Then Cut Them. Transportation & Distribution* 36, no. 12, December 1995: 94.

Roser, Christoph. *An Introduction to Capacity Leveling*. In *Collected Blog Posts of AllAboutLean.Com 2014*, 281–86. Collected Blog Posts of AllAboutLean.Com 2. Offenbach, Germany: AllAboutLean Publishing, 2020. ISBN 978-3-96382-010-6.

Roser, Christoph. *Basics of Value Stream Maps*. In *Collected Blog Posts of AllAboutLean.Com 2015*, 229–36. Collected Blog Posts of AllAboutLean.Com 3. Offenbach, Germany: AllAboutLean Publishing, 2020. ISBN 978-3-96382-013-7.

Roser, Christoph. *Bottleneck Management Part 1 – Introduction and Utilization*. In *Collected Blog Posts of AllAboutLean.Com 2014*, 246–51. Collected Blog Posts of AllAboutLean.Com 2. Offenbach, Germany: AllAboutLean Publishing, 2020. ISBN 978-3-96382-010-6.

Roser, Christoph. *Calculating the Material for Your Milk Run*. In *Collected Blog Posts of AllAboutLean.Com 2018*, 268–72. Collected Blog Posts of AllAboutLean.Com 6. Offenbach, Germany: AllAboutLean Publishing, 2020. ISBN 978-3-96382-022-9.

Roser, Christoph. *Changeover Sequencing – Part 1*. In *Collected Blog Posts of AllAboutLean.Com 2017*, 149–54. Collected Blog Posts of AllAboutLean.Com 5. Offenbach, Germany: AllAboutLean Publishing, 2020. ISBN 978-3-96382-019-9.

Roser, Christoph. *Determining the Size of Your FiFo Lane – The FiFo Formula*. In *Collected Blog Posts of AllAboutLean.Com 2014*, 185–91. Collected Blog Posts of AllAboutLean.Com 2. Offenbach, Germany: AllAboutLean Publishing, 2020. ISBN 978-3-96382-010-6.

Roser, Christoph. *Effect of Prioritization on Waiting Times*. In *Collected Blog Posts of AllAboutLean.Com 2018*, 113–20. Collected Blog Posts of AllAboutLean.Com 6. Offenbach, Germany: AllAboutLean Publishing, 2020. ISBN 978-3-96382-022-9.

Roser, Christoph. *External Milk Runs*. In *Collected Blog Posts of AllAboutLean.Com 2018*, 286–93. Collected Blog Posts of AllAboutLean.Com 6. Offenbach, Germany: AllAboutLean Publishing, 2020. ISBN 978-3-96382-022-9.

Roser, Christoph. *"Faster, Better, Cheaper" in the History of Manufacturing: From the Stone Age to Lean Manufacturing and Beyond*. 1st ed. Productivity Press, 2016. ISBN 978-1-4987-5630-3.

Roser, Christoph. *How to Determine Your Lot Size – Part 1*. In *Collected Blog Posts of AllAboutLean.Com 2017*, 12–16. Collected Blog Posts of AllAboutLean.Com 5. Offenbach, Germany: AllAboutLean Publishing, 2020. ISBN 978-3-96382-019-9.

Roser, Christoph. *How to Prioritize Your Work Orders – Basics*. In *Collected Blog Posts of AllAboutLean.Com 2016*, 156–59. Collected Blog Posts of AllAboutLean.Com 4. Offenbach, Germany: AllAboutLean Publishing, 2020. ISBN 978-3-96382-016-8.

Roser, Christoph. *Introduction to One-Piece Flow Leveling – Part 1 Theory*. In *Collected Blog Posts of AllAboutLean.Com 2015*, 1–5. Collected Blog Posts of AllAboutLean.Com 3. Offenbach, Germany: AllAboutLean Publishing, 2020. ISBN 978-3-96382-013-7.

Roser, Christoph. *Mathematically Accurate Bottleneck Detection 1 – The Average Active Period Method.* In *Collected Blog Posts of AllAboutLean.Com 2014*, 133–36. Collected Blog Posts of AllAboutLean.Com 2. Offenbach, Germany: AllAboutLean Publishing, 2020. ISBN 978-3-96382-010-6.

Roser, Christoph. *Mixed Model Sequencing – Basic Example Introduction.* In *Collected Blog Posts of AllAboutLean.Com 2019*, 143–47. Collected Blog Posts of AllAboutLean.Com 7. Offenbach, Germany: AllAboutLean Publishing, 2020. ISBN 978-3-96382-025-0.

Roser, Christoph. *Mixed Model Sequencing – Complex Example Introduction.* In *Collected Blog Posts of AllAboutLean.Com 2019*, 159–64. Collected Blog Posts of AllAboutLean.Com 7. Offenbach, Germany: AllAboutLean Publishing, 2020. ISBN 978-3-96382-025-0.

Roser, Christoph. *Mixed Model Sequencing – Introduction.* In *Collected Blog Posts of AllAboutLean.Com 2019*, 128–32. Collected Blog Posts of AllAboutLean.Com 7. Offenbach, Germany: AllAboutLean Publishing, 2020. ISBN 978-3-96382-025-0.

Roser, Christoph. *Mixed Model Sequencing – Summary.* In *Collected Blog Posts of AllAboutLean.Com 2019*, 189–93. Collected Blog Posts of AllAboutLean.Com 7. Offenbach, Germany: AllAboutLean Publishing, 2020. ISBN 978-3-96382-025-0.

Roser, Christoph. *Overview of Value Stream Mapping Symbols.* In *Collected Blog Posts of AllAboutLean.Com 2015*, 220–28. Collected Blog Posts of AllAboutLean.Com 3. Offenbach, Germany: AllAboutLean Publishing, 2020. ISBN 978-3-96382-013-7.

Roser, Christoph. *Practical Tips for Value Stream Mapping.* In *Collected Blog Posts of AllAboutLean.Com 2015*, 237–44. Collected Blog Posts of AllAboutLean.Com 3. Offenbach, Germany: AllAboutLean Publishing, 2020. ISBN 978-3-96382-013-7.

Roser, Christoph. *Supermarket vs. FiFo – What Requires Less Inventory?* In *Collected Blog Posts of AllAboutLean.Com 2016*, 82–88. Collected Blog Posts of AllAboutLean.Com 4. Offenbach, Germany: AllAboutLean Publishing, 2020. ISBN 978-3-96382-016-8.

Roser, Christoph. *The Bottleneck Walk – Practical Bottleneck Detection Part 1.* In *Collected Blog Posts of AllAboutLean.Com 2014*, 142–48. Collected

Blog Posts of AllAboutLean.Com 2. Offenbach, Germany: AllAboutLean Publishing, 2020. ISBN 978-3-96382-010-6.

Roser, Christoph. *The FiFo Calculator – Determining the Size of Your Buffers.* In *Collected Blog Posts of AllAboutLean.Com 2014*, 209–12. Collected Blog Posts of AllAboutLean.Com 2. Offenbach, Germany: AllAboutLean Publishing, 2020. ISBN 978-3-96382-010-6.

Roser, Christoph. *Theory of Every Part Every Interval (EPEI) Leveling & Heijunka.* In *Collected Blog Posts of AllAboutLean.Com 2014*, 287–92. Collected Blog Posts of AllAboutLean.Com 2. Offenbach, Germany: AllAboutLean Publishing, 2020. ISBN 978-3-96382-010-6.

Roser, Christoph. *Toyota's and Denso's Relentless Quest for Lot Size One.* In *Collected Blog Posts of AllAboutLean.Com 2016*, 250–55. Collected Blog Posts of AllAboutLean.Com 4. Offenbach, Germany: AllAboutLean Publishing, 2020. ISBN 978-3-96382-016-8.

Roser, Christoph. *Value Stream Mapping – Why to Start at the Customer Side.* In *Collected Blog Posts of AllAboutLean.Com 2013*, 92–97. Collected Blog Posts of AllAboutLean.Com 1. Offenbach, Germany: AllAboutLean Publishing, 2020. ISBN 978-3-96382-007-6.

Roser, Christoph. *When to Do Value Stream Maps (and When Not!).* In *Collected Blog Posts of AllAboutLean.Com 2015*, 212–19. Collected Blog Posts of AllAboutLean.Com 3. Offenbach, Germany: AllAboutLean Publishing, 2020. ISBN 978-3-96382-013-7.

Roser, Christoph, Kai Lorentzen, David Lenze, Jochen Deuse, Ferdinand Klenner, Ralph Richter, Jacqueline Schmitt, and Peter Willats. *Bottleneck Prediction Using the Active Period Method in Combination with Buffer Inventories.* In *Proceedings of the International Conference on the Advances in Production Management System.* Hamburg, Germany, 2017.

Rother, Mike, and John Shook. *Learning to See: Value-Stream Mapping to Create Value and Eliminate Muda: Value Stream Mapping to Add Value and Eliminate Muda.* Lean Enterprise Institute, 1999. ISBN 0-9667843-0-8.

Sato, Masaaki. *The Toyota Leaders: An Executive Guide.* New York: Vertical, 2008. ISBN 1-934287-23-7.

Shimokawa, Koichi, Takahiro Fujimoto, Brian Miller, and John Shook. *The Birth of Lean*. Cambridge, Massachusetts: Lean Enterprise Institute, Inc., 2009. ISBN 1-934109-22-3.

Spearman, Mark L., David L. Woodruff, and Wallace J. Hopp. *CONWIP: A Pull Alternative to Kanban. International Journal of Production Research* 28, no. 5, May 1, 1990: 879–94.

Suri, Rajan. *Quick Response Manufacturing: A Companywide Approach to Reducing Lead Times*. Portland, Oregon, USA: Taylor & Francis Inc, 1998. ISBN 978-1-56327-201-1.

Suri, Rajan. *The Practitioner's Guide to POLCA: The Production Control System for High-Mix, Low-Volume and Custom Products*. Productivity Press, 2018. ISBN 978-1-138-21064-6.

Terlep, Sharon, and Annie Gasparro. *Why Are There Still Not Enough Paper Towels? Wall Street Journal*, August 21, 2020, sec. US. https://www.wsj.com/articles/why-arent-there-enough-paper-towels-11598020793.

The Economist. *Supple Supplies - Businesses Are Proving Quite Resilient to the Pandemic | Briefing. The Economist*, May 16, 2020. https://www.economist.com/briefing/2020/05/16/businesses-are-proving-quite-resilient-to-the-pandemic.

Thürer, Matthias. *Card-Based Control Systems for a Lean Work Design: The Fundamentals of Kanban, ConWIP, POLCA, and COBACABANA*. Productivity Press, 2017. ISBN 978-1-138-43790-6.

Thürer, Matthias, Nuno O. Fernandes, and Mark Stevenson. *Material Flow Control in High-Variety Make-to-Order Shops: Combining COBACABANA and POLCA. Production and Operations Management* 29, no. 9, 2020: 2138–52.

Thürer, Matthias, Nuno O. Fernandes, Mark Stevenson, and Ting Qu. *On the Backlog-Sequencing Decision for Extending the Applicability of ConWIP to High-Variety Contexts: An Assessment by Simulation. International Journal of Production Research* 55, no. 16, August 18, 2017: 4695–4711.

Thürer, Matthias, Nuno O. Fernandes, Nick Ziengs, and Mark Stevenson. *On the Meaning of ConWIP Cards: An Assessment by Simulation. Journal of Industrial and Production Engineering* 36, no. 1, January 2, 2019: 49–58.

Thürer, Matthias, Mark Stevenson, and Charles W. Protzman. *COBACABANA (Control of Balance by Card Based Navigation): An Alternative to Kanban in the Pure Flow Shop? International Journal of Production Economics* 166, August 1, 2015: 143–51.

Trietsch, Dan. *From Management by Constraints (MBC) to Management by Criticalities (MBC II). Human Systems Management* 24, January 1, 2005: 105–15.

Trietsch, Dan. *Why a Critical Path by Any Other Name Would Smell Less Sweet? Towards a Holistic Approach to PERT/CPM. Project Management Journal* 36, 2005: 27–36.

Wiendahl, Hans-Peter. *Die belastungsorientierte Fertigungssteuerung.* In *Fertigungssteuerung: Grundlagen und Systeme,* edited by Dietrich Adam, 207–43. Schriften zur Unternehmensführung. Wiesbaden: Gabler Verlag, 1992. ISBN 978-3-322-89141-9.

Wiesse, Denis. *Analyse des Umlaufbestandes von Verbrauchssteuerungen in Abhängigkeit von der Nutzung von Supermärkten und FiFo-Strecken.* Master Thesis, Karlsruhe University of Applied Sciences, 2015.

Wiesse, Denis, and Christoph Roser. *Supermarkets vs. FIFO Lanes – A Comparison of Work-in-Process Inventories and Delivery Performance.* In *Proceedings of the International Conference on the Advances in Production Management System.* Iguassu Falls, Brazil, 2016.

Womack, James P. *The Machine That Changed the World: Based on the Massachusetts Institute of Technology 5-Million-Dollar 5-Year Study on the Future of the Automobile.* New York: Rawson Associates, 1990. ISBN 0-89256-350-8.

Image Credits

Most of the images and illustrations in this book are my own work. Below are the details on the licenses and sources of images by others. Some of them are available under a Creative Commons license. I support this license by also licensing most of the images on my blog under a Creative Commons license. I also uploaded selected images of mine on Wikimedia. Creative common licenses require a link to the source and the license. The links to the different licenses are listed below, and the images and their sources farther below. More information on the Creative Commons and their licenses is available at https://creativecommons.org/.

- CC-BY 3.0: https://creativecommons.org/licenses/by/3.0/
- CC-BY-SA 3.0: https://creativecommons.org/licenses/by-sa/3.0/

Here is the list of figures that originate partially or completely from other authors, including details on the source and the license. Special thanks to those contributors who provided images freely to the public!

- Chapter art based on bicycle ball bearing from the 1911 Encyclopedia Britannica, Vol. 3, p. 916. Original in public domain, redrawn as vector art by Roser.
- Figure 2 by unknown author, in public domain, available at http://digitalcollections.sjlibrary.org/cdm/ref/collection/arbuckle/id/266
- Figure 3 by Clarence Saunders, in public domain, available at https://commons.wikimedia.org/wiki/File:Piggly_Wiggly_store,_1918.png
- Figure 5 by David Falconer, in public domain, available at https://commons.wikimedia.org/wiki/file:"no_gas"_signs_were_a_common_sight_in_oregon_during_the_fall_of_1973._this_station_on_the_coast_was_open_for_any..._-_nara_-_555415.jpg
- Figure 32 by Peabody Energy, Inc. licensed under the CC-BY 3.0 License, available at https://commons.wikimedia.org/wiki/File:Coal_Stockpiles_at_Kayenta_Mine.png
- Figure 34 by mulderphoto with permission from BigStock
- Figure 61 by Cschirp licensed under the CC-BY 3.0 License, available at https://commons.wikimedia.org/wiki/File:Wheel_hub_assembly.jpg

- Figure 62 by Ypy31, in public domain, available at https://commons.wikimedia.org/wiki/File:2ZR-FE.jpg
- Figure 92 manager by Thomas Karol, in public domain, available at https://www.ellsworth.af.mil/News/Photos/igphoto/2001807165/; operator by style-photographs with permission from BigStock
- Figure 104 by Siyuwj licensed under the CC-BY-SA 3.0 License, available at https://commons.wikimedia.org/wiki/File:Geely_assembly_line_in_Beilun,_Ningbo.JPG
- Figure 212 by Schönwälder, copyright transferred to Roser

About the Author

Figure 212: Christoph Roser (Image Roser)

Prof. Dr. Christoph Roser is an expert for lean production and a professor of production management at the University of Applied Sciences in Karlsruhe, Germany. He studied automation engineering at the University of Applied Sciences in Ulm, Germany, and did his Ph.D. in mechanical engineering at the University of Massachusetts, Amherst, Massachusetts, USA, researching flexible design methodologies.

Afterwards he worked for five years at the **Toyota Central Research and Development Laboratories** in Nagoya, Japan, studying the Toyota Production System and developing bottleneck detection and buffer allocation methods. Following Toyota, he joined **McKinsey & Company** in Munich, Germany, specializing in lean manufacturing and driving numerous projects in all segments of industry. Before becoming a professor, he worked for the **Robert Bosch GmbH**, Germany, first as a lean expert for research and training, then using his expertise as a production logistics manager in the **Bosch Thermotechnik** Division. In 2013, he was appointed professor for production management at the **Karlsruhe University of Applied Sciences** to continue his research and teaching on lean manufacturing.

Throughout his career, Dr. Roser worked on lean projects in almost two hundred different plants, including automotive, machine construction, solar cells, chip manufacturing, gas turbines, paper making, logistics, power tools, heating, packaging, food processing, white goods, security technology, finance, and many more.

He is an award-winning author of over fifty academic publications and has written multiple books. Besides research, teaching, speaking, and consulting on lean manufacturing, he is very interested in different approaches to manufacturing organization, both historical and current. He blogs about his experiences and research on AllAboutLean.com.

Now, Go Out and Organize Your Industry!

Made in United States
Troutdale, OR
01/10/2024

16862366R00246